STUDENT'S
SOLUTIONS MANUAL

to accompany

Finite
Mathematics

Third Edition

Howard Rolf
Baylor University

Wm. C. Brown Publishers
Dubuque, Iowa•Melbourne, Australia•Oxford, England

ISBN 0-697-16173-0

Printed in the United States of America by Wm. C. Brown Communications, Inc., 2460 Kerper Boulevard, Dubuque, Iowa, 52001

10 9 8 7 6 5 4 3 2 1

Contents

Solutions to Odd-Numbered Exercises

Preface

This Student's Solutions Manual accompanies **Finite Mathematics, Third Edition** by Howard L. Rolf. All references to chapters, sections, and exercises refer to the textbook. This manual contains worked out solutions to the odd-numbered exercises in the textbook.

Do not use this manual as a substitute for working the homework problems yourself. In one sense you should use this manual as a last resort in solving a problem.

You may find it useful to compare your solution with the solution in this manual. Be aware that your solution may be different, yet correct. In fact, you may have a clever solution that is better. Quite often the steps to a solution may occur in a different order and still be correct. Therefore, do not assume your solution is incorrect if it differs from the one in this manual.

Chapter 1
Functions and Lines

Section 1-1

1. $y = 15x + 20$ 3. (a) $f(5) = \$23.75$ (b) $f(3) = \$14.25$

5. (a) $f(1) = 4(1) - 3 = 4 - 3 = 1$
   (b) $f(-2) = 4(-2) - 3 = -8 - 3 = -11$
   (c) $f(1/2) = 4(1/2) - 3 = 2 - 3 = -1$
   (d) $f(a) = 4a - 3$

7. (a) $f(5) = \dfrac{5 + 1}{5 - 1} = \dfrac{6}{4} = \dfrac{3}{2}$ (b) $f(-6) = \dfrac{-6 + 1}{-6 - 1} = \dfrac{5}{7}$

   (c) $f(0) = \dfrac{0 + 1}{0 - 1} = \dfrac{1}{-1} = -1$ (d) $f(2c) = \dfrac{(2c + 1)}{(2c - 1)}$

9. (a) $f(5) = 78(5) = 390; \ f(2.5) = 78(2.5) = 195;$
      $f(6.4) = 78(6.4) = 499.2$
   (b) Solve $78x = 741$ $x = 9.5$ ounces

11. (a) $f(60) = 9(60) = 540$ calories
    (b) Solve $9x = 750$ $x = 83.3$ minutes

13. $y = 1.80x + 25$ 15. $y = x - .20x$ or $y = 0.80x$

17. $y = 0.60x + 12$ 19. $y = 3500x + 5,000,000$ 21. $y = 0.88x$

23. (a) $f(450) = 30(450) = 13,500 \text{ ft}^2$
    (b) $f(125) = 30(125) = 3,750 \text{ ft}^2$
    (c) $0.4f(650) = 30(650)(0.4) = 19,500(0.4) = \$7,800$
    (d) Solve $30x = 15,900$ $x = 530$ ft

Section 1-2

1. $f(x) = 3x + 8$
   $f(0) = 8, \ f(1) = 11$

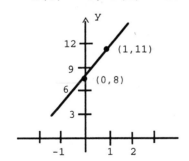

3. $f(x) = x + 7$
   $f(1) = 8, \ f(-1) = 6$

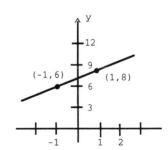

Section 1-2

5. $f(x) = -3x - 1$
    $f(0) = -1$, $f(-1) = 2$

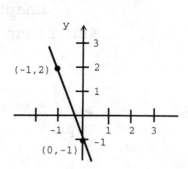

7. Slope = 7, y-intercept = 22   9. Slope = -2/5, y-intercept = 6

11. $2x + 5y - 3 = 0$
    $5y = -2x + 3$
    $y = -\frac{2}{5} x + \frac{3}{5}$
    Slope = -2/5, y-intercept = 3/5

13. $x - 3y + 6 = 0$
    $3y = x + 6$
    $y = 1/3 \ x + 2$
    Slope = 1/3,
    y-intercept = 2

15. $m = \frac{4 - 2}{3 - 1} = \frac{2}{2} = 1$ 17. $m = \frac{-5 - (-1)}{-1 - (-4)} = -\frac{4}{3}$

19. $y = -2$ 21. $y = 0$

23.

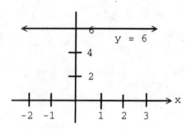

25.

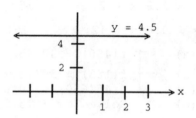

27. $m = \frac{5 - 2}{3 - 3} = \frac{3}{0}$. undefined → vertical line x = 3

29. Vertical line x = 10

31.

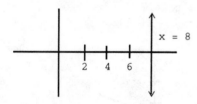

33.

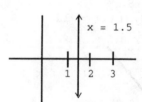

35. $y = 4x + 3$ 37. $y = -x + 6$ 39. $y = \frac{1}{2} x$

41. $y = -4x + b$ 43. $y = \frac{1}{2}x + b$
     $1 = -4(2) + b$
     $b = 9$ $4 = \frac{1}{2}(5) + b$
     $y = -4x + 9$
                                $b = \frac{3}{2}$

                                $y = \frac{1}{2} x + \frac{3}{2}$
                          or x - 2y = -3

45. $y - 5 = 7(x - 1)$
     $y = 7x - 7 + 5$
     $y = 7x - 2$

47. $y - 6 = \frac{1}{5}(x - 9)$
     $y = \frac{1}{5}x - \frac{9}{5} + 6$
     $y = \frac{1}{5}x + \frac{21}{5}$

49. $m = \frac{1 - 0}{2 + 1} = \frac{1}{3}$
     $y - 0 = \frac{1}{3}(x + 1)$
     $y = \frac{1}{3}x + \frac{1}{3}$

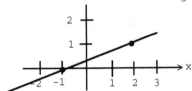

51. $m = \frac{2 - 0}{1 - 0} = \frac{2}{1} = 2$
     $y - 0 = 2(x - 0)$
     $y = 2x$

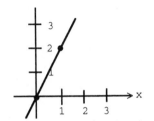

53. $y = 4$

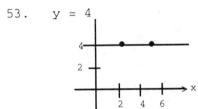

55. $x = 0$: $-3y = 15 \rightarrow y = -5$, y-intercept
     $y = 0$: $5x = 15 \rightarrow x = 3$, x-intercept

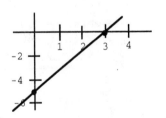

57. $x = 0$: $-5y = 25 \rightarrow y = -5$, y-intercept
     $y = 0$: $2x = 25 \rightarrow x = 12.5$, x-intercept

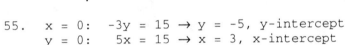

59. Line through $(8, 2)$ and $(3, -3)$ has slope $m_1 = \frac{-3 - 2}{3 - 8} = \frac{-5}{-5} = 1$

     Line through $(6, -1)$ and $(16, 9)$ has slope $m_2 = \frac{9 + 1}{16 - 6} = \frac{10}{10} = 1$

     The lines are parallel.

61. Line through $(5, 4)$ and $(1, -2)$ has slope $m_1 = \frac{-2 - 4}{1 - 5} = \frac{-6}{-4} = \frac{3}{2}$

     Line through $(1, 2)$ and $(6, 8)$ has slope $m_2 = \frac{8 - 2}{6 - 1} = \frac{6}{5}$

     The lines are not parallel.

63. $m_1 = 6 = m_2$ (parallel)

65. The first line may be written $y = \frac{1}{2}x - \frac{3}{2} \rightarrow m_1 = \frac{1}{2}$

The second line may be written $y = -2x + 1 \rightarrow m_2 = -2$

The lines are not parallel.

67. $m = 3$

$y - 5 = 3(x + 1)$

$y = 3x + 3 + 5$

$y = 3x + 8$

69. $m = -\frac{5}{7}$

$y = -\frac{5}{7}x + 8$

71. Horizontal line, $y = -4$

73. $y - 5 = \frac{2}{3}(x - 2)$

When $x = 0$, $y = \frac{2}{3}(0 - 2) + 5 = -\frac{4}{3} + 5 = \frac{11}{3}$, so the y-intercept is $\frac{11}{3}$

75. Let x = no. of weeks from start of the diet and y = weight. Then $m = -3$, and $(14, 196)$ is a point on the line.

(a) $y - 196 = -3(x - 14)$

$y = -3x + 42 + 196$

$y = -3x + 238$

(b) $y = -3(0) + 238 = 238$ pounds

77. Let x = number of items and y = the cost. Then $(500, 1340)$ and $(800, 1760)$ are points on the line, so

$m = \frac{1760 - 1340}{800 - 500} = \frac{420}{300} = 1.4$

$y - 1340 = 1.4(x - 500)$

$y = 1.4x - 700 + 1340$

$y = 1.4x + 640$

79. (a) $\frac{y - 3}{-1 - 2} = 3$

$y - 3 = -9$

$y = -6$

(b) $\frac{3 - 2}{x - 1} = -4$

$-4x + 4 = 1$

$-4x = -3$

$x = \frac{3}{4}$

(c) $\frac{y - 0}{5 + 2} = \frac{3}{4}$

$y = 7(\frac{3}{4})$

$y = \frac{21}{4}$

(d) $\frac{4 + 3}{x + 1} = -\frac{1}{2}$

$-\frac{1}{2}x - \frac{1}{2} = 7$

$-\frac{1}{2}x = \frac{15}{2}$

$x = -15$

81. A y-intercept of 9 indicates that $(0, 9)$ is a point on the line.

Then $m = \frac{9 - 4}{0 - 6} = \frac{5}{-6} = -\frac{5}{6}$ and $y = -\frac{5}{6}x + 9$

83. Let x = the number of years since 1980 and y = value of the coin. Then $(0, 185)$ and $(10, 220)$ are points on the line, so

$m = \frac{220 - 185}{10 - 0} = \frac{35}{10} = 3.5$

$y - 220 = 3.5(x - 10)$

$y = 3.5x - 35 + 220$

$y = 3.5x + 185$ is the value.

85. $y = 0.078x + 5$

87. (a) Increases 4   (b) Decreases 3   (c) Increases 2/3

    (d) Decreases 1/2   (e) $y = -\frac{2}{3}x + \frac{4}{3}$ so it decreases $\frac{2}{3}$

    (f) No change

89. Let x = number of miles and y = cost. Then the points (125, 35.75) and (265, 51.15) are on the line, so

$$m = \frac{51.15 - 35.75}{265 - 125} = \frac{15.40}{140} = .11$$

    y - 35.75 = 0.11(x - 125)

    y = 0.11x - 13.75 + 35.75

    y = 0.11x + 22

Section 1-3

1. (a) C(180) = 43(180) + 2300 = $10,040
    (b) Solve 43x + 2300 = 11,889
        43x = 9589   x = 223 bikes
    (c) Unit cost is $43, fixed cost is $2,300

3. (a) Fixed cost is $400, unit cost is $3
    (b) For 600 units, C(600) = 3(600) + 400 = $2,200
        For 1,000 units, C(1000) = 3(1000) + 400 = $3,400

5. (a) R(x) = 32x   (b) R(78) = 32(78) = $2,496
    (c) Solve 32x = 672   x = 21 pairs

7. (a) R(x) = 3.39x   (b) R(834) = 3.39(834) = $2,827.26

9. (a) C(x) = 57x + 780   (b) R(x) = 79x
    (c) 79x = 57x + 780   22x = 780   x = 35.45, so
        the break-even number is 36 coats.

11. C(x) = 4x + 500   C(800) = 4(800) + 500 = $3,700

13. (a) Let x = number of T-shirts and C = the cost. Then the points
    (600, 1400) and (700, 1600) lie on the line, so

$$m = \frac{1600 - 1400}{700 - 600} = \frac{200}{100} = 2$$

        y - 1600 = 2(x - 700)

        y = 2x - 1400 + 1600

        C(x) = 2x + 200

    (b) $200   (c) $2

15. (a) C(x) = 649x + 1500   (b) R(x) = 899x
    (c) C(37) = 649(37) + 1500 = $25,513
    (d) R(37) = 899(37) = $33,263
    (e) 899x = 649x + 1500
        250x = 1500   x = 6 computers

17. (a) Let x = number of years and BV = the book value.
    Then the points (0, 425) and (8, 25) are on the line, so

$$m = \frac{425 - 25}{0 - 8} = \frac{400}{-8} = -50$$

    BV - 425 = -50x

    BV = -50x + 425

    (b) Annual depreciation is $50
    (c) BV(3) = -50(3) + 425 = -150 + 425 = $275

Section 1-3

19. (a) Let x = number of years and BV = the book value. Then the points (0, 9750) and (6, 300) lie on the line, so

$$m = \frac{9750 - 300}{0 - 6} = \frac{9450}{-6} = -1575$$

BV - 9750 = -1575x

BV = -1575x + 9750

(b) $1,575

(c) BV(2) = -1575(2) + 9750 = $6600

BV(5) = -1575(5) + 9750 = $1875

21. Revenue must be greater than costs, so

0.45x > 0.23x + 475

0.22x > 475

x > 2159.09 at break-even, so at least 2,160 cookies must be sold to make a profit.

23. The weekly costs for Company A, C(x) = .14x + 105, must be less than the weekly costs for Company B, C(x) = .10x + 161.

0.14x + 105 < 0.10x + 161

0.04x < 56

x < 1400

Company A is the better deal when the weekly mileage is less than 1400 miles.

25. A profit occurs when

.85x + .20x > .40x + 1400

.65x > 1400

x > 2153.846, so at least 2,154 copies must be sold to make a profit.

27. The unit cost gives m = 12.65. The point (2700, 36295) lies on the line so

y - 36295 = 12.65(x - 2700)

C(x) = 12.65x + 2140

29. (a) 6x = 650 + 45 + 2.20x

3.8x = 695

x = 182.89, so 183 tickets must be sold to break even.

(b) 6x = 650 + 45 + 2.20x + 700

3.8x = 1395

x = 367.105, so 368 tickets must be sold to clear $700.

(c) 7.5x = 2.20x + 1395

5.3x = 1395

x = 263.208, so 264 tickets must be sold to clear $700.

31. (a) R(x) = 35x   (b)   R(1238) = 35(1238) = $43,330

(c) Solve 35x = 595

x = 17

33. (a) Let x = number of years and y = book value, so the points (3, 14175) and (7, 8475) lie on the line, so

$$m = \frac{8475 - 14175}{7 - 3} = \frac{-5700}{4} = -1425$$

y - 14175 = -1425(x - 3)

BV = -1425x + 18,450

(b) $1,425   (c)   BV(0) = $18,450

35. (a) Solve c(260) = 3120
          c = 12 so R(x) = 12x
     (b) Since the break-even membership is 260 and the break-even
          revenue is 3120, the point (260, 3120) is on the cost line.
          The revenue for 200 memberships is $2400 and is $330 less
          than the cost, so the point (200, 2730) is on the cost line.
          From these two points m = $\frac{3120 - 2730}{260 - 200}$ = $\frac{390}{60}$ = 6.5
          y - 2730 = 6.5(x - 200)
          y = 6.5x - 1300 + 2730
          C(x) = 6.5x + 1430

37. (a) Solve c(1465) = 32962.50
          c = 22.5, so R(x) = 22.5x
     (b) The points (1465, 26405.50) and (940, 17638) lie on
          the line, so m = $\frac{26405.50 - 17638}{1465 - 940}$
                         = $\frac{8767.5}{525}$ = 16.7
          y - 17638 = 16.7(x - 940)
          y = 16.7x - 15698 + 17638
          C(x) = 16.7x + 1940
     (c) Solve 22.5x = 16.7x + 1940
          5.8x = 1940
          x = 334.48 so use 335 for break-even quantity.

Review Exercises, Chapter 1

1.   (a) f(5) = $\frac{7 \times 5 - 3}{2}$ = 16   (b) f(1) = 2

     (c) f(4) = 12.5   (d) f(b) = $\frac{7b - 3}{2}$

3.   f(2) + g(3) = $\frac{2 + 2}{2 - 1}$ + 5(3) + 3 = $\frac{4}{1}$ + 15 + 3 = 22

5.   (a) f(3.5) = 1.20(3.5) = $4.20
     (b) Solve 1.20x = 3.30
          x = 2.75 pounds

7.   (a) f(x) = 29.95x   (b) f(x) = 1.25x + 40

9.   (a)   (b)

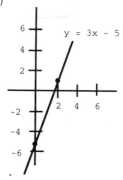
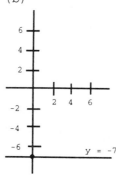

Review, Chapter 1

(c)

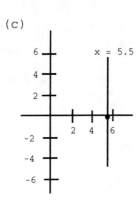

(d)

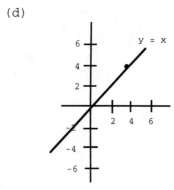

11. (a) Slope is -2, y-intercept is 3
    (b) Slope is 2/3, y-intercept is -4

    (c) $y = \frac{5}{4}x + \frac{3}{2}$ slope is $\frac{5}{4}$, y-intercept is $\frac{3}{2}$

    (d) $y = -\frac{6}{7}x - \frac{5}{7}$ slope is $-\frac{6}{7}$, y-intercept is $-\frac{5}{7}$

13. $y = -\frac{6}{5}x + 3$ (a) $m = -\frac{6}{5}$ (b) y-intercept = 3

    (c) When y = 0, x = 5/2, so x-intercept = 5/2

15. (a) $y = -\frac{3}{4}x + 5$ (b) $y = 8x - 3$

    (c) $y + 1 = -2(x - 5)$ (d) Horizontal line, $y = 6$
         $y = -2x + 10 - 1$
         $y = -2x + 9$

    (e) $m = \frac{4 - 3}{-1 - 5} = \frac{1}{-6}$ (f) Vertical line, $x = -2$

         $y - 3 = -\frac{1}{6}(x - 5)$

         $y = -\frac{1}{6}x + \frac{5}{6} + 3$

         $y = -\frac{1}{6}x + \frac{23}{6}$

    (g) $y = \frac{4}{3}x - \frac{22}{3}$, so $m = \frac{4}{3}$

         $y - 7 = \frac{4}{3}(x - 2)$

         $y = \frac{4}{3}x + \frac{13}{3}$ or $4x - 3y = -13$

17. (a) $m = \frac{2 - 2}{-3 - 6} = 0$ (b) $m = \frac{-2 - 5}{-4 + 4}$
         $y - 2 = 0(x - 6)$ slope undefined, $x = -4$
         $y = 2$

    (c) $m = \frac{10 - 0}{5 - 5}$ slope undefined, $x = 5$

    (d) $m = \frac{6 - 6}{7 + 7} = 0$ $y = 6$

19. The line through (5, 19) and (-2, 7) has slope $m_1 = \frac{19 - 7}{5 + 2} = \frac{12}{7}$

    The line through (11, 3) and (-1, -5) has slope $m_2 = \frac{3 + 5}{11 + 1} = \frac{8}{12} = \frac{2}{3}$

    The lines are not parallel.

21. The given line has slope m = -2. The line through (8, 6) and
$(-3, 14)$ has slope $m = \dfrac{14 - 6}{-3 - 8} = \dfrac{8}{-11} = -\dfrac{8}{11}$
The lines are not parallel.

23. The given line has slope $m = \dfrac{3}{2}$. The line through (9, 10) and
(5, 6) has slope $m = \dfrac{10 - 6}{9 - 5} = 1$ The lines are not parallel.

25. $C(x) = 36x + 12,800$

27. (a) $C(580) = 3.60(580) + 2850 = \$4,938$
   (b) Solve $3.60x + 2850 = 5208$
   $3.60x = 2358$
   $x = 655$ bags

29. (a) $R(x) = 11x$ (b) $C(x) = 6.5x + 675$
   (c) Solve $11x = 6.5x + 675$
   $4.5x = 675$
   $x = 150$

31. $R(x) = 19.5x$
   The points (1840, 25260) and (2315, 31102.5) lie on the cost line
   so, $m = \dfrac{31102.5 - 25260}{2315 - 1840} = \dfrac{5842.5}{475} = 12.3$
   $y - 25260 = 12.3(x - 1840)$
   $C(x) = 12.3x + 2628$
   To find the break-even quantity, solve
   $19.5x = 12.3x + 2628$
   $7.2x = 2628$
   $x = 365$ watches

33. (a) The points (0, 17500) and (8, 900) lie on the line
   so $m = \dfrac{900 - 17500}{8 - 0} = \dfrac{-16600}{8} = -2075$
   $BV = -2075x + 17500$
   (b) $\$2,075$
   (c) $BV(5) = -2075(5) + 17500 = \$7,125$

35. The points (0, 1540) and (5, 60) lie on the line, so
   $m = \dfrac{1540 - 60}{0 - 5} = \dfrac{1480}{-5} = -296$
   $BV = -296x + 1540$

37. The slope of the given line is 4/5, so
   $\dfrac{k - 9}{-3 - 2} = \dfrac{4}{5}$
   $k - 9 = -4$
   $k = 5$

39. The points (0, 12000) and (5, 1500) lie on the line, so
   $m = \dfrac{1500 - 12000}{5 - 0} = \dfrac{-10500}{5} = -2100$
   $BV = -2100x + 12,000$

41. Let x = number of hamburgers and y = cost. Then m = 0.67, and the
   point (1150, 1250.5) lies on the line,
   so $y - 1250.5 = 0.67(x - 1150)$
   $y = 0.67x - 770.5 + 1250.5$
   $C(x) = 0.67x + 480$

43. $0.75x + 2000 > 17000$
     $0.75x > 15000 \qquad x > 20,000$
     The second plan is better when sales exceed \$20,000.

45. $\dfrac{k - 4}{-2 - 9} = -2$
     $k - 4 = 22$
     $k = 26$

47. Let x = number of tapes and C(x) = total cost. Since the unit
     cost is \$6.82, m = 6.82, and the point (1730, 12813.60) lies on
     the line,
     $y - 12813.60 = 6.82(x - 1730)$
     $C(x) = 6.82x + 1015$
     The fixed cost is \$1015.

Chapter 2
Linear Systems

Section 2-1

1. $4x - y = 5$
    $x + 2y = 8$

    $x = 8 - 2y$
    $4(8 - 2y) - y = 5$
    $32 - 8y - y = 5$
    $-9y = -27$
    $y = 3$
    $x = 8 - 2(3) = 2 \qquad (2, 3)$

3. $5x - y = -15$
    $x + y = -3$

    $x = -3 - y$
    $5(-3 - y) - y = -15$
    $-15 - 5y - y = -15$
    $-6y = 0$
    $y = 0$
    $x = -3 - 0 = -3 \qquad (-3, 0)$

5. $y = 5x$
    $6x - 2y = 12$

    $6x - 2(5x) = 12$
    $-4x = 12$
    $x = -3$
    $y = 5(-3) = -15 \qquad (-3, -15)$

7. $7x - y = 32$
    $2x + 3y = 19$

    $y = 7x - 32$
    $2x + 3(7x - 32) = 19$
    $2x + 21x - 96 = 19$
    $23x = 115$
    $x = 5$
    $y = 7(5) - 32 = 3 \qquad (5, 3)$

9. $5x + 2y = 14$
    $x - 3y = 30$

    $x = 3y + 30$
    $5(3y + 30) + 2y = 14$
    $15y + 150 + 2y = 14$
    $17y = -136$
    $y = -8$
    $x = 3(-8) + 30 = 6 \qquad (6, -8)$

11. $22x + y = 81$
    $8x - 3y = 16$

    $y = 81 - 22x$
    $8x - 3(81 - 22x) = 16$
    $8x - 243 + 66x = 16$
    $74x = 259$
    $x = 3.5$
    $y = 81 - 22(3.5) = 4 \qquad (3.5, 4)$

13. $6x - 3y = 9$
    $9x - 15y = 31$

    $3y = 6x - 9$
    $y = 2x - 3$
    $9x - 15(2x - 3) = 31$
    $9x - 30x + 45 = 31$
    $-21x = -14$
    $x = 2/3$
    $y = 2(2/3) - 3 = 4/3 - 3 = -5/3 \quad (2/3, -5/3)$

15. $y = 3x - 5$
    $8x - 4y - 30 = 0$

    $8x - 4(3x - 5) - 30 = 0$
    $8x - 12x + 20 - 30 = 0$
    $-4x - 10 = 0$
    $x = -2.5$
    $y = -12.5 \qquad (-2.5, -12.5)$

Section 2-1

17. $3x - 4y = 22$ $6x - 8y = 44$
     $2x + 5y = 7$ $\underline{-6x - 15y = -21}$
                                     $-23y = 23$
                             $y = -1$
                             $3x - 4(-1) = 22$
                             $3x + 4 = 22$
                             $x = 6$ $(6, -1)$

19. $6x - y = 18$ $6x - y = 18$
     $2x + y = 2$ $\underline{2x + y = 2}$
                         $8x = 20$
                         $x = 5/2$
                         $2(5/2) + y = 2$
                         $5 + y = 2$
                         $y = -3$ $(5/2, -3)$

21. $-2x + y = 7$ $-6x + 3y = 21$
     $6x + 12y = 24$ $\underline{6x + 12y = 24}$
                                     $15y = 45$
                             $y = 3$
                             $-2x + 3 = 7$
                             $-2x = 4$
                             $x = -2$ $(-2, 3)$

23. $2x + y = -9$ $-4x - 2y = 18$
     $4x + 3y = 1$ $\underline{4x + 3y = 1}$
                                 $y = 19$
                          $2x + 19 = -9$
                          $2x = -28$
                          $x = -14$
                          $(-14, 19)$

25. $7x + 3y = -1.5$ $35x + 15y = -7.5$
     $2x - 5y = -30.3$ $\underline{6x - 15y = -90.9}$
                               $41x = -98.4$
                               $x = -2.4$
                               $2(-2.4) - 5y = -30.3$
                               $-5y = -25.5$
                               $y = 5.1$ $(-2.4, 5.1)$

27. $2x - 3y = -0.27$ $-4x + 6y = 0.54$
     $5x - 2y = 0.04$ $\underline{15x - 6y = 0.12}$
                                $11x = 0.66$
                                $x = 0.06$
                                $2(0.06) - 3y = -0.27$
                                $-3y = -0.39$
                                $y = 0.13$ $(0.06, 0.13)$

29. $6x - 9y = 8$ $30x - 45y = 40$
     $10x - 15y = -20$ $\underline{-30x + 45y = 60}$
                                   $0 = 100$
                            No solution

31. $8x + 10y = 2$ $4x + 5y = 1$
     $12x + 15y = 3$ $\underline{-4x - 5y = -1}$
                                   $0 = 0$
                            Infinite number

33. $\begin{array}{l} x - 6y = 4 \\ 5x - 30y = 20 \end{array}$

$\begin{array}{l} x - 6y = 4 \\ \underline{-x + 6y = -4} \\ 0 = 0 \end{array}$

Infinite number

35. $\begin{array}{l} y = -3x + 15 \\ y = 2x - 5 \end{array}$

$\begin{array}{l} 2x - 5 = -3x + 15 \\ 5x = 20 \\ x = 4 \\ y = -3(4) + 15 = 3 \qquad (4, 3) \end{array}$

37. $\begin{array}{l} y = -4x + 130 \\ y = x - 20 \end{array}$

$\begin{array}{l} x - 20 = -4x + 130 \\ 5x = 150 \\ x = 30 \\ y = 30 - 20 = 10 \qquad (30, 10) \end{array}$

39. $\begin{array}{l} y = -5x + 83 \\ y = 4x - 52 \end{array}$

$\begin{array}{l} 4x - 52 = -5x + 83 \\ 9x = 135 \\ x = 15 \\ y = 4(15) - 52 = 8 \qquad (15, 8) \end{array}$

41. $\begin{array}{l} y = -2.5x + 148 \\ y = 1.7x + 43 \end{array}$

$\begin{array}{l} 1.7x + 43 = -2.5x + 148 \\ 4.2x = 105 \\ x = 25 \\ y = 1.7(25) + 43 = 85.5 \qquad (25, 85.5) \end{array}$

43. Let x = number of oranges and y = number of apples.

$\begin{array}{l} 50x + 8y = 151 \\ 0.5x + 0.4y = 2.55 \end{array}$

$\begin{array}{l} 50x + 8y = 151 \\ \underline{-50x - 40y = -255} \\ -32y = -104 \\ y = 3.25 \\ 50x + 8(3.25) = 151 \\ 50x = 125 \\ x = 2.5 \\ (2.5 \text{ oranges}, 3.25 \text{ apples}) \end{array}$

45. Let n number of nickels and d = number of dimes.

$\begin{array}{l} n + d = 165 \\ 5n + 10d = 1435 \end{array}$

$\begin{array}{l} d = 165 - n \\ 5n + 10(165 - n) = 1435 \\ 5n + 1650 - 10n = 1435 \\ -5n = -215 \\ n = 43 \\ d = 165 - 43 = 122 \\ (43 \text{ nickels}, 122 \text{ dimes}) \end{array}$

47. Let x = number of gallons of 20% acid and y = number of gallons of 55% acid.

$\begin{array}{l} x + y = 840 \\ .20x + .55y = .30(840) \end{array}$

$\begin{array}{l} x = 840 - y \\ 20(840 - y) + 55y = 25200 \\ 35y = 8400 \\ y = 240 \\ x = 840 - 240 = 600 \\ (600 \text{ gallons of 20%}, 240 \text{ gallons of 55%}) \end{array}$

49. Let x = number produced at McGregor and y = number produced at Ennis.

$$x + y = 1500 \qquad\qquad x = 1500 - y$$
$$8.4x + 7480 = 7.8y + 5419 \qquad 84(1500 - y) - 78y = -20610$$
$$162y = 146610$$
$$y = 905$$
$$x = 1500 - 905 = 595$$

(595 at McGregor, 905 at Ennis)

51. Let P = weight of peanuts and C = weight of cashews.

$$P + C = 80 \qquad\qquad P = 80 - C$$
$$3P + 7C = 4(80) \qquad 3(80 - C) + 7C = 320$$
$$4C = 80$$
$$C = 20$$
$$P = 80 - 20 = 60$$

(60 lb of peanuts, 20 lb of cashews)

53. Let x = cases of Golden Punch and y = cases of Light Punch.

$$4x + 7y = 142 \qquad 12x + 21y = 426$$
$$6x + 3y = 108 \qquad -12x - 6y = -216$$
$$15y = 210$$
$$y = 14$$
$$x = 11$$

(11 cases of Golden, 14 cases of Light Punch)

55. Let B = number of beef and S = number of sausage sandwiches.

$$B + S = 115 \qquad S = 115 - B$$
$$2.3B + 2.1S = 253.90 \qquad 23B + 21(115 - B) = 2539$$
$$2B = 124$$
$$B = 62$$
$$S = 115 - 62 = 53$$

(62 chopped beef, 53 sausage)

57. Let x = amount in tax-free and y = amount in money market.

$$x + y = 50000 \qquad x = 50000 - y$$
$$.074x + .088y = 4071 \qquad 74(50000 - y) + 88y = 4071000$$
$$14y = 371,000$$
$$y = 26,500$$
$$x = 23,500$$

($23,500 in tax-free, $26,500 in money market)

59. Let x = amount of federal tax and y = amount of state tax.

$$x + .2y = 39600 \qquad .05x + .01y = 1980$$
$$.05x + y = 9900 \qquad \underline{-.05x - y = -9900}$$
$$-.99y = -7920$$
$$y = 8,000$$
$$x = .2(190,000) = 38,000$$

Federal tax is $38,000, state tax is $8,000

Section 2-2

1. $\begin{aligned} x + 2y &= 7 \\ 3x + 5y &= 19 \end{aligned}$

    $\begin{aligned} 3x + 6y &= 21 \\ \underline{3x + 5y} &= \underline{19} \\ y &= 2 \end{aligned}$

    $x + 2(2) = 7$
    $x = 3$
    $(3, 2)$

3. $\begin{aligned} 2x + 5y &= -1 \\ 6x - 4y &= 16 \end{aligned}$

    $\begin{aligned} 6x + 15y &= -3 \\ \underline{6x - 4y} &= \underline{16} \\ 19y &= -19 \\ y &= -1 \end{aligned}$

    $2x + 5(-1) = -1$
    $x = 2 \qquad (2, -1)$

5. $\begin{aligned} x + y - z &= -1 \\ x - y + z &= 5 \\ x - y - z &= 1 \end{aligned}$

    $\begin{aligned} x + y - z &= -1 \\ \underline{x - y + z} &= \underline{5} \qquad \text{subtract second from first} \\ 2y - 2z &= -6 \end{aligned}$

    $\begin{aligned} x - y + z &= 5 \\ \underline{x - y - z} &= \underline{1} \qquad \text{subtract third from second} \\ 2z &= 4 \\ z &= 2 \end{aligned}$

    Substitute $z = 2$
    $2y - 2(2) = -6$
    $2y = -2$
    $y = -1$
    Substitute $y = -1$ and $z = 2$
    $x + (-1) - 2 = -1$
    $x = 2$
    $x = 2, y = -1, z = 2$

7. $\begin{aligned} x + 4y - 2z &= 21 \\ 3x - 6y - 3z &= -18 \\ 2x + 4y + z &= 37 \end{aligned}$

    $\begin{aligned} 3x + 12y - 6z &= 63 \qquad \text{multiply first equation by 3} \\ \underline{3x - 6y - 3z} &= \underline{-18} \qquad \text{subtract second} \\ 18y - 3z &= 81 \end{aligned}$

    $\begin{aligned} 2x + 8y - 4z &= 42 \qquad \text{multiply first equation by 2} \\ \underline{2x + 4y + z} &= \underline{37} \qquad \text{subtract third} \\ 4y - 5z &= 5 \end{aligned}$

    Use these two new equations
    $18y - 3z = 81$
    $4y - 5z = 5$

    $\begin{aligned} 36y - 6z &= 162 \\ \underline{36y - 45z} &= \underline{45} \\ 39z &= 117 \\ z &= 3 \end{aligned}$

    Substitute $z = 3$
    $18y - 3(3) = 81$
    $18y = 90$
    $y = 5$
    Substitute $z = 3$ and $y = 5$
    $x + 4(5) - 2(3) = 21$
    $x = 7 \qquad\qquad (7, 5, 3)$

Section 2-2

9. $2x + 4y - 6z = -2$
     $4x - 3y + z = 11$
     $3x + 2y - 2z = 7$

   $4x + 8y - 12z = -4$ multiply first equation by 2
   $\underline{4x - 3y + z = 11}$ subtract second
   $ 11y - 13z = -15$

   $6x + 12y - 18z = -6$ multiply first equation by 3
   $\underline{6x + 4y - 4z = 14}$ multiply equation 3 by 2
   $ 8y - 14z = -20$ subtract

   Now solve $11y - 13z = -15$
                 $8y - 14z = -20$

   $88y - 104z = -120$
   $\underline{88y - 154z = -220}$
   $ 50z = 100$
   $ z = 2$

   $11y - 13(2) = -15$
   $11y = 11$
   $ y = 1$
   $2x + 4(1) - 6(2) = -2$
   $2x = 6$
   $ x = 3$
   $x = 3, \ y = 1, \ z = 2$

11. (a) $a_{11} = 2$ $a_{22} = 3$ $a_{33} = 6$ $a_{43} = 11$
     (b) $(2, 3)$
     (c) $a_{12} = 4$ $a_{32} = 0$ $a_{41} = 9$

13. coeff: $\begin{bmatrix} 5 & -2 \\ 3 & 1 \end{bmatrix}$ aug: $\left[\begin{array}{cc|c} 5 & -2 & 1 \\ 3 & 1 & 7 \end{array}\right]$

15. coeff: $\begin{bmatrix} 1 & 1 & -1 \\ 3 & 4 & -2 \\ 2 & 0 & 1 \end{bmatrix}$ aug: $\left[\begin{array}{ccc|c} 1 & 1 & -1 & 14 \\ 3 & 4 & -2 & 9 \\ 2 & 0 & 1 & 7 \end{array}\right]$

17. coeff: $\begin{bmatrix} 1 & 5 & -2 & 1 \\ 1 & -1 & 2 & 4 \\ 6 & 3 & -11 & 1 \\ 5 & -3 & -7 & 1 \end{bmatrix}$ aug: $\left[\begin{array}{cccc|c} 1 & 5 & -2 & 1 & 12 \\ 1 & -1 & 2 & 4 & -5 \\ 6 & 3 & -11 & 1 & 14 \\ 5 & -3 & -7 & 1 & 22 \end{array}\right]$

19. $5x + 3y = -2$
     $-x + 4y = 4$

21. $5x_1 + 2x_2 - x_3 = 3$
     $-2x_1 + 7x_2 + 8x_3 = 7$
     $3x_1 + x_3 = 5$

23. $3x_1 + 2x_3 + 6x_4 = 4$
     $-4x_1 + 5x_2 + 7x_3 + 2x_4 = 2$
     $x_1 + 3x_2 + 2x_3 + 5x_4 = 0$
     $-2x_1 + 6x_2 - 5x_3 + 3x_4 = 4$

25. $\begin{bmatrix} 1 & 2 & -4 & 6 \\ 4 & 2 & 5 & 7 \\ 1 & -1 & 0 & 4 \end{bmatrix}$

27. $\begin{bmatrix} 1 & 3 & 2 & -4 \\ 0 & -7 & -1 & 13 \\ 0 & -6 & -10 & 19 \end{bmatrix}$ 29. $\begin{bmatrix} 1 & -3 & 2 & -6 \\ 0 & 1 & -2 & 4 \\ 0 & 4 & 3 & 8 \end{bmatrix}$

31. $\begin{bmatrix} 2 & 3 & | & 5 \\ 1 & -2 & | & -1 \end{bmatrix}$ R1 ↔ R2 $\begin{bmatrix} 1 & -2 & | & -1 \\ 2 & 3 & | & 5 \end{bmatrix}$ -2R1 + R2 → R2

$\begin{bmatrix} 1 & -2 & | & -1 \\ 0 & 7 & | & 7 \end{bmatrix}$ (1/7)R2 → R2 $\begin{bmatrix} 1 & -2 & | & -1 \\ 0 & 1 & | & 1 \end{bmatrix}$ 2R2 + R1 → R1

$\begin{bmatrix} 1 & 0 & | & 1 \\ 0 & 1 & | & 1 \end{bmatrix}$ x = 1, y = 1

33. $\begin{bmatrix} 1 & -3 & | & -1 \\ 4 & 5 & | & 30 \end{bmatrix}$ -4R1 + R2 → R2 $\begin{bmatrix} 1 & -3 & | & -1 \\ 0 & 17 & | & 34 \end{bmatrix}$ (1/17)R2 → R2

$\begin{bmatrix} 1 & -3 & | & -1 \\ 0 & 1 & | & 2 \end{bmatrix}$ 3R2 + R1 → R1 $\begin{bmatrix} 1 & 0 & | & 5 \\ 0 & 1 & | & 2 \end{bmatrix}$ x = 5, y = 2

35. $\begin{bmatrix} 2 & 4 & | & -7 \\ 1 & -3 & | & 9 \end{bmatrix}$ R1 ↔ R2 $\begin{bmatrix} 1 & -3 & | & 9 \\ 2 & 4 & | & -7 \end{bmatrix}$ -2R1 + R2 → R2

$\begin{bmatrix} 1 & -3 & | & 9 \\ 0 & 10 & | & -25 \end{bmatrix}$ (1/10)R2 → R2 $\begin{bmatrix} 1 & -3 & | & 9 \\ 0 & 1 & | & -5/2 \end{bmatrix}$ 3R2 + R1 → R1

$\begin{bmatrix} 1 & 0 & | & 3/2 \\ 0 & 1 & | & -5/2 \end{bmatrix}$ x = 3/2, y = -5/2

37. $\begin{bmatrix} 1 & 2 & -1 & | & 3 \\ 1 & 3 & -1 & | & 4 \\ 1 & -1 & 1 & | & 4 \end{bmatrix}$ -R1 + R2 → R2 $\begin{bmatrix} 1 & 2 & -1 & | & 3 \\ 0 & 1 & 0 & | & 1 \\ 0 & -3 & 2 & | & 1 \end{bmatrix}$ -2R1 + R1 → R1

-R1 + R3 → R3   3R2 + R3 → R3

$\begin{bmatrix} 1 & 0 & -1 & | & 1 \\ 0 & 1 & 0 & | & 1 \\ 0 & 0 & 2 & | & 4 \end{bmatrix}$ (1/2)R3 → R3 $\begin{bmatrix} 1 & 0 & -1 & | & 1 \\ 0 & 1 & 0 & | & 1 \\ 0 & 0 & 1 & | & 2 \end{bmatrix}$ R3 + R1 → R1

$\begin{bmatrix} 1 & 0 & 0 & | & 3 \\ 0 & 1 & 0 & | & 1 \\ 0 & 0 & 1 & | & 2 \end{bmatrix}$ $x_1 = 3,\ x_2 = 1,\ x_3 = 2$

39. $\begin{bmatrix} 2 & 4 & 2 & | & 6 \\ 2 & 1 & 1 & | & 16 \\ 1 & 1 & 2 & | & 9 \end{bmatrix}$ R1 ↔ R3 $\begin{bmatrix} 1 & 1 & 2 & | & 9 \\ 2 & 1 & 1 & | & 16 \\ 2 & 4 & 2 & | & 6 \end{bmatrix}$ -2R1 + R2 → R2

-2R1 + R3 → R3

$\begin{bmatrix} 1 & 1 & 2 & | & 9 \\ 0 & -1 & -3 & | & -2 \\ 0 & 2 & -2 & | & -12 \end{bmatrix}$ R2 + R1 → R1 $\begin{bmatrix} 1 & 0 & -1 & | & 7 \\ 0 & 1 & 3 & | & 2 \\ 0 & 0 & -8 & | & -16 \end{bmatrix}$ -(1/8)R3 → R3

-R2 → R2

2R2 + R3 → R3

$\begin{bmatrix} 1 & 0 & -1 & | & 7 \\ 0 & 1 & 3 & | & 2 \\ 0 & 0 & 1 & | & 2 \end{bmatrix}$ R3 + R1 → R1 $\begin{bmatrix} 1 & 0 & 0 & | & 9 \\ 0 & 1 & 0 & | & -4 \\ 0 & 0 & 1 & | & 2 \end{bmatrix}$ (9, -4, 2)

-3R3 + R2 → R2

41. $\begin{bmatrix} 1 & 2 & -1 & | & -1 \\ 2 & -3 & 2 & | & 15 \\ 0 & 1 & 4 & | & -7 \end{bmatrix}$ -2R1 + R2 → R2 $\begin{bmatrix} 1 & 2 & -1 & | & -1 \\ 0 & -7 & 4 & | & 17 \\ 0 & 1 & 4 & | & -7 \end{bmatrix}$ R2 ↔ R3

$\begin{bmatrix} 1 & 2 & -1 & | & -1 \\ 0 & 1 & 4 & | & -7 \\ 0 & -7 & 4 & | & 17 \end{bmatrix}$ -2R2 + R1 → R1 $\begin{bmatrix} 1 & 0 & -9 & | & 13 \\ 0 & 1 & 4 & | & -7 \\ 0 & 0 & 32 & | & -32 \end{bmatrix}$

7R2 + R3 → R3

$\begin{bmatrix} 1 & 0 & -9 & | & 13 \\ 0 & 1 & 4 & | & -7 \\ 0 & 0 & 1 & | & -1 \end{bmatrix}$ $\begin{bmatrix} 1 & 0 & 0 & | & 4 \\ 0 & 1 & 0 & | & -3 \\ 0 & 0 & 1 & | & -1 \end{bmatrix}$ (4, -3, -1)

43.
$$\begin{bmatrix} 1 & 5 & -1 & | & 1 \\ 4 & -2 & -3 & | & 6 \\ -3 & 1 & 3 & | & -3 \end{bmatrix} \qquad \begin{bmatrix} 1 & 5 & -1 & | & 1 \\ 0 & -22 & 1 & | & 2 \\ 0 & 16 & 0 & | & 0 \end{bmatrix}$$

$$\begin{bmatrix} 1 & 0 & -1 & | & 1 \\ 0 & 0 & 1 & | & 2 \\ 0 & 1 & 0 & | & 0 \end{bmatrix} \qquad \begin{bmatrix} 1 & 0 & 0 & | & 3 \\ 0 & 0 & 1 & | & 2 \\ 0 & 1 & 0 & | & 0 \end{bmatrix} \qquad (3, 0, 2)$$

45.
$$\begin{bmatrix} 2 & 2 & 4 & | & 16 \\ 1 & 2 & -1 & | & 6 \\ -3 & 1 & -2 & | & 0 \end{bmatrix} \qquad \begin{bmatrix} 1 & 1 & 2 & | & 8 \\ 0 & 1 & -3 & | & -2 \\ 0 & 1 & 1 & | & 6 \end{bmatrix}$$

$$\begin{bmatrix} 1 & 0 & 5 & | & 10 \\ 0 & 1 & -3 & | & -2 \\ 0 & 0 & 1 & | & 2 \end{bmatrix} \qquad \begin{bmatrix} 1 & 0 & 0 & | & 0 \\ 0 & 1 & 0 & | & 4 \\ 0 & 0 & 1 & | & 2 \end{bmatrix} \qquad (0, 4, 2)$$

47.
$$\begin{bmatrix} 1 & 2 & -3 & | & -6 \\ 1 & -3 & -7 & | & 10 \\ 1 & -1 & 1 & | & 10 \end{bmatrix} \qquad \begin{bmatrix} 1 & 2 & -3 & | & -6 \\ 0 & 5 & 4 & | & -16 \\ 0 & -3 & 4 & | & 16 \end{bmatrix}$$

$$\begin{bmatrix} 1 & 0 & -23/5 & | & 2/5 \\ 0 & 1 & 4/5 & | & -16/5 \\ 0 & 0 & 32/5 & | & 32/5 \end{bmatrix} \qquad \begin{bmatrix} 1 & 0 & 0 & | & 5 \\ 0 & 1 & 0 & | & -4 \\ 0 & 0 & 1 & | & 1 \end{bmatrix} \qquad (5, -4, 1)$$

49.
$$\begin{bmatrix} 1 & 1 & 1 & 1 & | & 4 \\ 1 & 2 & -1 & -1 & | & 7 \\ 2 & -1 & -1 & -1 & | & 8 \\ 1 & -1 & 2 & -2 & | & -7 \end{bmatrix} \begin{matrix} \\ -R1 + R2 \to R2 \\ -2R1 + R3 \to R3 \\ -R1 + R4 \to R4 \end{matrix}$$

$$\begin{bmatrix} 1 & 1 & 1 & 1 & | & 4 \\ 0 & 1 & -2 & -2 & | & 3 \\ 0 & -3 & -3 & -3 & | & 0 \\ 0 & -2 & 1 & -3 & | & -11 \end{bmatrix} \begin{matrix} -R2 + R1 \to R1 \\ \\ 3R2 + R3 \to R3 \\ 2R2 + R4 \to R4 \end{matrix}$$

$$\begin{bmatrix} 1 & 0 & 3 & 3 & | & 1 \\ 0 & 1 & -2 & -2 & | & 3 \\ 0 & 0 & -9 & -9 & | & 9 \\ 0 & 0 & -3 & -7 & | & -5 \end{bmatrix} \begin{matrix} \\ \\ (-1/9)R3 \to R3 \\ \end{matrix}$$

$$\begin{bmatrix} 1 & 0 & 3 & 3 & | & 1 \\ 0 & 1 & -2 & -2 & | & 3 \\ 0 & 0 & 1 & 1 & | & -1 \\ 0 & 0 & -3 & -7 & | & -5 \end{bmatrix} \begin{matrix} -3R3 + R1 \to R1 \\ 2R3 + R2 \to R2 \\ \\ 3R3 + R4 \to R4 \end{matrix}$$

$$\begin{bmatrix} 1 & 0 & 0 & 0 & | & 4 \\ 0 & 1 & 0 & 0 & | & 1 \\ 0 & 0 & 1 & 1 & | & -1 \\ 0 & 0 & 0 & -4 & | & -8 \end{bmatrix} \begin{matrix} \\ \\ \\ (-1/4)R4 \to R4 \end{matrix}$$

$$\begin{bmatrix} 1 & 0 & 0 & 0 & | & 4 \\ 0 & 1 & 0 & 0 & | & 1 \\ 0 & 0 & 1 & 1 & | & -1 \\ 0 & 0 & 0 & 1 & | & 2 \end{bmatrix} \begin{matrix} \\ \\ \\ -R4 + R3 \to R3 \end{matrix}$$

$$\begin{bmatrix} 1 & 0 & 0 & 0 & | & 4 \\ 0 & 1 & 0 & 0 & | & 1 \\ 0 & 0 & 1 & 0 & | & -3 \\ 0 & 0 & 0 & 1 & | & 2 \end{bmatrix} \qquad (4, 1, -3, 2)$$

51. $\begin{bmatrix} 2 & 6 & 4 & -2 & | & 18 \\ 1 & 4 & -2 & -1 & | & -1 \\ 3 & -1 & -1 & 2 & | & 6 \\ -1 & -2 & -5 & 0 & | & -20 \end{bmatrix}$ $\begin{bmatrix} 1 & 3 & 2 & -1 & | & 9 \\ 0 & 1 & -4 & 0 & | & -10 \\ 0 & -10 & -7 & 5 & | & -21 \\ 0 & 1 & -3 & -1 & | & -11 \end{bmatrix}$

$\begin{bmatrix} 1 & 0 & 14 & -1 & | & 39 \\ 0 & 1 & -4 & 0 & | & -10 \\ 0 & 0 & -47 & 5 & | & -121 \\ 0 & 0 & 1 & -1 & | & -1 \end{bmatrix}$ $\begin{bmatrix} 1 & 0 & 14 & -1 & | & 39 \\ 0 & 1 & -4 & 0 & | & -10 \\ 0 & 0 & 1 & -1 & | & -1 \\ 0 & 0 & -47 & 5 & | & -121 \end{bmatrix}$

$\begin{bmatrix} 1 & 0 & 0 & 13 & | & 53 \\ 0 & 1 & 0 & -4 & | & -14 \\ 0 & 0 & 1 & -1 & | & -1 \\ 0 & 0 & 0 & -42 & | & -168 \end{bmatrix}$ $\begin{bmatrix} 1 & 0 & 0 & 0 & | & 1 \\ 0 & 1 & 0 & 0 & | & 2 \\ 0 & 0 & 1 & 0 & | & 3 \\ 0 & 0 & 0 & 1 & | & 4 \end{bmatrix}$ $(1, 2, 3, 4)$

53. Let x_1 = number cases of Regular, x_2 = number cases of Premium, x_3 = number cases of Classic.

$$4x_1 + 4x_2 + 5x_3 = 316 \quad \text{(Apple juice)}$$
$$5x_1 + 4x_2 + 2x_3 = 292 \quad \text{(Pineapple juice)}$$
$$x_1 + 2x_2 + 3x_3 = 142 \quad \text{(Cranberry juice)}$$

55. Let x_1 = number of student tickets, x_2 = number of faculty tickets, x_3 = number of general public tickets.

$$3x_1 + 5x_2 + 8x_3 = 2542$$
$$x_1 = 3x_2$$
$$x_3 = 2x_1$$

57. Let x = number shares of X, y = number shares of Y, z = number shares of Z.

$$44x + 22y + 64z = 20,480$$
$$42x + 28y + 62z = 20,720$$
$$42x + 30y + 60z = 20,580$$

59. Let x_1 = number of Portfolio I, x_2 = number of Portfolio II, x_3 = number of Portfolio III.

$$x_1 + 3x_2 + 2x_3 = 15$$
$$3x_1 + 2x_2 + x_3 = 14$$
$$x_1 + 2x_2 + 4x_3 = 16$$

$\begin{bmatrix} 1 & 3 & 2 & | & 15 \\ 3 & 2 & 1 & | & 14 \\ 1 & 2 & 4 & | & 16 \end{bmatrix}$ $\begin{bmatrix} 1 & 3 & 2 & | & 15 \\ 0 & -7 & -5 & | & -31 \\ 0 & -1 & 2 & | & 1 \end{bmatrix}$ $\begin{bmatrix} 1 & 0 & 8 & | & 18 \\ 0 & 1 & -2 & | & -1 \\ 0 & 0 & -19 & | & -38 \end{bmatrix}$

$\begin{bmatrix} 1 & 0 & 8 & | & 18 \\ 0 & 1 & -2 & | & -1 \\ 0 & 0 & 1 & | & 2 \end{bmatrix}$ $\begin{bmatrix} 1 & 0 & 0 & | & 2 \\ 0 & 1 & 0 & | & 3 \\ 0 & 0 & 1 & | & 2 \end{bmatrix}$

2 of Portfolio I, 3 of Portfolio II, 2 of Portfolio III

61. Let A = amount invested in stock A, B = amount invested in stock B, C = amount invested in stock C.

$$A + B + C = 40,000$$
$$.06A + .07B + .08C = 2730$$
$$.03A + .04B + .02C = 1080$$

$\begin{bmatrix} 1 & 1 & 1 & 40000 \\ .06 & .07 & .08 & 2730 \\ .03 & .04 & .02 & 1080 \end{bmatrix}$ $\begin{bmatrix} 1 & 1 & 1 & 40000 \\ 0 & 1 & 2 & 33000 \\ 0 & 1 & -1 & -12000 \end{bmatrix}$ $\begin{bmatrix} 1 & 0 & -1 & 7000 \\ 0 & 1 & 2 & 33000 \\ 0 & 0 & -3 & -45000 \end{bmatrix}$

Section 2-3

$$\left[\begin{array}{ccc|c} 1 & 0 & -1 & 7000 \\ 0 & 1 & 2 & 33000 \\ 0 & 0 & 1 & 15000 \end{array}\right] \qquad \left[\begin{array}{ccc|c} 1 & 0 & 0 & 22000 \\ 0 & 1 & 0 & 3000 \\ 0 & 0 & 1 & 15000 \end{array}\right]$$

$22,000 in stock A, $3,000 in stock B, $15,000 in stock C

63. Let x_1 = number high school tickets, x_2 = number college tickets, x_3 = number adult tickets.

$$4x_1 + 6x_2 + 8x_3 = 14980$$
$$4x_1 + 5x_2 + 9x_3 = 14430$$
$$2x_1 + 7x_2 + 7x_3 = 14450$$

$$\left[\begin{array}{ccc|c} 4 & 6 & 8 & 14980 \\ 4 & 5 & 9 & 14430 \\ 2 & 7 & 7 & 14450 \end{array}\right] \quad \left[\begin{array}{ccc|c} 1 & 3/2 & 2 & 3745 \\ 0 & -1 & 1 & -550 \\ 0 & 4 & 3 & 6960 \end{array}\right] \quad \left[\begin{array}{ccc|c} 1 & 0 & 7/2 & 2920 \\ 0 & 1 & -1 & 550 \\ 0 & 0 & 7 & 4760 \end{array}\right]$$

$$\left[\begin{array}{ccc|c} 1 & 0 & 7/2 & 2920 \\ 0 & 1 & -1 & 550 \\ 0 & 0 & 1 & 680 \end{array}\right] \quad \left[\begin{array}{ccc|c} 1 & 0 & 0 & 540 \\ 0 & 1 & 0 & 1230 \\ 0 & 0 & 1 & 680 \end{array}\right]$$

540 to high school students, 1230 to college students, 680 to adults

65. $$\left[\begin{array}{ccc|c} 1 & 2 & 3 & 142 \\ 5 & 4 & 2 & 292 \\ 4 & 4 & 5 & 316 \end{array}\right] \quad \left[\begin{array}{ccc|c} 1 & 2 & 3 & 142 \\ 0 & -6 & -13 & -418 \\ 0 & -4 & -7 & -252 \end{array}\right] \quad \left[\begin{array}{ccc|c} 1 & 0 & -4/3 & 8/3 \\ 0 & 1 & 13/6 & 209/3 \\ 0 & 0 & 5/3 & 80/3 \end{array}\right]$$

$$\left[\begin{array}{ccc|c} 1 & 0 & -4/3 & 8/3 \\ 0 & 1 & 13/6 & 209/3 \\ 0 & 0 & 1 & 16 \end{array}\right] \qquad \left[\begin{array}{ccc|c} 1 & 0 & 0 & 24 \\ 0 & 1 & 0 & 35 \\ 0 & 0 & 1 & 16 \end{array}\right] \begin{array}{l} 24 \text{ cases of Regular} \\ 35 \text{ cases of Premium} \\ 16 \text{ cases of Classic} \end{array}$$

67. $$\left[\begin{array}{ccc|c} 1 & -3 & 0 & 0 \\ -2 & 0 & 1 & 0 \\ 3 & 5 & 8 & 2542 \end{array}\right] \qquad \left[\begin{array}{ccc|c} 1 & -3 & 0 & 0 \\ 0 & -6 & 1 & 0 \\ 0 & 14 & 8 & 2542 \end{array}\right]$$

$$\left[\begin{array}{ccc|c} 1 & 0 & -1/2 & 0 \\ 0 & 1 & -1/6 & 0 \\ 0 & 0 & 31/3 & 2542 \end{array}\right] \qquad \left[\begin{array}{ccc|c} 1 & 0 & 0 & 123 \\ 0 & 1 & 0 & 41 \\ 0 & 0 & 1 & 246 \end{array}\right]$$

123 students, 41 faculty, 246 general public

69. $$\left[\begin{array}{ccc|c} 44 & 22 & 64 & 20480 \\ 42 & 28 & 62 & 20720 \\ 42 & 30 & 60 & 20580 \end{array}\right] \qquad \left[\begin{array}{ccc|c} 1 & 1/2 & 16/11 & 5120/11 \\ 0 & 7 & 10/11 & 12880/11 \\ 0 & 9 & -12/11 & 11340/11 \end{array}\right]$$

$$\left[\begin{array}{ccc|c} 1 & 0 & 107/77 & 4200/11 \\ 0 & 1 & 10/77 & 1840/11 \\ 0 & 0 & -174/77 & -5220/11 \end{array}\right] \quad \left[\begin{array}{ccc|c} 1 & 1 & 107/77 & 4200/11 \\ 0 & 1 & 10/77 & 1840/11 \\ 0 & 0 & 1 & 210 \end{array}\right]$$

$$\left[\begin{array}{ccc|c} 1 & 0 & 0 & 90 \\ 0 & 1 & 0 & 140 \\ 0 & 0 & 1 & 210 \end{array}\right] \begin{array}{l} 90 \text{ shares of X} \\ 140 \text{ shares of Y} \\ 210 \text{ shares of Z} \end{array}$$

Section 2-3

1. Yes   3. No, leftmost nonzero entry of Row 2 is 2, not 1.

5. No, Rows 2 and 3 should be switched.

7. No, should have 0's in column 4 of Rows 1 and 2, and in column 5 of Rows 1, 2, and 3.

9. No, leftmost nonzero entry of row 2 is 2, not 1.

11. $\begin{bmatrix} 1 & 0 & 1 & | & 4 \\ 0 & 1 & 2 & | & 3 \\ 0 & 0 & 1 & | & 2 \end{bmatrix}$
13. $\begin{bmatrix} 1 & 3 & 4 & | & -1 \\ 0 & 4 & 3 & | & 4 \\ 0 & 0 & 6 & | & 2 \end{bmatrix}$

15. $\begin{bmatrix} 1 & 4 & 2 & 4 & | & 5 \\ 0 & 0 & 3 & 1 & | & 2 \\ 0 & 0 & 0 & 2 & | & 3 \\ 0 & 0 & 0 & 0 & | & 6 \end{bmatrix}$
17. $\begin{bmatrix} 1 & 0 & 2 & | & 3 \\ 0 & 1 & 4 & | & 4 \\ 0 & 0 & 0 & | & 5 \\ 0 & 0 & 0 & | & 0 \end{bmatrix}$

19. $\begin{bmatrix} 1 & -1 & 7 & | & 1 \\ 1 & -2 & 1 & | & 4 \\ 2 & 1 & 0 & | & 1 \end{bmatrix}$ $\begin{bmatrix} 1 & -1 & 7 & | & 1 \\ 0 & -1 & -6 & | & 3 \\ 0 & 3 & -14 & | & -1 \end{bmatrix}$

$\begin{bmatrix} 1 & 0 & 13 & | & -2 \\ 0 & 1 & 6 & | & -3 \\ 0 & 0 & -32 & | & 8 \end{bmatrix}$ $\begin{bmatrix} 1 & 0 & 0 & | & 5/4 \\ 0 & 1 & 0 & | & -6/4 \\ 0 & 0 & 1 & | & -1/4 \end{bmatrix}$

21. $\begin{bmatrix} 2 & 4 & 8 & | & -4 \\ 3 & 5 & -1 & | & 6 \\ 1 & -1 & -9 & | & 10 \end{bmatrix}$ $\begin{bmatrix} 1 & 2 & 4 & | & -2 \\ 0 & -1 & -13 & | & 12 \\ 0 & -3 & -13 & | & 12 \end{bmatrix}$

$\begin{bmatrix} 1 & 0 & -22 & | & 22 \\ 0 & 1 & 13 & | & -12 \\ 0 & 0 & 26 & | & -24 \end{bmatrix}$ $\begin{bmatrix} 1 & 0 & 0 & | & 22/13 \\ 0 & 1 & 0 & | & 0 \\ 0 & 0 & 1 & | & -12/13 \end{bmatrix}$

23. $\begin{bmatrix} 1 & 2 & 1 & 0 & | & 3 \\ 0 & 1 & 4 & 1 & | & 2 \\ 2 & -1 & 3 & 1 & | & 4 \end{bmatrix}$ $\begin{bmatrix} 1 & 2 & 1 & 0 & | & 3 \\ 0 & 1 & 4 & 1 & | & 2 \\ 0 & -5 & 1 & 1 & | & -2 \end{bmatrix}$

$\begin{bmatrix} 1 & 0 & -7 & -2 & | & -1 \\ 0 & 1 & 4 & 1 & | & 2 \\ 0 & 0 & 21 & 6 & | & 8 \end{bmatrix}$ $\begin{bmatrix} 1 & 0 & 0 & 0 & | & 5/3 \\ 0 & 1 & 0 & -1/7 & | & 10/21 \\ 0 & 0 & 1 & 2/7 & | & 8/21 \end{bmatrix}$

25. $x_1 = 2$
$x_2 + 2x_3 = 3$
$x_4 = -1$ Solution: $x_1 = 2$, $x_2 = 3 - 2x_3$, $x_4 = -1$
         or $(2, 3 - 2k, k, -1)$

27. $x_1 + 2x_3 + 2x_5 = -1$
$x_2 + 4x_3 + 3x_5 = 2$
$x_4 + 4x_5 = 1$
Solution: $x_1 = -1 - 2x_3 - 2x_5$, $x_2 = 2 - 4x_3 - 3x_5$, $x_4 = 1 - 4x_5$
     or $(-1 - 2k - 2r, 2 - 4k - 3r, k, 1 - 4r, r)$

29. $x_1 + 2x_3 = 2$
$x_2 - 3x_3 = 1$
$x_4 = 3$ Solution: $x_1 = 2 - 2x_3$, $x_2 = 1 + 3x_3$, $x_4 = 3$
     or $(2 - k, 1 - 3k, k, 3)$

31. $x_1 + 2x_2 + x_4 = 4$
$x_3 + 3x_4 = -1$
$x_5 = 3$
$x_6 = 2$
Solution: $x_1 = 4 - 2x_2 - x_4$, $x_3 = -1 - 3x_4$, $x_5 = 3$, $x_6 = 2$
     or $(4 - 2k - r, k, -1 - 3r, r, 3, 2)$

Section 2-3

33. $\begin{bmatrix} 1 & 4 & -2 & | & 13 \\ 3 & -1 & 4 & | & 6 \\ 2 & -5 & 6 & | & -4 \end{bmatrix}$ $\qquad$ $\begin{bmatrix} 1 & 4 & -2 & | & 13 \\ 0 & -13 & 10 & | & -33 \\ 0 & -13 & 10 & | & -30 \end{bmatrix}$

$\begin{bmatrix} 1 & 0 & 14/13 & | & 37/13 \\ 0 & 1 & -10/13 & | & 33/13 \\ 0 & 0 & 0 & | & 3 \end{bmatrix}$ $\qquad$ No solution

35. $\begin{bmatrix} 3 & -2 & 2 & | & 10 \\ 2 & 1 & 3 & | & 3 \\ 1 & 1 & -1 & | & 5 \end{bmatrix}$ $\qquad$ $\begin{bmatrix} 1 & 1 & -1 & | & 5 \\ 2 & 1 & 3 & | & 3 \\ 3 & -2 & 2 & | & 10 \end{bmatrix}$

$\begin{bmatrix} 1 & 1 & -1 & | & 5 \\ 0 & -1 & 5 & | & -7 \\ 0 & -5 & 5 & | & -5 \end{bmatrix}$ $\qquad$ $\begin{bmatrix} 1 & 0 & 4 & | & -2 \\ 0 & 1 & -5 & | & 7 \\ 0 & 0 & -20 & | & 30 \end{bmatrix}$

$\begin{bmatrix} 1 & 0 & 0 & | & 4 \\ 0 & 1 & 0 & | & -1/2 \\ 0 & 0 & 1 & | & -3/2 \end{bmatrix}$ $\qquad$ $x_1 = 4, \quad x_2 = -1/2, \quad x_3 = -3/2$

37. $\begin{bmatrix} 1 & 1 & 1 & -1 & | & -3 \\ 2 & 3 & 1 & -5 & | & -9 \\ 1 & 3 & -1 & -6 & | & 7 \end{bmatrix}$ $\qquad$ $\begin{bmatrix} 1 & 1 & 1 & -1 & | & -3 \\ 0 & 1 & -1 & -3 & | & -3 \\ 0 & 2 & -2 & -5 & | & 10 \end{bmatrix}$

$\begin{bmatrix} 1 & 0 & 2 & 2 & | & 0 \\ 0 & 1 & -1 & -3 & | & -3 \\ 0 & 0 & 0 & 1 & | & 16 \end{bmatrix}$ $\qquad$ $\begin{bmatrix} 1 & 0 & 2 & 0 & | & -32 \\ 0 & 1 & -1 & 0 & | & 45 \\ 0 & 0 & 0 & 1 & | & 16 \end{bmatrix}$

$\qquad$ $x_1 = -32 - 2x_3, \quad x_2 = 45 + x_3, \quad x_4 = 16$

$\qquad$ or $(-32 - 2k, \; 45 + k, \; k, \; 16)$

39. $\begin{bmatrix} 1 & -1 & 1 & | & 3 \\ -2 & 3 & 1 & | & -8 \\ 4 & -2 & 10 & | & 10 \end{bmatrix}$ $\qquad$ $\begin{bmatrix} 1 & -1 & 1 & | & 3 \\ 0 & 1 & 3 & | & -2 \\ 0 & 2 & 6 & | & -2 \end{bmatrix}$

$\begin{bmatrix} 1 & 0 & 4 & | & 1 \\ 0 & 1 & 3 & | & -2 \\ 0 & 0 & 0 & | & 2 \end{bmatrix}$ $\qquad$ No solution

41. $\begin{bmatrix} 1 & 1 & 1 & | & 6 \\ 1 & -3 & 2 & | & 1 \\ 3 & -1 & 4 & | & 5 \end{bmatrix}$ $\qquad$ $\begin{bmatrix} 1 & 1 & 1 & | & 6 \\ 0 & -4 & 1 & | & -5 \\ 0 & -4 & 1 & | & -13 \end{bmatrix}$

$\begin{bmatrix} 1 & 1 & 1 & | & 6 \\ 0 & -4 & 1 & | & -5 \\ 0 & 0 & 0 & | & -8 \end{bmatrix}$ $\qquad$ No solution

43. $\begin{bmatrix} 1 & 2 & -1 & | & -13 \\ 2 & 5 & 3 & | & -3 \end{bmatrix}$ $\qquad$ $\begin{bmatrix} 1 & 2 & -1 & | & -13 \\ 0 & 1 & 5 & | & 23 \end{bmatrix}$

$\begin{bmatrix} 1 & 0 & -11 & | & -59 \\ 0 & 1 & 5 & | & 23 \end{bmatrix}$ $\qquad$ $x_1 = -59 + 11x_3, \quad x_2 = 23 - 5x_3$

$\qquad$ or $(-59 + 11k, \; 23 - 5k, \; k)$

45. $\begin{bmatrix} 1 & -2 & 1 & 1 & -2 & | & -9 \\ 5 & 1 & -6 & -6 & 1 & | & 21 \end{bmatrix}$ $\qquad$ $\begin{bmatrix} 1 & -2 & 1 & 1 & -2 & | & -9 \\ 0 & 11 & -11 & -11 & 11 & | & 66 \end{bmatrix}$

$\begin{bmatrix} 1 & 0 & -1 & -1 & 0 & | & 3 \\ 0 & 1 & -1 & -1 & 1 & | & 6 \end{bmatrix}$

$\qquad$ $x_1 = 3 + x_3 + x_4, \quad x_2 = 6 + x_3 + x_4 - x_5$

$\qquad$ or $(3 + k + r, \; 6 + k + r - s, \; k, \; r, \; s)$

47. $\begin{bmatrix} 1 & 1 & -3 & 1 & \bigm| & 4 \\ -2 & -2 & 6 & -2 & \bigm| & 3 \end{bmatrix}$ $\qquad$ $\begin{bmatrix} 1 & 1 & -3 & 1 & \bigm| & 4 \\ 0 & 0 & 0 & 0 & \bigm| & 11 \end{bmatrix}$

No solution

49. $\begin{bmatrix} 1 & 1 & -1 & -1 & \bigm| & -1 \\ 3 & -2 & -4 & 2 & \bigm| & 1 \\ 4 & -1 & -5 & 1 & \bigm| & 5 \end{bmatrix}$ $\qquad$ $\begin{bmatrix} 1 & 1 & -1 & -1 & \bigm| & -1 \\ 0 & -5 & -1 & 5 & \bigm| & 4 \\ 0 & -5 & -1 & 5 & \bigm| & 9 \end{bmatrix}$

$\begin{bmatrix} 1 & 1 & -1 & -1 & \bigm| & -1 \\ 0 & -5 & -1 & 5 & \bigm| & 4 \\ 0 & 0 & 0 & 0 & \bigm| & 5 \end{bmatrix}$ $\qquad$ No solution

51. $\begin{bmatrix} 1 & 4 & \bigm| & -10 \\ -2 & 3 & \bigm| & -13 \\ 5 & -2 & \bigm| & 16 \end{bmatrix}$ $\qquad$ $\begin{bmatrix} 1 & 4 & \bigm| & -10 \\ 0 & 11 & \bigm| & -33 \\ 0 & -22 & \bigm| & 66 \end{bmatrix}$

$\begin{bmatrix} 1 & 0 & \bigm| & 2 \\ 0 & 1 & \bigm| & -3 \\ 0 & 0 & \bigm| & 0 \end{bmatrix}$ $\qquad$ $x = 2$
$\qquad\qquad\qquad$ $y = -3$

53. $\begin{bmatrix} 1 & -1 & \bigm| & -7 \\ 1 & 1 & \bigm| & -3 \\ 3 & -1 & \bigm| & -17 \end{bmatrix}$ $\begin{bmatrix} 1 & -1 & \bigm| & -7 \\ 0 & 2 & \bigm| & 4 \\ 0 & 2 & \bigm| & 4 \end{bmatrix}$ $\begin{bmatrix} 1 & 0 & \bigm| & -5 \\ 0 & 1 & \bigm| & 2 \\ 0 & 0 & \bigm| & 0 \end{bmatrix}$ $\quad x = -5, \ y = 2$

55. $\begin{bmatrix} 0 & 1 & 2 & \bigm| & 7 \\ 1 & -2 & -6 & \bigm| & -18 \\ 1 & -1 & -2 & \bigm| & -5 \\ 2 & -5 & -15 & \bigm| & -46 \end{bmatrix}$ $\begin{bmatrix} 1 & -2 & -6 & \bigm| & -18 \\ 0 & 1 & 2 & \bigm| & 7 \\ 1 & -1 & -2 & \bigm| & -5 \\ 2 & -5 & -15 & \bigm| & -46 \end{bmatrix}$ $\begin{bmatrix} 1 & -2 & -6 & \bigm| & -18 \\ 0 & 1 & 2 & \bigm| & 7 \\ 0 & 1 & 4 & \bigm| & 13 \\ 0 & -1 & -3 & \bigm| & -10 \end{bmatrix}$

$\begin{bmatrix} 1 & 0 & -2 & \bigm| & -4 \\ 0 & 1 & 2 & \bigm| & 7 \\ 0 & 0 & 2 & \bigm| & 6 \\ 0 & 0 & -1 & \bigm| & -3 \end{bmatrix}$ $\begin{bmatrix} 1 & 0 & 0 & \bigm| & 2 \\ 0 & 1 & 0 & \bigm| & 1 \\ 0 & 0 & 1 & \bigm| & 3 \\ 0 & 0 & 0 & \bigm| & 0 \end{bmatrix}$ $\quad x_1 = 2, \ x_2 = 1, \ x_3 = 3$

57. $\begin{bmatrix} 3 & -2 & 4 & \bigm| & 4 \\ 2 & 5 & -1 & \bigm| & -2 \\ 1 & -7 & 5 & \bigm| & 6 \\ 5 & 3 & 3 & \bigm| & 3 \end{bmatrix}$ $\begin{bmatrix} 1 & -7 & 5 & \bigm| & 6 \\ 3 & -2 & 4 & \bigm| & 4 \\ 2 & 5 & -1 & \bigm| & -2 \\ 5 & 3 & 3 & \bigm| & 3 \end{bmatrix}$

$\begin{bmatrix} 1 & -7 & 5 & \bigm| & 6 \\ 0 & 19 & -11 & \bigm| & -14 \\ 0 & 19 & -11 & \bigm| & -14 \\ 0 & 38 & -22 & \bigm| & -27 \end{bmatrix}$ $\begin{bmatrix} 1 & 0 & 18/19 & \bigm| & 16/19 \\ 0 & 1 & -11/19 & \bigm| & -14/19 \\ 0 & 0 & 0 & \bigm| & 0 \\ 0 & 0 & 0 & \bigm| & 1 \end{bmatrix}$

No solution

59. $\begin{bmatrix} 2 & -5 & \bigm| & 5 \\ 6 & 1 & \bigm| & 31 \\ 2 & 11 & \bigm| & 18 \end{bmatrix}$ $\begin{bmatrix} 1 & -5/2 & \bigm| & 5/2 \\ 0 & 16 & \bigm| & 16 \\ 0 & 16 & \bigm| & 13 \end{bmatrix}$ $\begin{bmatrix} 1 & -5/2 & \bigm| & 5/2 \\ 0 & 16 & \bigm| & 16 \\ 0 & 0 & \bigm| & -3 \end{bmatrix}$

No solution

61. $\begin{bmatrix} 1 & -1 & 2 & 0 & \bigm| & 7 \\ 3 & -4 & 18 & -13 & \bigm| & 17 \\ 2 & -2 & 2 & -4 & \bigm| & 12 \\ -1 & 1 & -1 & 2 & \bigm| & -6 \\ -3 & 1 & -8 & -10 & \bigm| & -21 \end{bmatrix}$ $\begin{bmatrix} 1 & -1 & 2 & 0 & \bigm| & 7 \\ 0 & -1 & 12 & -13 & \bigm| & -4 \\ 0 & 0 & -2 & -4 & \bigm| & -2 \\ 0 & 0 & 1 & 2 & \bigm| & 1 \\ 0 & -2 & -2 & -10 & \bigm| & 0 \end{bmatrix}$

Section 2-3

$$\begin{bmatrix} 1 & 0 & -10 & 13 & | & 11 \\ 0 & 1 & -12 & 13 & | & 4 \\ 0 & 0 & -2 & -4 & | & -2 \\ 0 & 0 & 1 & 2 & | & 1 \\ 0 & 0 & -26 & 16 & | & 8 \end{bmatrix} \qquad \begin{bmatrix} 1 & 0 & 0 & 33 & | & 21 \\ 0 & 1 & 0 & 37 & | & 16 \\ 0 & 0 & 1 & 2 & | & 1 \\ 0 & 0 & 0 & 0 & | & 0 \\ 0 & 0 & 0 & 68 & | & 34 \end{bmatrix}$$

$$\begin{bmatrix} 1 & 0 & 0 & 0 & | & 9/2 \\ 0 & 1 & 0 & 0 & | & -5/2 \\ 0 & 0 & 1 & 0 & | & 0 \\ 0 & 0 & 0 & 0 & | & 0 \\ 0 & 0 & 0 & 1 & | & 1/2 \end{bmatrix} \qquad x_1 = \frac{9}{2}, \; x_2 = -\frac{5}{2}, \; x_3 = 0, \; x_4 = \frac{1}{2}$$

63.
$$\begin{bmatrix} 1 & 2 & -1 & -1 & | & 0 \\ 1 & 2 & 0 & 1 & | & 4 \\ -1 & -2 & 2 & 4 & | & 5 \\ -1 & -1 & -1 & 0 & | & 1 \end{bmatrix} \begin{bmatrix} 1 & 2 & -1 & -1 & | & 0 \\ 0 & 0 & 1 & 2 & | & 4 \\ 0 & 0 & 1 & 3 & | & 5 \\ 0 & 1 & -2 & -1 & | & 1 \end{bmatrix} \begin{bmatrix} 1 & 0 & 3 & 1 & | & -2 \\ 0 & 1 & -2 & -1 & | & 1 \\ 0 & 0 & 1 & 3 & | & 5 \\ 0 & 0 & 1 & 2 & | & 4 \end{bmatrix}$$

$$\begin{bmatrix} 1 & 0 & 0 & -8 & | & -17 \\ 0 & 1 & 0 & 5 & | & 11 \\ 0 & 0 & 1 & 3 & | & 5 \\ 0 & 0 & 0 & -1 & | & -1 \end{bmatrix} \begin{bmatrix} 1 & 0 & 0 & 0 & | & -9 \\ 0 & 1 & 0 & 0 & | & 6 \\ 0 & 0 & 1 & 0 & | & 2 \\ 0 & 0 & 0 & 1 & | & 1 \end{bmatrix} \qquad (-9, \; 6, \; 2, \; 1)$$

65.
$$\begin{bmatrix} 1 & 2 & -3 & 2 & 5 & -1 & | & 0 \\ -2 & -4 & 6 & -1 & -4 & 5 & | & 0 \\ 3 & 6 & -9 & 5 & 13 & -4 & | & 0 \end{bmatrix} \begin{bmatrix} 1 & 2 & -3 & 2 & 5 & -1 & | & 0 \\ 0 & 0 & 0 & 3 & 6 & 3 & | & 0 \\ 0 & 0 & 0 & -1 & -2 & -1 & | & 0 \end{bmatrix}$$

$$\begin{bmatrix} 1 & 2 & -3 & 0 & 1 & -3 & | & 0 \\ 0 & 0 & 0 & 1 & 2 & 1 & | & 0 \\ 0 & 0 & 0 & 0 & 0 & 0 & | & 0 \end{bmatrix}$$

$$x_1 = -2x_2 + 3x_3 - x_5 + 3x_6, \quad x_4 = -2x_5 - x_6$$
$$\text{or } (-2k + 3r - s + 3t, \; k, \; r, \; -2s - t, \; s, \; t)$$

67. Let x_1 = amount in stocks, x_2 = amount in bonds,
x_3 = amount in money markets.

$$x_1 + x_2 + x_3 = 45{,}000$$
$$-2x_1 + x_2 + x_3 = 0$$
$$.10x_1 + .07x_2 + .075x_3 = 3{,}660$$

$$\begin{bmatrix} 1 & 1 & 1 & | & 45{,}000 \\ -2 & 1 & 1 & | & 0 \\ .10 & .07 & .075 & | & 3{,}660 \end{bmatrix} \qquad \begin{bmatrix} 1 & 1 & 1 & | & 45{,}000 \\ 0 & 3 & 3 & | & 90{,}000 \\ 0 & -30 & -25 & | & -840{,}000 \end{bmatrix}$$

$$\begin{bmatrix} 1 & 0 & 0 & | & 15{,}000 \\ 0 & 1 & 1 & | & 30{,}000 \\ 0 & 0 & 5 & | & 60{,}000 \end{bmatrix} \qquad \begin{bmatrix} 1 & 0 & 0 & | & 15{,}000 \\ 0 & 1 & 0 & | & 18{,}000 \\ 0 & 0 & 1 & | & 12{,}000 \end{bmatrix}$$

$15,000 in stocks, $18,000 in bonds, $12,000 in money market

69. Let x = minutes jogging, y = minutes playing handball,
z = minutes biking.

$$x + y + z = 60$$
$$13x + 11y + 7z = 660$$
$$x \qquad - 2z = 0$$

$$\begin{bmatrix} 1 & 1 & 1 & | & 60 \\ 13 & 11 & 7 & | & 660 \\ 1 & 0 & -2 & | & 0 \end{bmatrix} \begin{bmatrix} 1 & 1 & 1 & | & 60 \\ 0 & -2 & -6 & | & -120 \\ 0 & -1 & -3 & | & -60 \end{bmatrix} \begin{bmatrix} 1 & 0 & -2 & | & 0 \\ 0 & 1 & 3 & | & 60 \\ 0 & 0 & 0 & | & 0 \end{bmatrix}$$

$x = 2z, \quad y = 60 - 3z$

She may bike from $z = 0$ to $z = 20$ min., then should jog for $x = 2z$
min. and play handball for $y = 60 - 3z$ min.

Section 2-4

1.

	Alpha	Beta
Salv. Army	50	65
Boys' Club	85	32
Girl Scouts	68	94

3.

	Joe	Jane	Judy
Checking	12	11	5
Savings	15	18	8
Boxes	8	9	21

5. 2×2 (square)   7. 3×3 (square)   9. 3×1 (column matrix)

11. 2×3 13. 2×1 (column matrix)

15. 2×2 (square)   17. Not equal   19. Equal   21. Not equal

23. $\begin{bmatrix} 3 & 3 & 2 \\ 7 & 4 & 3 \end{bmatrix}$ 25. $\begin{bmatrix} 2 \\ 58 \end{bmatrix}$ 27. Can not add them

29. $\begin{bmatrix} 6 & 5 & 8 \\ 5 & 1 & 3 \\ 5 & -3 & 4 \end{bmatrix}$ 31. $\begin{bmatrix} 12 & 3 \\ 6 & 15 \end{bmatrix}$ 33. $\begin{bmatrix} 20 \\ 15 \\ 5 \\ 10 \end{bmatrix}$

35. $\begin{bmatrix} -12 & 6 & -15 \end{bmatrix}$ 37. $\begin{bmatrix} 0 & 0 \\ 0 & 0 \end{bmatrix}$

39. (a) $2A = \begin{bmatrix} 2 & 4 \\ 6 & 0 \end{bmatrix}$, $3B = \begin{bmatrix} -3 & 6 \\ 3 & 3 \end{bmatrix}$, $-2C = \begin{bmatrix} 0 & -2 \\ -2 & -8 \end{bmatrix}$

(b) $A + B = \begin{bmatrix} 0 & 4 \\ 4 & 1 \end{bmatrix}$, $B + A = \begin{bmatrix} 0 & 4 \\ 4 & 1 \end{bmatrix}$,

$A + C = \begin{bmatrix} 1 & 3 \\ 4 & 4 \end{bmatrix}$, $B + C = \begin{bmatrix} -1 & 3 \\ 2 & 5 \end{bmatrix}$

(c) $A + 2B = \begin{bmatrix} -1 & 6 \\ 5 & 2 \end{bmatrix}$, $3A + C = \begin{bmatrix} 3 & 7 \\ 10 & 4 \end{bmatrix}$,

$2A + B - C = \begin{bmatrix} 1 & 5 \\ 6 & -3 \end{bmatrix}$

41.

	I	II	III
PC	23	17	20
Print	19	22	11
Disk	151	151	105

43. $x = 3$

45. $6x + 4 = 14x - 13$ so $x = \dfrac{17}{8}$

47.

	A	B	C	
$\frac{1}{12} A =$	65/12	55/6	20/3	small
	30/4	45/4	5	reg.
	25/4	28/3	7	giant

49.

		S.D.	N.O.	P.M.
$12M =$	Fairfield	2760	1080	1680
	Tyler	3120	1380	1992

51. $\dfrac{1}{3}$ (A + B + C) = $\dfrac{1}{3}\begin{bmatrix} 269 \\ 204 \\ 226 \\ 246 \\ 227 \end{bmatrix} = \begin{bmatrix} 89.7 \\ 68.0 \\ 75.3 \\ 82.0 \\ 75.7 \end{bmatrix}$

Section 2-5

1. $2 + 12 = 14$ 3. $12 + 0 = 12$ 5. $6 + 0 + 8 = 14$

7. $[.90 \quad 1.85 \quad .65]\begin{bmatrix} 2 \\ 1 \\ 4 \end{bmatrix} = 1.80 + 1.85 + 2.60 = \$6.25$

9. $\begin{bmatrix} -5 & 11 \\ 0 & 14 \end{bmatrix}$ 11. $\begin{bmatrix} 30 & 2 \\ 39 & -3 \end{bmatrix}$ 13. $\begin{bmatrix} 14 & 6 \\ 16 & -1 \end{bmatrix}$

15. $\begin{bmatrix} 10 \\ 20 \end{bmatrix}$ 17. $\begin{bmatrix} 7 & 4 \\ 0 & 5 \\ 22 & 14 \end{bmatrix}$ 19. $\begin{bmatrix} -12 & 4 & -3 \\ -14 & 22 & 5 \\ 6 & 14 & 9 \end{bmatrix}$

21. $\begin{bmatrix} 2 & 3 \\ 8 & 7 \end{bmatrix}$ 23. Not possible   25. Not possible

27. Not possible   29. AB = $\begin{bmatrix} 1 & 8 \\ -1 & 2 \end{bmatrix}$ BA = $\begin{bmatrix} 3 & 10 \\ -1 & 0 \end{bmatrix}$

31. AB = $\begin{bmatrix} -3 & 10 \\ -2 & 5 \end{bmatrix}$ BA = $\begin{bmatrix} -1 & 2 \\ -4 & 3 \end{bmatrix}$

33. AB = $\begin{bmatrix} 6 & 2 & 13 \\ -11 & -6 & -4 \end{bmatrix}$ BA not possible

35. AB = [27 38] BA not possible

37. $[13 \quad 13]\begin{bmatrix} 1 & 3 \\ 2 & 4 \end{bmatrix} = [39 \quad 91]$ 39. $\begin{bmatrix} 5 & 37 & 5/2 & 29 & 20 \\ 7 & 59 & 31/2 & 53 & 52 \\ 11 & 31 & -1/2 & 9 & 11 \\ 25 & 113 & 17/2 & 103 & 65 \end{bmatrix}$

41. $\begin{bmatrix} 4 & 1 \\ 9 & 10 \end{bmatrix} + \begin{bmatrix} 7 & 8 \\ 1 & 9 \end{bmatrix} = \begin{bmatrix} 11 & 9 \\ 10 & 19 \end{bmatrix}$ 43. $\begin{bmatrix} 1 & 2 \\ 3 & 1 \end{bmatrix}$

45. $\begin{bmatrix} 1 & 2 & 3 \\ 4 & -1 & 0 \\ 2 & 1 & 7 \end{bmatrix}$ 47. $\begin{bmatrix} 3x + y \\ 2x + 4y \end{bmatrix}$ 49. $\begin{bmatrix} x_1 + 2x_2 - x_3 \\ 3x_1 + x_2 + 4x_3 \\ 2x_1 - x_2 - x_3 \end{bmatrix}$

51. $\begin{bmatrix} x_1 + 3x_2 + 5x_3 + 6x_4 \\ -2x_1 + 9x_2 + 6x_3 + x_4 \\ 8x_1 \quad\quad + 17x_3 + 5x_4 \end{bmatrix}$

53. $\begin{bmatrix} 4 & 5.5 \\ 1 & 2 \end{bmatrix}\begin{bmatrix} 300 \\ 450 \end{bmatrix} = \begin{bmatrix} 3675 \\ 1200 \end{bmatrix}$

    3675 hrs assembly time, 1200 hrs checking

55. $\begin{bmatrix} 114 & 85 \\ 118 & 84 \\ 116 & 86 \end{bmatrix} \begin{bmatrix} 60 \\ 140 \end{bmatrix} = \begin{bmatrix} 18740 \\ 18840 \\ 19000 \end{bmatrix}$

$18,740 on Monday, $18,840 on Wednesday, $19,000 on Friday

57. $\begin{bmatrix} .5 & 1.5 & .5 & 1.0 & 1.0 \\ 0 & 1.0 & 1.0 & 3.0 & 2.0 \end{bmatrix} \begin{bmatrix} 500 & .2 & 0 & 129 \\ 0 & .2 & 0 & 0 \\ 1560 & .32 & 1.7 & 6 \\ 0 & 0 & 0 & 0 \\ 460 & 0 & 0 & 0 \end{bmatrix}$

 A B_1 B_2 C

$= \begin{bmatrix} 1490 & .56 & .85 & 67.5 \\ 2480 & .52 & 1.70 & 6 \end{bmatrix}$ I
II

Section 2-6

1. $25^{-1} = .04, \quad (2/3)^{-1} = 3/2, \quad (-5)^{-1} = -1/5, \quad (.75)^{-1} = 4/3,$

$11^{-1} = 1/11$

3. $AB = \begin{bmatrix} 1 & 0 & 0 \\ 0 & 1 & 0 \\ 0 & 0 & 1 \end{bmatrix}$ Yes $\qquad$ 5. $AB = \begin{bmatrix} 1 & -3 \\ 0 & 10 \end{bmatrix}$ No

7. $AB = \begin{bmatrix} 1 & 0 & 0 \\ 0 & 1 & 0 \\ 0 & 0 & 1 \end{bmatrix}$ Yes

9. $\left[\begin{array}{cc|cc} 1 & 2 & 1 & 0 \\ 3 & 5 & 0 & 1 \end{array}\right]$ $\qquad$ $\left[\begin{array}{cc|cc} 1 & 2 & 1 & 0 \\ 0 & -1 & -3 & 1 \end{array}\right]$

$\left[\begin{array}{cc|cc} 1 & 0 & -5 & 2 \\ 0 & 1 & 3 & -1 \end{array}\right]$ $\qquad A^{-1} = \begin{bmatrix} -5 & 2 \\ 3 & -1 \end{bmatrix}$

11. $\left[\begin{array}{cc|cc} 3 & 2 & 1 & 0 \\ 4 & 3 & 0 & 1 \end{array}\right]$ $\qquad$ $\left[\begin{array}{cc|cc} 1 & 2/3 & 1/3 & 0 \\ 0 & 1/3 & -4/3 & 1 \end{array}\right]$

$\left[\begin{array}{cc|cc} 1 & 0 & 3 & -2 \\ 0 & 1 & -4 & 1 \end{array}\right]$ $\qquad A^{-1} = \begin{bmatrix} 3 & -2 \\ -4 & 3 \end{bmatrix}$

13. $\left[\begin{array}{ccc|ccc} 1 & 3 & 9 & 1 & 0 & 0 \\ 0 & 1 & 4 & 0 & 1 & 0 \\ 3 & 2 & 3 & 0 & 0 & 1 \end{array}\right]$ $\quad$ $\left[\begin{array}{ccc|ccc} 1 & 3 & 9 & 1 & 0 & 0 \\ 0 & 1 & 4 & 0 & 1 & 0 \\ 0 & -7 & -24 & -3 & 0 & 1 \end{array}\right]$

$\left[\begin{array}{ccc|ccc} 1 & 0 & -3 & 1 & -3 & 0 \\ 0 & 1 & 4 & 0 & 1 & 0 \\ 0 & 0 & 4 & -3 & 7 & 1 \end{array}\right]$ $\quad$ $\left[\begin{array}{ccc|ccc} 1 & 0 & 0 & -5/4 & 9/4 & 3/4 \\ 0 & 1 & 0 & 3 & -6 & -1 \\ 0 & 0 & 1 & -3/4 & 7/4 & 1/4 \end{array}\right]$

$A^{-1} = \begin{bmatrix} -5/4 & 9/4 & 3/4 \\ 3 & -6 & -1 \\ -3/4 & 7/4 & 1/4 \end{bmatrix}$

15. $\left[\begin{array}{ccc|ccc} 0 & 4 & -2 & 1 & 0 & 0 \\ 1 & 3 & 5 & 0 & 1 & 0 \\ 1 & 4 & 2 & 0 & 0 & 1 \end{array}\right]$ $\qquad$ $\left[\begin{array}{ccc|ccc} 1 & 3 & 5 & 0 & 1 & 0 \\ 0 & 4 & -2 & 1 & 0 & 0 \\ 1 & 4 & 2 & 0 & 0 & 1 \end{array}\right]$

$$\begin{bmatrix} 1 & 3 & 5 & \bigm| & 0 & 1 & 0 \\ 0 & 4 & -2 & \bigm| & 1 & 0 & 0 \\ 0 & 1 & -3 & \bigm| & 0 & -1 & 1 \end{bmatrix} \qquad \begin{bmatrix} 1 & 0 & 13/2 & \bigm| & -3/4 & 1 & 0 \\ 0 & 1 & -1/2 & \bigm| & 1/4 & 0 & 0 \\ 0 & 0 & -5/2 & \bigm| & -1/4 & -1 & 1 \end{bmatrix}$$

$$\begin{bmatrix} 1 & 0 & 0 & \bigm| & -7/5 & -8/5 & 13/5 \\ 0 & 1 & 0 & \bigm| & 3/10 & 1/5 & -1/5 \\ 0 & 0 & 1 & \bigm| & 1/10 & 2/5 & -2/5 \end{bmatrix} \qquad A^{-1} = \begin{bmatrix} -7/5 & -8/5 & 13/5 \\ 3/10 & 1/5 & -1/5 \\ 1/10 & 2/5 & -2/5 \end{bmatrix}$$

17. $\begin{bmatrix} 4 & -2 & \bigm| & 1 & 0 \\ -2 & 1 & \bigm| & 0 & 1 \end{bmatrix} \qquad \begin{bmatrix} 0 & 0 & \bigm| & 1 & 2 \\ -2 & 1 & \bigm| & 0 & 1 \end{bmatrix}$ No inverse

19. $\begin{bmatrix} 1 & 3 & 1 & \bigm| & 1 & 0 & 0 \\ 2 & 0 & -2 & \bigm| & 0 & 1 & 0 \\ 3 & 3 & -1 & \bigm| & 0 & 0 & 1 \end{bmatrix} \qquad \begin{bmatrix} 1 & 3 & 1 & \bigm| & 1 & 0 & 0 \\ 0 & -6 & -4 & \bigm| & -2 & 1 & 0 \\ 0 & -6 & -4 & \bigm| & -3 & 0 & 1 \end{bmatrix}$

$\begin{bmatrix} 1 & 3 & 1 & \bigm| & 1 & 0 & 0 \\ 0 & -6 & -4 & \bigm| & -2 & 1 & 0 \\ 0 & 0 & 0 & \bigm| & -1 & -1 & 1 \end{bmatrix}$ No inverse

21. $\begin{bmatrix} 1 & 2 & 1 & \bigm| & 1 & 0 & 0 \\ 1 & -3 & 2 & \bigm| & 0 & 1 & 0 \\ 2 & -1 & 3 & \bigm| & 0 & 0 & 1 \end{bmatrix} \qquad \begin{bmatrix} 1 & 2 & 1 & \bigm| & 1 & 0 & 0 \\ 0 & -5 & 1 & \bigm| & -1 & 1 & 0 \\ 0 & -5 & 1 & \bigm| & -2 & 0 & 1 \end{bmatrix}$

$\begin{bmatrix} 1 & 2 & 1 & \bigm| & 1 & 0 & 0 \\ 0 & -5 & 1 & \bigm| & -1 & 1 & 0 \\ 0 & 0 & 0 & \bigm| & -1 & -1 & 1 \end{bmatrix}$ No inverse

23. $\begin{bmatrix} 2 & 1 & \bigm| & 1 & 0 \\ 4 & 3 & \bigm| & 0 & 1 \end{bmatrix} \qquad \begin{bmatrix} 1 & 1/2 & \bigm| & 1/2 & 0 \\ 0 & 1 & \bigm| & -2 & 1 \end{bmatrix} \qquad \begin{bmatrix} 1 & 0 & \bigm| & 3/2 & -1/2 \\ 0 & 1 & \bigm| & -2 & 1 \end{bmatrix}$

$A^{-1} = \begin{bmatrix} 3/2 & -1/2 \\ -2 & 1 \end{bmatrix}$

25. $\begin{bmatrix} 1 & 2 & 3 & \bigm| & 1 & 0 & 0 \\ 2 & -1 & 4 & \bigm| & 0 & 1 & 0 \\ 0 & -1 & 1 & \bigm| & 0 & 0 & 1 \end{bmatrix} \qquad \begin{bmatrix} 1 & 2 & 3 & \bigm| & 1 & 0 & 0 \\ 0 & -5 & -2 & \bigm| & -2 & 1 & 0 \\ 0 & -1 & 1 & \bigm| & 0 & 0 & 1 \end{bmatrix}$

$\begin{bmatrix} 1 & 2 & 3 & \bigm| & 1 & 0 & 0 \\ 0 & -1 & 1 & \bigm| & 0 & 0 & 1 \\ 0 & -5 & -2 & \bigm| & -2 & 1 & 0 \end{bmatrix} \qquad \begin{bmatrix} 1 & 0 & 5 & \bigm| & 1 & 0 & 2 \\ 0 & 1 & -1 & \bigm| & 0 & 0 & -1 \\ 0 & 0 & -7 & \bigm| & -2 & 1 & -5 \end{bmatrix}$

$\begin{bmatrix} 1 & 0 & 0 & \bigm| & -3/7 & 5/7 & -11/7 \\ 0 & 1 & 0 & \bigm| & 2/7 & -1/7 & -2/7 \\ 0 & 0 & 1 & \bigm| & 2/7 & -1/7 & 5/7 \end{bmatrix} \qquad A^{-1} = \begin{bmatrix} -3/7 & 5/7 & -11/7 \\ 2/7 & -1/7 & -2/7 \\ 2/7 & -1/7 & 5/7 \end{bmatrix}$

27. (a) $\begin{bmatrix} 3 & 4 & -5 & \bigm| & 4 \\ 2 & -1 & 3 & \bigm| & -1 \\ 1 & 1 & -1 & \bigm| & 2 \end{bmatrix}$ (b) $\begin{bmatrix} 3 & 4 & -5 \\ 2 & -1 & 3 \\ 1 & 1 & -1 \end{bmatrix}$

(c) $\begin{bmatrix} 3 & 4 & -5 \\ 2 & -1 & 3 \\ 1 & 1 & -1 \end{bmatrix} \begin{bmatrix} x_1 \\ x_2 \\ x_3 \end{bmatrix} = \begin{bmatrix} 4 \\ -1 \\ 2 \end{bmatrix}$

29. (a) $\begin{bmatrix} 4 & 5 & \bigm| & 2 \\ 3 & -2 & \bigm| & 7 \end{bmatrix}$ (b) $\begin{bmatrix} 4 & 5 \\ 3 & -2 \end{bmatrix}$

(c) $\begin{bmatrix} 4 & 5 \\ 3 & -2 \end{bmatrix} \begin{bmatrix} x \\ y \end{bmatrix} = \begin{bmatrix} 2 \\ 7 \end{bmatrix}$

31. $\begin{bmatrix} 1 & 3 \\ 2 & -1 \end{bmatrix} \begin{bmatrix} x_1 \\ x_2 \end{bmatrix} = \begin{bmatrix} 5 \\ 6 \end{bmatrix}$

33. $\begin{bmatrix} 1 & 2 & -3 & 4 \\ 1 & 1 & 0 & 1 \\ 3 & 2 & 1 & 2 \end{bmatrix} \begin{bmatrix} x_1 \\ x_2 \\ x_3 \\ x_4 \end{bmatrix} = \begin{bmatrix} 0 \\ 5 \\ 4 \end{bmatrix}$

35. $\left[\begin{array}{cccc|cccc} 1 & 1 & 0 & 0 & 1 & 0 & 0 & 0 \\ 0 & 1 & 1 & 0 & 0 & 1 & 0 & 0 \\ 1 & 0 & 0 & 1 & 0 & 0 & 1 & 0 \\ 0 & 0 & 1 & 1 & 0 & 0 & 0 & 1 \end{array}\right]$
$\left[\begin{array}{cccc|cccc} 1 & 1 & 0 & 0 & 1 & 0 & 0 & 0 \\ 0 & 1 & 1 & 0 & 0 & 1 & 0 & 0 \\ 0 & -1 & 0 & 1 & -1 & 0 & 1 & 0 \\ 0 & 0 & 1 & 1 & 0 & 0 & 0 & 1 \end{array}\right]$

$\left[\begin{array}{cccc|cccc} 1 & 0 & -1 & 0 & 1 & -1 & 0 & 0 \\ 0 & 1 & 1 & 0 & 0 & 1 & 0 & 0 \\ 0 & 0 & 1 & 1 & -1 & 1 & 1 & 0 \\ 0 & 0 & 1 & 1 & 0 & 0 & 0 & 1 \end{array}\right]$ No inverse

37. $\left[\begin{array}{ccc|ccc} 1 & 2 & -1 & 1 & 0 & 0 \\ 1 & 1 & 2 & 0 & 1 & 0 \\ 1 & -1 & -1 & 0 & 0 & 1 \end{array}\right]$
$\left[\begin{array}{ccc|ccc} 1 & 2 & -1 & 1 & 0 & 0 \\ 0 & -1 & 3 & -1 & 1 & 0 \\ 0 & -3 & 0 & -1 & 0 & 1 \end{array}\right]$

$\left[\begin{array}{ccc|ccc} 1 & 0 & 5 & -1 & 2 & 0 \\ 0 & 1 & -3 & 1 & -1 & 0 \\ 0 & 0 & -9 & 2 & -3 & 1 \end{array}\right]$
$\left[\begin{array}{ccc|ccc} 1 & 0 & 5 & -1 & 2 & 0 \\ 0 & 1 & -3 & 1 & -1 & 0 \\ 0 & 0 & 1 & -2/9 & 1/3 & -1/9 \end{array}\right]$

$\left[\begin{array}{ccc|ccc} 1 & 0 & 0 & 1/9 & 1/3 & 5/9 \\ 0 & 1 & 0 & 1/3 & 0 & -1/3 \\ 0 & 0 & 1 & -2/9 & 1/3 & -1/9 \end{array}\right]$ $A^{-1} = \begin{bmatrix} 1/9 & 1/3 & 5/9 \\ 1/3 & 0 & -1/3 \\ -2/9 & 1/3 & -1/9 \end{bmatrix}$

$\begin{bmatrix} 1/9 & 1/3 & 5/9 \\ 1/3 & 0 & -1/3 \\ -2/9 & 1/3 & -1/9 \end{bmatrix} \begin{bmatrix} 2 \\ 0 \\ 1 \end{bmatrix} = \begin{bmatrix} 7/9 \\ 1/3 \\ -5/9 \end{bmatrix}$ $x_1 = \dfrac{7}{9}, \; x_2 = \dfrac{1}{3}, \; x_3 = \dfrac{-5}{9}$

39. $\left[\begin{array}{cccc|cccc} 1 & 1 & 2 & 1 & 1 & 0 & 0 & 0 \\ 2 & 0 & -1 & 1 & 0 & 1 & 0 & 0 \\ 0 & 1 & 3 & -1 & 0 & 0 & 1 & 0 \\ 3 & 2 & 0 & 1 & 0 & 0 & 0 & 1 \end{array}\right]$
$\left[\begin{array}{cccc|cccc} 1 & 1 & 2 & 1 & 1 & 0 & 0 & 0 \\ 0 & -2 & -5 & -1 & -2 & 1 & 0 & 0 \\ 0 & 1 & 3 & -1 & 0 & 0 & 1 & 0 \\ 0 & -1 & -6 & -2 & -3 & 0 & 0 & 1 \end{array}\right]$

$\left[\begin{array}{cccc|cccc} 1 & 1 & 2 & 1 & 1 & 0 & 0 & 0 \\ 0 & 1 & 3 & -1 & 0 & 0 & 1 & 0 \\ 0 & -2 & -5 & -1 & -2 & 1 & 0 & 0 \\ 0 & -1 & -6 & -2 & -3 & 0 & 0 & 1 \end{array}\right]$
$\left[\begin{array}{cccc|cccc} 1 & 0 & -1 & 2 & 1 & 0 & -1 & 0 \\ 0 & 1 & 3 & -1 & 0 & 0 & 1 & 0 \\ 0 & 0 & 1 & -3 & -2 & 1 & 2 & 0 \\ 0 & 0 & -3 & -3 & -3 & 0 & 1 & 1 \end{array}\right]$

$\left[\begin{array}{cccc|cccc} 1 & 0 & 0 & -1 & -1 & 1 & 1 & 0 \\ 0 & 1 & 0 & 8 & 6 & -3 & -5 & 0 \\ 0 & 0 & 1 & -3 & -2 & 1 & 2 & 0 \\ 0 & 0 & 0 & -12 & -9 & 3 & 7 & 1 \end{array}\right]$

$\left[\begin{array}{cccc|cccc} 1 & 0 & 0 & 0 & -1/4 & 3/4 & 5/12 & -1/12 \\ 0 & 1 & 0 & 0 & 0 & -1 & -1/3 & 2/3 \\ 0 & 0 & 1 & 0 & 1/4 & 1/4 & 1/4 & -1/4 \\ 0 & 0 & 0 & 1 & 3/4 & -1/4 & -7/12 & -1/12 \end{array}\right]$

$A^{-1} = \begin{bmatrix} -1/4 & 3/4 & 5/12 & -1/12 \\ 0 & -1 & -1/3 & 2/3 \\ 1/4 & 1/4 & 1/4 & -1/4 \\ 3/4 & -1/4 & -7/12 & -1/12 \end{bmatrix}$

$$A^{-1}\begin{bmatrix} 4 \\ 6 \\ 3 \\ 9 \end{bmatrix} = \begin{bmatrix} 4 \\ -1 \\ 1 \\ -1 \end{bmatrix} \qquad x_1 = 4, \ x_2 = -1, \ x_3 = 1, \ x_4 = -1$$

41. $$\left[\begin{array}{ccc|ccc} -2 & 1 & 3 & 1 & 0 & 0 \\ 2 & 4 & -1 & 0 & 1 & 0 \\ 3 & 0 & -4 & 0 & 0 & 1 \end{array}\right] \qquad \left[\begin{array}{ccc|ccc} 1 & -1/2 & -3/2 & -1/2 & 0 & 0 \\ 0 & 5 & 2 & 1 & 1 & 0 \\ 0 & 3/2 & 1/2 & 3/2 & 0 & 1 \end{array}\right]$$

$$\left[\begin{array}{ccc|ccc} 1 & 0 & -13/10 & -2/5 & 1/10 & 0 \\ 0 & 1 & 2/5 & 1/5 & 1/5 & 0 \\ 0 & 0 & -1/10 & 6/5 & -3/10 & 1 \end{array}\right] \qquad \left[\begin{array}{ccc|ccc} 1 & 0 & 0 & -16 & 4 & -13 \\ 0 & 1 & 0 & 5 & -1 & 4 \\ 0 & 0 & 1 & -12 & 3 & -10 \end{array}\right]$$

$$A^{-1} = \begin{bmatrix} -16 & 4 & -13 \\ 5 & -1 & 4 \\ -12 & 3 & -10 \end{bmatrix} \qquad A^{-1}\begin{bmatrix} 1 \\ 5 \\ 2 \end{bmatrix} = \begin{bmatrix} -22 \\ 8 \\ -17 \end{bmatrix} \qquad x_1 = -22, \ x_2 = 8, \ x_3 = -17$$

$$A^{-1}\begin{bmatrix} -1 \\ 3 \\ 1 \end{bmatrix} = \begin{bmatrix} 15 \\ -4 \\ 11 \end{bmatrix} \qquad x_1 = 15, \ x_2 = -4, \ x_3 = 11$$

$$A^{-1}\begin{bmatrix} 0 \\ 1 \\ 2 \end{bmatrix} = \begin{bmatrix} -22 \\ 7 \\ -17 \end{bmatrix} \qquad x_1 = -22, \ x_2 = 7, \ x_3 = -17$$

43. $$\left[\begin{array}{cc|cc} 1 & 2 & 1 & 0 \\ 3 & 5 & 0 & 1 \end{array}\right] \qquad \left[\begin{array}{cc|cc} 1 & 2 & 1 & 0 \\ 0 & -1 & -3 & 1 \end{array}\right]$$

$$\left[\begin{array}{cc|cc} 1 & 0 & -5 & 2 \\ 0 & 1 & 3 & -1 \end{array}\right] \qquad A^{-1} = \begin{bmatrix} -5 & 2 \\ 3 & -1 \end{bmatrix}$$

(a) $A^{-1}\begin{bmatrix} 3 \\ 8 \end{bmatrix} = \begin{bmatrix} 1 \\ 1 \end{bmatrix} \qquad x_1 = 1, \ x_2 = 1$

(b) $A^{-1}\begin{bmatrix} 4 \\ 9 \end{bmatrix} = \begin{bmatrix} -2 \\ 3 \end{bmatrix} \qquad x_1 = -2, \ x_2 = 3$

(c) $A^{-1}\begin{bmatrix} 3 \\ 7 \end{bmatrix} = \begin{bmatrix} -1 \\ 2 \end{bmatrix} \qquad x_1 = -1, \ x_2 = 2$

45. (a) Vitamin C intake = 32x + 24y
Vitamin A intake = 900x + 425y

$$\text{so} \quad \begin{bmatrix} 32 & 24 \\ 900 & 425 \end{bmatrix} \begin{bmatrix} x \\ y \end{bmatrix} = \begin{bmatrix} b_1 \\ b_2 \end{bmatrix}$$

where b_1 = vitamin C intake and b_2 = vitamin A intake

(b) $$\begin{bmatrix} 32 & 24 \\ 900 & 425 \end{bmatrix} \begin{bmatrix} 3.2 \\ 2.5 \end{bmatrix} = \begin{bmatrix} 162.4 \\ 3942.5 \end{bmatrix}$$
162.4 mg of C, 3,942.5 iu of A

(c) $$\begin{bmatrix} 32 & 24 \\ 900 & 425 \end{bmatrix} \begin{bmatrix} 1.5 \\ 3.0 \end{bmatrix} = \begin{bmatrix} 120 \\ 2625 \end{bmatrix}$$
120 mg of C, 2,625 iu of A

(d) $$\begin{bmatrix} -.053125 & .003 \\ .1125 & -.004 \end{bmatrix} \begin{bmatrix} 107.2 \\ 2315.0 \end{bmatrix} = \begin{bmatrix} 1.25 \\ 2.8 \end{bmatrix}$$
1.25 units of A, 2.8 units of B

(e) $$\begin{bmatrix} -.053125 & .003 \\ .1125 & -.004 \end{bmatrix} \begin{bmatrix} 104 \\ 2575 \end{bmatrix} = \begin{bmatrix} 2.2 \\ 1.4 \end{bmatrix}$$
2.2 units of A, 1.4 units of B

47. (a) $\begin{bmatrix} 2 & -.25 \\ -1 & .25 \end{bmatrix} \begin{bmatrix} 900 \\ 5840 \end{bmatrix} = \begin{bmatrix} 340 \\ 560 \end{bmatrix}$

340 children, 560 adults

(b) $\begin{bmatrix} 2 & -.25 \\ -1 & .25 \end{bmatrix} \begin{bmatrix} 1000 \\ 6260 \end{bmatrix} = \begin{bmatrix} 435 \\ 565 \end{bmatrix}$

435 children, 565 adults

(c) $\begin{bmatrix} 2 & -.25 \\ -1 & .25 \end{bmatrix} \begin{bmatrix} 750 \\ 5560 \end{bmatrix} = \begin{bmatrix} 110 \\ 640 \end{bmatrix}$

110 children, 640 adults

Section 2-7

1. Solve $(A - I)X = 0$ $\begin{bmatrix} -9/16 & 1/2 & 3/16 & 0 \\ 5/16 & -5/6 & 5/16 & 0 \\ 4/16 & 1/3 & -8/16 & 0 \end{bmatrix}$

$\begin{bmatrix} 1 & -8/9 & -1/3 & 0 \\ 0 & -5/9 & 5/12 & 0 \\ 0 & 5/9 & -5/12 & 0 \end{bmatrix}$ $\begin{bmatrix} 1 & 0 & -1 & 0 \\ 0 & 1 & -3/4 & 0 \\ 0 & 0 & 0 & 0 \end{bmatrix}$

$x_1 = x_3, \; x_2 = \dfrac{3}{4} x_3$

If $x_3 = \$8,000$, then $x_2 = \$6,000$, $x_1 = \$8,000$

3. Solve $\begin{bmatrix} -.4 & .2 & .5 & 0 \\ .1 & -.8 & .5 & 0 \\ .3 & .6 & -1 & 0 \end{bmatrix}$ $\begin{bmatrix} 1 & -.50 & -1.25 & 0 \\ 0 & -.75 & .625 & 0 \\ 0 & .75 & -.625 & 0 \end{bmatrix}$

$\begin{bmatrix} 1 & 0 & -5/3 & 0 \\ 0 & 1 & -5/6 & 0 \\ 0 & 0 & 0 & 0 \end{bmatrix}$ $x_1 = \dfrac{5}{3} x_3, \; x_2 = \dfrac{5}{6} x_3$

Use $x_3 = 6000$, then the incomes are $\$10,000$, $\$5,000$, and $\$6,000$.

5. $AX = \begin{bmatrix} .15 & .08 \\ .30 & .20 \end{bmatrix} \begin{bmatrix} 8 \\ 12 \end{bmatrix} = \begin{bmatrix} 2.16 \\ 4.8 \end{bmatrix}$

7. $\begin{bmatrix} .06 & .12 & .09 \\ .15 & .05 & .10 \\ .08 & .04 & .02 \end{bmatrix} \begin{bmatrix} 8 \\ 14 \\ 10 \end{bmatrix} = \begin{bmatrix} 3.06 \\ 2.90 \\ 1.40 \end{bmatrix}$

9. $\begin{bmatrix} .8 & -.3 & 1 & 0 \\ -.2 & .7 & 0 & 1 \end{bmatrix}$ $\begin{bmatrix} 1 & -.375 & 1.25 & 0 \\ 0 & .625 & .25 & 1 \end{bmatrix}$

$\begin{bmatrix} 1 & 0 & 1.4 & .6 \\ 0 & 1 & .4 & 1.6 \end{bmatrix}$ $(I - A)^{-1} = \begin{bmatrix} 1.4 & .6 \\ .4 & 1.6 \end{bmatrix}$

Section 2-7

11. Find $(I-A)^{-1}D$

$$\left[\begin{array}{cc|cc} .76 & -.08 & 1 & 0 \\ -.12 & .96 & 0 & 1 \end{array}\right] \qquad \left[\begin{array}{cc|cc} 1 & -.1053 & 1.3158 & 0 \\ 0 & .9474 & 0.15789 & 1 \end{array}\right]$$

$$\left[\begin{array}{cc|cc} 1 & 0 & 1.333 & 0.1111 \\ 0 & 1 & 0.1667 & 1.0555 \end{array}\right]$$

$$(I - A)^{-1}D = \left[\begin{array}{cc} 1.3333 & 0.1111 \\ 0.1667 & 1.0555 \end{array}\right] \left[\begin{array}{c} 15 \\ 12 \end{array}\right] = \left[\begin{array}{c} 21.33 \\ 15.17 \end{array}\right]$$

13. Find $(I - A)^{-1}D$

$$\left[\begin{array}{cc|cc} .90 & -.40 & 1 & 0 \\ -.30 & .80 & 0 & 1 \end{array}\right] \qquad \left[\begin{array}{cc|cc} 1 & -.4444 & 1.1111 & 0 \\ 0 & .6667 & 0.3333 & 1 \end{array}\right]$$

$$\left[\begin{array}{cc|cc} 1 & 0 & 1.3333 & 0.6666 \\ 0 & 1 & 0.50 & 1.50 \end{array}\right] \qquad (I - A)^{-1} = \left[\begin{array}{cc} 1.3333 & 0.6666 \\ 0.50 & 1.50 \end{array}\right]$$

(a) $(I - A)^{-1} \left[\begin{array}{c} 6 \\ 12 \end{array}\right] = \left[\begin{array}{c} 16 \\ 21 \end{array}\right]$ (b) $(I - A)^{-1} \left[\begin{array}{c} 18 \\ 6 \end{array}\right] = \left[\begin{array}{c} 28 \\ 18 \end{array}\right]$

(c) $(I - A)^{-1} \left[\begin{array}{c} 24 \\ 12 \end{array}\right] = \left[\begin{array}{c} 40 \\ 30 \end{array}\right]$

15. Find $(I - A)^{-1}D$

$$\left[\begin{array}{ccc|ccc} .80 & -.20 & -.10 & 1 & 0 & 0 \\ 0 & .60 & -.20 & 0 & 1 & 0 \\ 0 & -.20 & .40 & 0 & 0 & 1 \end{array}\right]$$

$$\left[\begin{array}{ccc|ccc} 1 & -.25 & -.125 & 1.25 & 0 & 0 \\ 0 & 1 & -.3333 & 0 & 1.6667 & 0 \\ 0 & -.20 & .40 & 0 & 0 & 1 \end{array}\right]$$

$$\left[\begin{array}{ccc|ccc} 1 & 0 & -.2083 & 1.25 & .4167 & 0 \\ 0 & 1 & -.3333 & 0 & 1.6667 & 0 \\ 0 & 0 & .3333 & 0 & .3333 & 1 \end{array}\right]$$

$$\left[\begin{array}{ccc|ccc} 1 & 0 & 0 & 1.25 & .625 & .625 \\ 0 & 1 & 0 & 0 & 2.00 & 1.00 \\ 0 & 0 & 1 & 0 & 1.00 & 3.00 \end{array}\right]$$

$$(I - A)^{-1} = \left[\begin{array}{ccc} 1.25 & .625 & .625 \\ 0 & 2.00 & 1.00 \\ 0 & 1.00 & 3.00 \end{array}\right]$$

(a) $(I - A)^{-1} \left[\begin{array}{c} 4 \\ 8 \\ 8 \end{array}\right] = \left[\begin{array}{c} 15 \\ 24 \\ 32 \end{array}\right]$ (b) $(I - A)^{-1} \left[\begin{array}{c} 0 \\ 8 \\ 16 \end{array}\right] = \left[\begin{array}{c} 15 \\ 32 \\ 56 \end{array}\right]$

(c) $(I - A)^{-1} \left[\begin{array}{c} 8 \\ 24 \\ 8 \end{array}\right] = \left[\begin{array}{c} 30 \\ 56 \\ 48 \end{array}\right]$

17. (a) $AX = \left[\begin{array}{c} 5.6 \\ 5.0 \end{array}\right]$ (b) $X - AX = \left[\begin{array}{c} 2.4 \\ 5.0 \end{array}\right]$

19. (a) $AX = \left[\begin{array}{c} 21.6 \\ 64.8 \\ 36.0 \end{array}\right]$ (b) $X - AX = \left[\begin{array}{c} 14.4 \\ 7.2 \\ 0 \end{array}\right]$

Review Exercises, Chapter 2

1. $3x + 2y = 5$ $x = 9/2 - 2y$ $x = 9/2 - 2(17/8)$
     $2x + 4y = 9$ $3(9/2 - 2y) + 2y = 5$ $= 9/2 - 17/4$
                        $-4y = 5 - 27/2$ $= 1/4$
                          $4y = 17/2$
                          $y = 17/8$ $(1/4,\ 17/8)$

3. $5x - y = 34$
     $2x + 3y = 0$

     $15x - 3y = 102$
     $\underline{\ 2x + 3y = \ \ 0\ }$
     $17x \qquad = 102$

       $x = 6$
       $y = -4$

5. $x - 2y + 3z = 3$
     $4x + 7y - 6z = 6$
     $-2x + 4y + 12z = 0$

     $4x - 8y + 12z = 12$
     $\underline{4x + 7y - \ 6z = \ 6}$
         $-15y + 18z = 6$

     $2x - 4y + 6z = 6$
     $\underline{-2x + 4y + 12z = 0}$
              $18z = 6$
               $z = 1/3$

     $-15y + 6 = 6$
           $y = 0$

     $x - 0 + 1 = 3$
     $x = 2$ $(2,\ 0,\ 1/3)$

7.
$$\begin{bmatrix} 2 & -4 & -14 & | & 50 \\ 1 & -1 & -5 & | & 17 \\ 2 & -4 & -17 & | & 65 \end{bmatrix} \quad \begin{bmatrix} 1 & -1 & -5 & | & 17 \\ 2 & -4 & -14 & | & 50 \\ 2 & -4 & -17 & | & 65 \end{bmatrix} \quad \begin{bmatrix} 1 & -1 & -5 & | & 17 \\ 0 & -2 & -4 & | & 16 \\ 0 & -2 & -7 & | & 31 \end{bmatrix}$$

$$\begin{bmatrix} 1 & 0 & -3 & | & 9 \\ 0 & 1 & 2 & | & -8 \\ 0 & 0 & -3 & | & 15 \end{bmatrix} \quad \begin{bmatrix} 1 & 0 & 0 & | & -6 \\ 0 & 1 & 0 & | & 2 \\ 0 & 0 & 1 & | & -5 \end{bmatrix} \quad x_1 = -6,\ x_2 = 2,\ x_3 = -5$$

9.
$$\begin{bmatrix} 1 & -1 & | & 3 \\ 4 & 3 & | & 5 \\ 6 & 1 & | & 9 \end{bmatrix} \quad \begin{bmatrix} 1 & -1 & | & 3 \\ 0 & 7 & | & -7 \\ 0 & 7 & | & -9 \end{bmatrix} \quad \begin{bmatrix} 1 & -1 & | & 3 \\ 0 & 7 & | & -7 \\ 0 & 0 & | & -2 \end{bmatrix}$$
               No solution

11.
$$\begin{bmatrix} 1 & 0 & 1 & | & 0 \\ 2 & -1 & 1 & | & -1 \\ 1 & -1 & 0 & | & -1 \end{bmatrix} \quad \begin{bmatrix} 1 & 0 & 1 & | & 0 \\ 0 & -1 & -1 & | & -1 \\ 0 & -1 & -1 & | & -1 \end{bmatrix} \quad \begin{bmatrix} 1 & 0 & 1 & | & 0 \\ 0 & 1 & 1 & | & 1 \\ 0 & 0 & 0 & | & 0 \end{bmatrix}$$
            $x = -z,\ y = 1 - z$

13.
$$\begin{bmatrix} 1 & 2 & -1 & 3 & | & 3 \\ 1 & 3 & 1 & -1 & | & 0 \\ 2 & 1 & -6 & 2 & | & -11 \\ 3 & 7 & -1 & 5 & | & 6 \end{bmatrix} \quad \begin{bmatrix} 1 & 2 & -1 & 3 & | & 3 \\ 0 & 1 & 2 & -4 & | & -3 \\ 0 & -3 & -4 & -4 & | & -17 \\ 0 & 1 & 2 & -4 & | & -3 \end{bmatrix}$$

$$\begin{bmatrix} 1 & 0 & -5 & 11 & | & 9 \\ 0 & 1 & 2 & -4 & | & -3 \\ 0 & 0 & 2 & -16 & | & -26 \\ 0 & 0 & 0 & 0 & | & 0 \end{bmatrix} \quad \begin{bmatrix} 1 & 0 & 0 & -29 & | & -56 \\ 0 & 1 & 0 & 12 & | & 23 \\ 0 & 0 & 1 & -8 & | & -13 \\ 0 & 0 & 0 & 0 & | & 0 \end{bmatrix}$$

           $x_1 = -56 + 29x_4,\ x_2 = 23 - 12x_4,\ x_3 = -13 + 8x_4$

15. $\begin{bmatrix} 2 & 3 & -5 & | & 8 \\ 6 & -3 & 1 & | & 16 \end{bmatrix}$ $\qquad$ $\begin{bmatrix} 1 & 3/2 & -5/2 & | & 4 \\ 0 & -12 & 16 & | & -8 \end{bmatrix}$

$\begin{bmatrix} 1 & 0 & -1/2 & | & 3 \\ 0 & 1 & -4/3 & | & 2/3 \end{bmatrix}$ $\quad x_1 = 3 + (1/2)x_3, \ x_2 = 2/3 + (4/3)x_3$

17. $3x + 2 = 5 - x$ $\qquad\qquad\qquad\qquad$ 19. $\begin{bmatrix} -3 & -2 \\ 6 & 7 \end{bmatrix}$
    $4x = 3$
    $x = 3/4$

21. $\begin{bmatrix} 11 & -3 \\ 7 & -1 \\ 3 & 0 \end{bmatrix}$ $\qquad$ 23. $[3]$ $\qquad\qquad$ 25. Cannot multiply them

27. $\begin{bmatrix} 8 & 6 & | & 1 & 0 \\ 7 & 5 & | & 0 & 1 \end{bmatrix}$ $\qquad$ $\begin{bmatrix} 1 & 3/4 & | & 1/8 & 0 \\ 0 & -1/4 & | & -7/8 & 1 \end{bmatrix}$

$\begin{bmatrix} 1 & 0 & | & -5/2 & 3 \\ 0 & 1 & | & 7/2 & -4 \end{bmatrix}$ $\qquad A^{-1} = \begin{bmatrix} -5/2 & 3 \\ 7/2 & -4 \end{bmatrix}$

29. $\begin{bmatrix} 1 & 0 & 3 & | & 1 & 0 & 0 \\ 2 & -5 & 4 & | & 0 & 1 & 0 \\ 1 & -2 & 2 & | & 0 & 0 & 1 \end{bmatrix}$ $\qquad$ $\begin{bmatrix} 1 & 0 & 3 & | & 1 & 0 & 0 \\ 0 & -5 & -2 & | & -2 & 1 & 0 \\ 0 & -2 & -1 & | & -1 & 0 & 1 \end{bmatrix}$

$\begin{bmatrix} 1 & 0 & 3 & | & 1 & 0 & 0 \\ 0 & 1 & 2/5 & | & 2/5 & -1/5 & 0 \\ 0 & 0 & -1/5 & | & -1/5 & -2/5 & 1 \end{bmatrix}$ $\qquad$ $\begin{bmatrix} 1 & 0 & 0 & | & -2 & -6 & 15 \\ 0 & 1 & 0 & | & 0 & -1 & 2 \\ 0 & 0 & 1 & | & 1 & 2 & -5 \end{bmatrix}$

$$A^{-1} = \begin{bmatrix} -2 & -6 & 15 \\ 0 & -1 & 2 \\ 1 & 2 & -5 \end{bmatrix}$$

31. $\begin{bmatrix} 6 & 4 & -5 & | & 10 \\ 3 & -2 & 0 & | & 12 \\ 1 & 1 & -4 & | & -2 \end{bmatrix}$

33. $\begin{bmatrix} 2 & 4 & 6 & -2 \\ 3 & 1 & 0 & 5 \\ -2 & 1 & 3 & -11 \end{bmatrix}$ $\qquad$ $\begin{bmatrix} 1 & 2 & 3 & -1 \\ 0 & -5 & -9 & 8 \\ 0 & 5 & 9 & -13 \end{bmatrix}$

$\begin{bmatrix} 1 & 0 & -3/5 & 11/5 \\ 0 & 1 & 9/5 & -8/5 \\ 0 & 0 & 0 & -5 \end{bmatrix}$ $\qquad$ $\begin{bmatrix} 1 & 0 & -3/5 & 0 \\ 0 & 1 & 9/5 & 0 \\ 0 & 0 & 0 & 1 \end{bmatrix}$

35. Let x = number of field goals, y = number of free throws.
    $x + y = 36$
    $2x + y = 59$
    $\begin{bmatrix} 1 & 1 & | & 36 \\ 2 & 1 & | & 59 \end{bmatrix}$ $\qquad$ $\begin{bmatrix} 1 & 1 & | & 36 \\ 0 & -1 & | & -13 \end{bmatrix}$ $\qquad$ $\begin{bmatrix} 1 & 0 & | & 23 \\ 0 & 1 & | & 13 \end{bmatrix}$

    23 field goals, 13 free throws

37. Let x = amount invested in bonds, y = amount invested in stocks.
    $x + \ y = 50{,}000$
    $.07x + .12y = 5{,}000$
    $\begin{bmatrix} 1 & 1 & | & 50{,}000 \\ .07 & .12 & | & 5{,}000 \end{bmatrix}$ $\qquad$ $\begin{bmatrix} 1 & 1 & | & 50{,}000 \\ 0 & .05 & | & 1{,}500 \end{bmatrix}$ $\qquad$ $\begin{bmatrix} 1 & 0 & | & 20{,}000 \\ 0 & 1 & | & 30{,}000 \end{bmatrix}$

    $\$20{,}000$ in bonds, $\$30{,}000$ in stocks

39. Let x = shares of High-Tech, y = shares of Big Burger

$$38x + 16y = 5648$$
$$40.5x + 15.75y = 5931$$

$$\begin{bmatrix} 1 & 8/19 & | & 2824/19 \\ 0 & -99/76 & | & -1683/19 \end{bmatrix} \qquad \begin{bmatrix} 1 & 0 & | & 120 \\ 0 & 1 & | & 68 \end{bmatrix}$$

120 of High-Tech, 68 of Big Burger

41. Let x = number at plant A, y = number at plant B.

$$x + y = 900$$
$$3.6x + 1260 = 3.3y + 2637$$
$$3.6x + 1260 = 3.3(900 - x) + 2637$$
$$6.9x = 4347$$
$$x = 630, \ y = 270$$

630 at plant A and 270 at plant B.

43. $P(-6) = 4600$, $P(0) = 5400$ so the slope of the line is

$$m = \frac{5400 - 4600}{0 - (-6)} = \frac{400}{3}$$

The y-intercept is 5400 so the equation is

$$P(t) = \frac{400}{3}t + 5400$$

$$P(15) = \frac{400}{3}(15) + 5400 = 2000 + 5400 = 7400$$

Chapter 3
Linear Programming

Section 3-1

1.   (1, -1): $5(1) + 2(-1) = 5 - 2 = 3 \leq 17$ yes
       (4, 1) : $5(4) + 2(1) = 20 + 2 \nleq 17$ no
       (3, 1) : $5(3) + 2(1) = 15 + 2 = 17 \leq 17$ yes
       (4, 4) : $5(4) + 2(4) = 20 + 8 = 28 \nleq 17$ no
       (2, 3) : $5(2) + 2(3) = 10 + 6 = 16 \leq 17$ yes

3. $6x + 8y \leq 24$
       $x = 0$: $8y = 24$ $y = 3$
       $y = 0$: $6x = 24$ $x = 4$

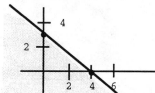

5. $3x - 7y \leq 21$
       $x = 0$: $-7y = 21$ $y = -3$
       $y = 0$: $3x = 21$ $x = 7$

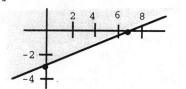

7. $5x + 4y < 20$
       $x = 0$: $4y = 20$ $y = 5$
       $y = 0$: $5x = 20$ $x = 4$

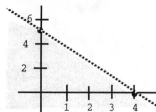

9. $6x + 5y < 30$
       $x = 0$: $5y = 30$ $y = 6$
       $y = 0$: $6x = 30$ $x = 5$

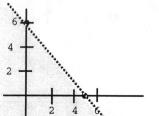

11. $x \leq 10$

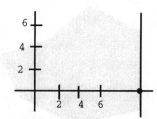

13. $y \geq -3$

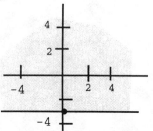

15. $9x - 6y > 30$
       $x = 0$: $-6y = 30$ $y = -5$
       $y = 0$: $9x = 30$ $x = 10/3$

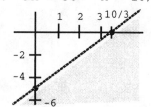

17. $4x - 3y > 12$
       $x = 0$: $-3y = 12$ $y = -4$
       $y = 0$: $4x = 12$ $x = 3$

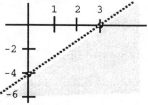

19. $-2x - 5y > 10$
   $x = 0$: $-5y = 10$ $y = -2$
   $y = 0$: $-2x = 10$ $x = -5$

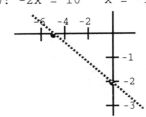

21. Let x = number of air
   conditioners, y = number
   of fans.
   $3.2x + 1.8y \leq 144$
   $x = 0$: $1.8y = 144$ $y = 80$
   $y = 0$: $3.2x = 144$ $x = 45$

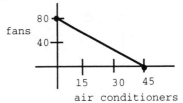

23. Let x = number of members, y = number of pledges.
   (a) $4x + 6y \geq 500$
   (b) $x = 0$: $6y = 500$ $y = 83.33$
       $y = 0$: $4x = 500$ $x = 125$

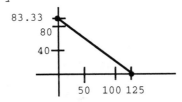

25. Let x = number of TV spots, y = number of newspaper ads.
   $900x + 830y \leq 75,000$

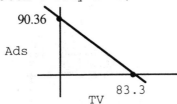

27. Let x = number of acres of strawberries, y = number of acres of
   tomatoes. $9x + 6y \leq 750$

29. Let x = number of days the Glen Echo plant operates, y = number of
   days the Speegleville Road plant operates.
       (a) $200x + 300y \geq 2400$ (paperbacks)
       (b) $300x + 200y \geq 2100$ (hardbacks)

31. Let x = number of drills and y = number of screwdrivers. The
   constraints are
           $2x + 4y \geq 900$ (Production time)
           $x + y \leq 300$ (Packing capacity)
             $y \geq 2x$ (More screwdrivers than drills)
   Maximize $z = 40x + 30y$ (income)

Section 3-2

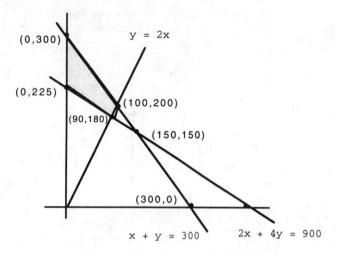

(0,300)

y = 2x

(0,225)

(100,200)

(90,180)

(150,150)

(300,0)

x + y = 300   2x + 4y = 900

Check z at each corner	
Point	z
(0,300)	9,000
(0,225)	6,750
(90,180)	9,000
(100,200)	10,000

The maximum daily income, $10,000, occurs when 100 drills and 200 screwdrivers are produced.

Section 3-2

1.   x + y ≤ 3   (3,0),(0,3)
      2x − y < −2   (−1,0),(0,2)

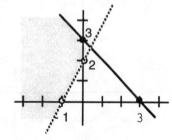

3.   x ≥ 3
      y ≥ 2
      3x + 2y < 18(6,0),(0,9)

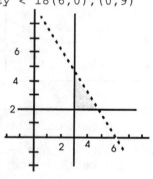

5. 4x + 6y ≤ 18   (9/2,0),(0,3)
   x + 3y ≤ 6   (6,0),(0,2)
   x ≥ 0

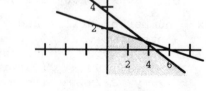

7.   2x + y ≤ 60   (30,0), (0,60)
      2x + 3y ≤ 120   (60,0), 0,40)
      x ≥ 0, y ≥ 0

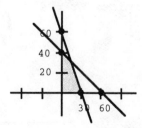

9.   x + y > 4   (4,0), (0,4)
      2x - 3y ≥ 8 (4,0), (0,-8/3)

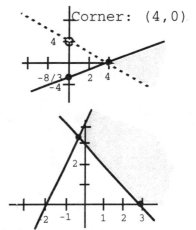

Corner: (4,0)

11.   -2x + y < 4 (-2,0),(0,4)
       x + y ≥ 3   (3,0),(0,3)

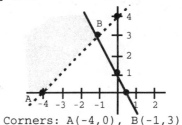

Corner: (-1/3, 10/3)

13.   x ≥ 0
     y < 0

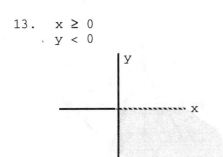

Corner: (0, 0)

15.   2x + y ≤ 1 (1/2,0),(0,1)
      -x + y > 4 (-4,0),(0,4)
      y ≥ 0

Corners: A(-4,0), B(-1,3)

17.   3x + 4y > 24   (8,0),(0,6)
      4x + 5y < 20   (5,0),(0,4)
      x > 0

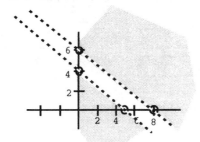

No feasible solution

19.   x + y ≤ 2   (2,0),(0,2)
      2x + y ≥ 6   (3,0),(0,6)
      y ≥ 0

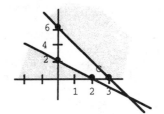

No feasible region

21.   x + y ≥ 1   (1,0),(0,1)
      -x + y ≥ 2 (-2,0),(0,2)
      5x - y ≤ 4 (4/5,0),(0,-4)

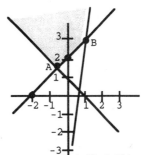

Corners: A(-1/2,3/2), B(3/2,7/2)

Section 3-3

23. $8x + y \geq -10$ $(-5/4,0)$, $(0,-10)$
       $-2x + y \leq 6$ $(-3,0)$, $(0,6)$
       $4x + y \leq 2$ $(1/2,0)$, $(0,2)$
       $3x - y \leq -1$ $(-1/3,0)$, $(0,1)$

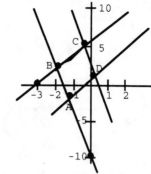

Corners: A$(-1,-2)$
         B$(-8/5,14/5)$
         C$(-2/3,14/3)$
         D$(1/7,10/7)$

25. $-2x + y \leq 2$ $(-1,0)$, $(0,2)$
       $3x + y \leq 3$ $(1,0)$, $(0,3)$
       $-x + y \geq -4$ $(4,0)$, $(0,-4)$
       $x + y \geq -3$ $(-3,0)$, $(0,-3)$

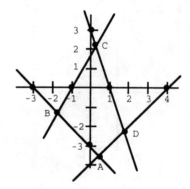

Corners: A$(1/2,-7/2)$
         B$(-5/3,-4/3)$
         C$(1/5,12/5)$
         D$(7/4,-9/4)$

27.   Let x = amount of High Fibre, y = amount of Corn Bits.
         $.25x + .02y \geq .40$
         $.04x + .10y \geq .25$
         $x \geq 0$, $y \geq 0$

29.   Let x = number of student tickets, y = number of adult tickets.
         $x + y \geq 500$
         $3x + 8y \geq 2500$
         $x \geq 0$, $y \geq 0$

31.   Let x = number correct, y = number incorrect.
         $x + y \geq 60$
         $4x - y \geq 200$
         $x \geq 0$, $y \geq 0$

Section 3-3

1.   Let x = number of style A, y = number of style B.
       Maximize $z = 50x + 40y$ Subject to: $x + y \leq 80$
                                              $x + 2y \leq 110$
                                              $x \geq 0$, $y \geq 0$

3. $3x + 2y \le 18$ (6, 0),(0, 9)
     $3x + y \le 15$ (5, 0),(0, 15)

	$z = 20x + 12y$
A(0, 0)	0
B(0, 9)	108
C(4, 3)	116
D(5, 0)	100

Maximum is 116 at (4, 3)

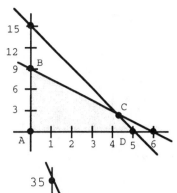

5. $5x + y \le 35$ (7, 0),(0, 35)
     $3x + y \le 27$ (9, 0),(0, 27)

	$z = 9x + 2y$
A(0, 0)	0
B(0, 27)	54
C(4, 15)	66
D(7, 0)	63

Maximum is 66 at (4, 15)

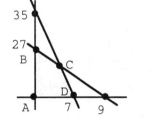

7. $4x + y \ge 40$ (10,0), (0,40)
     $4x + 3y \ge 64$ (16,0), (0,64/3)

	$z = 2x + 3y$
A(0,40)	120
B(7,12)	50
C(16,0)	32

Minimum is 32 at (16, 0)

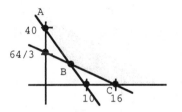

9. $10x + 11y \le 330$ (33, 0),(0, 30)
      $4x + 6y \le 156$ (39, 0),(0, 26)

	$z = 9x + 13y$
A(0, 0)	0
B(0, 26)	338
C(33/2, 15)	343.5
D(33, 0)	297

Maximum is 343.5 at (16.5, 15)

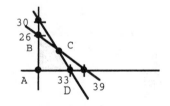

11. $-x + 2y \le 40$ (-40, 0),(0, 20)
       $x + 4y \le 54$ (54, 0),(0, 27/2)
      $3x + y \le 63$ (21, 0),(0, 63)

	$z = 20x + 30y$
A(0, 0)	0
B(0, 27/2)	405
C(18, 9)	630
D(21, 0)	420

Maximum is 630 at (18, 9)

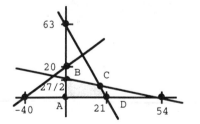

13. $x + 5y \le 250$ (250, 0),(0, 50)
      $2x + 5y \le 300$ (150, 0),(0, 60)
      $x \le 75$

	$z = 320x + 140y$
A(0, 0)	0
B(0, 50)	7,000
C(50, 40)	21,600
D(75, 30)	28,200
E(75, 0)	24,000

Maximum is 28,200 at (75, 30)

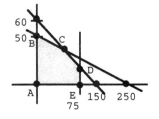

15. $6x + y \geq 52$ (26/3, 0), (0, 52)
     $2x + y \geq 20$ (10, 0), (0, 20)
     $x + 4y \geq 24$ (24, 0), (0, 6)

	$z = 5x + 3y$
A(0, 52)	156
B(8, 4)	52
C(24, 0)	120

Minimum is 52 at (8, 4)

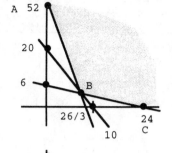

17. $3x + y \geq 30$ (10, 0), (0, 30)
     $4x + 3y \geq 60$ (15, 0), (0, 20)
     $x + 2y \geq 20$ (20, 0), (0, 10)

	$z = 5x + 3y$
A(0, 30)	90
B(6, 12)	66
C(12, 4)	72
D(20, 0)	100

Minimum is 66 at (6, 12)

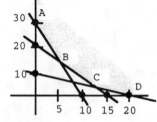

19. $2x + 10y \leq 80$ (40, 0), (0, 8)
     $6x + 2y \leq 72$ (12, 0), (0, 36)
     $3x + 2y \geq 6$ (2, 0), (0, 3)

	$z = 20x + 30y$
A(2, 0)	40
B(0, 3)	90
C(0, 8)	240
D(10, 6)	380
E(12, 0)	240

Maximum is 380 at (10, 6)
Minimum is 40 at (2, 0)

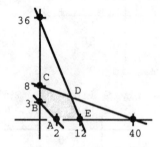

21. $6x + 8y \leq 300$ (50, 0), (0, 37.5)
     $15x + 22y \geq 330$ (22, 0), (0, 15)
     $x \leq 40, y \leq 21$

	$z = 5x + 6y$
A(0, 15)	90
B(0, 21)	126
C(22, 21)	236
D(40, 7.5)	245
E(40, 0)	200
F(22, 0)	110

Maximum is 245 at (40, 7.5)
Minimum is 90 at (0, 15)

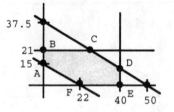

23. $5x + 3y \leq 30$ (6, 0), (0, 10)
     $5x + y \leq 20$ (4, 0), (0, 20)

	$z = 15x + 9y$
A(0, 0)	0
B(0, 10)	90
C(3, 5)	90
D(4, 0)	60

Maximum is 90 at any pt. on line
$5x + 3y = 30$ from (0, 10) to (3, 5)

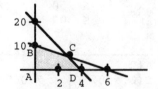

25. $3x + 2y \geq 60$ (20, 0),(0, 30)
$10x + 3y \leq 180$ (18, 0),(0, 60)
$y \leq 24$

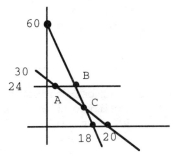

	$z = 9x + 6y$
A(4, 24)	180
B(10.8, 24)	241.2
C($\frac{180}{11}$, $\frac{60}{11}$)	180

Minimum is 180 at (4, 24),
($\frac{180}{11}$, $\frac{60}{11}$) and points between

Maximum is 144 at (0, 24),(12, 20) and points between

27. $3x + y \geq 150$ (50, 0)(0, 150)
$x + 2y \geq 100$ (100, 0)(0, 50)
$y \geq 20$ (0, 20)

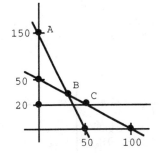

	$z = 5x + 10y$
A(0, 150)	1500
B(40, 30)	500
C(60, 20)	500

Minimum is 500 at (40, 30), (60, 20) and points between

29. $2x - 3y \geq 10$ (5, 0),(0, -10/3)
$x \geq 8$
Unbounded feasible region,
no maximum

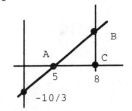

31. $-3x + y \leq 4$ (-4/3, 0),(0, 4)
$-2x - y \geq 1$ (-1/2, 0),(0, -1)
No feasible region, no minimum

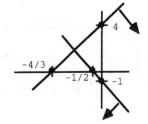

33. $3x - y \leq 8$ (8/3, 0),(0, -8)
$x - 2y \geq 5$ (5, 0),(0, -5/2)
No feasible region

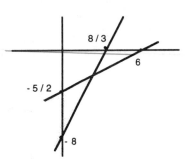

35. Let x = number of standard VCR's, y = number of deluxe VCR's.
Maximize $P = 39x + 26y$
Subject to $8x + 9y \leq 2200$
$115x + 136y \leq 18,000$
$x \geq 35, y \geq 0$

Section 3-3

37. Let x = number shipped to A, y = number shipped to B.
            Minimize C = 13x + 11y
            Subject to x + y ≥ 250
                        x + 30 ≤ 140
                        y + 18 ≤ 165
                        x ≥ 0, y ≥ 0

39. Let x = number cartons of regular, y = number cartons of diet.
            Maximize z = .15x + .17y
            Subject to x + 1.2y ≤ 5400
                        x +   y ≤ 5000
                        x ≥ 0, y ≥ 0

41. Let x = number of desk lamps y = number of floor lamps.
     Maximize z = 2.65x + 3.15y
     Subject to .8x + y ≤ 1200   (1500, 0) (0, 1200)
                 4x + 3y ≤ 4200   (1050, 0) (0, 1400)
                 x ≥ 0, y ≥ 0

	z = 2.65x + 3.15y
A (0,0)	0
B (0,1200)	3780
C (375,900)	3828.75
D (1050,0)	2782.50

Maximum profit is $3828.75 at 375 desk lamps, 900 floor lamps.

43. Let x = number acres for cattle, y = number acres for sheep.
     Maximize z = 30x + 32y
     Subject to   x + y ≤ 1000   (1000, 0),(0, 1000)
                 2x + 8y ≤ 3200   (1600, 0),(0, 400)
                 x ≥ 0, y ≥ 0

	z = 30x +32y
A(0, 0)	0
B(0, 400)	12,800
C(800, 200)	30,400
D(1000, 0)	30,000

Maximum profit is $30,400 for 800 acres for cattle and 200 acres for sheep.

45. Let x = weight of food I, y = weight of food II.
     Minimize z = .03x + .04y
     Subject to   .4x + .6y ≥ 10   (25, 0),(0, 50/3)
                   .5x + .2y ≥ 7.5   (15, 0),(0, 37.5)
                  .06x + .04y ≥ 1.2   (20, 0),(0, 30)
                   x ≥ 0, y ≥ 0

	z = .03x + .04y
A(0,37.5)	1.50
B(7.5,18.75)	.975
C(16,6)	.72
D(25,0)	.75

Minimum cost is $.72 using 16 g of food I and 6 g of food II.

45

47. Let x = number of standard gears, y = number of heavy duty gears.
Minimize z = 15x + 22y
subject to 8x + 10y ≥ 12,000   (1500, 0),(0, 1200)
            3x + 10y ≥ 8,400   (2800, 0),(0, 840)
            x ≥ 0, y ≥ 0

z = 15x + 22y	
A (0,1200)	26,400
B (720,624)	24,528
C (2800. 0)	42,000

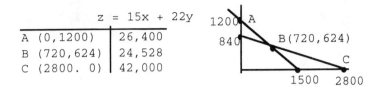

Minimum cost is $24,528 producing 720 standard gears and 624 heavy
duty gears.

49. Let x = number of SE vans, y = number of LE vans.
Minimize z = 2700x + 2400y
subject to   x + y ≥ 9   (9, 0),(0, 9)
           16,000x + 20,000y ≤ 160,000   (10, 0),(0, 8)
                    x ≥ 0, y ≥ 0

	2700x + 2400y
A(9,0)	24,300
B(10,0)	27,000
C(5,4)	23,100

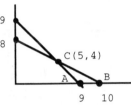

Minimum maintenance cost = $23,100 with 5 SE vans and 4 LE vans.

51. Let x = number cartons of regular, y = number cartons of diet.
Maximize z = .15x + .17y
subject to   x + 1.2y ≤ 5400   (5400, 0),(0, 4500)
             x + y ≤ 5000   (5000, 0),(0, 5000)
             x ≥ 0, y ≥ 0

	z = .15x + .17y
A(0,0)	0
B(0,4500)	765
C(3000,2000)	790
D(5000,0)	750

Maximum profit is $790 with 3,000 cartons of regular
and 2,000 cartons of diet.

53. Let x = number of square feet of type A, y = number of square feet
of type B glass.
(a) Minimize z = x + .25y subject to
        x + y ≥ 4000   (4000, 0),(0, 4000)
       .8x + 1.2y ≤ 4500 (5625, 0),(0, 3750)
             x ≥ 0, y ≥ 0

	z = x + .25y
A(4000, 0)	4000
B(750, 3250)	1562.5
C(5625, 0)	5625

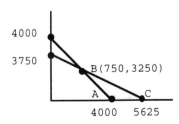

Minimum conductance is 1562.5 using 750 square feet of type A glass
and 3250 square feet of type B.

(b) Minimize z = .8x + 1.2y, subject to
        x + .25y ≤ 2200   (2200, 0),(0, 8800)
        x +   y ≥ 4000   (4000, 0),(0, 4000)

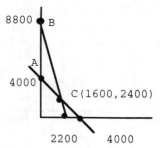

	z = .8x + 1.2y
A(0, 4000)	4,800
B(0, 8800)	10,560
C(1600, 2400)	4,160

Minimum cost is $4,160 using 1600 square feet of type A and 2400 square feet of type B.

55. Let x = number of days the Glen Echo plant operates,
     y = number of days the Speegleville Road plant operates.
     Minimize z = x + y, subject to
            200x + 300y ≥ 2400   (12, 0), (0, 8)
            200x + 300y ≥ 2400   (12, 0),(0, 8)
            300x + 200y ≥ 2100   (7, 0),(0,10.5)
                   x ≥ 0, y ≥ 0

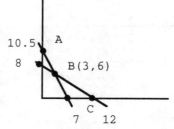

	z = x + y
A(0, 10.5)	10.5
B(3, 6)	9
C(12, 0)	12

Minimum number of days is 9 with 3 at Glen Echo and 6 at Speegleville Road.

57. (a)   5x + 2y ≤ 50   (10, 0),(0, 25)
            x + 4y ≤ 28   (28, 0),(0, 7)

	z = 10x + 4y	
A(0, 0)	0	
B(0, 7)	28	
C(8, 5)	100	multiple
D(10, 0)	100	solutions

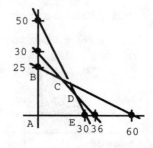

	Slope
z = 10x + 4y	-5/2
5x + 2y = 50	-5/2

     (b)   5x + 12y ≤ 300   (60, 0),(0, 25)
           10x + 12y ≤ 360   (36, 0),(0, 30)
           10x + 6y ≤ 300   (30, 0),(0, 50)

	z = 5x + 6y	
A(0, 0)	0	
B(0, 25)	150	
C(12, 20)	180	multiple
D(24, 10)	180	solutions
E(20, 0)	100	

	Slope
z = 5x + 6y	-5/6
10x + 12y = 360	-5/6

(c) $3x + 2y \geq 50$ $(50/3, 0), (0, 25)$
    $2x + 3y \geq 60$ $(30, 0), (0, 20)$
     $x + 4y \geq 40$ $(40, 0), (0, 10)$

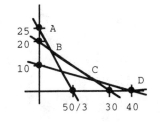

	$z = 10x + 15y$	
A(0, 25)	375	
B(6, 16)	300	multiple
C(24, 4)	300	solutions
D(40, 0)	400	

	Slope
$z = 10x + 15y$	$-2/3$
$2x + 3y = 60$	$-2/3$

(d) $5x + 12y \leq 1200$ $(240, 0), (0, 100)$
    $5x + 4y \leq 600$ $(120, 0), (0, 150)$

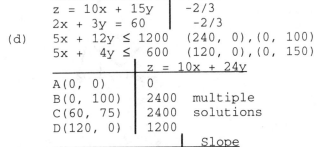

	$z = 10x + 24y$	
A(0, 0)	0	
B(0, 100)	2400	multiple
C(60, 75)	2400	solutions
D(120, 0)	1200	

	Slope
$z = 10x + 24y$	$-5/12$
$5x + 12y = 1200$	$-5/12$

Review Exercises, Chapter 3

1. (a) $5x + 7y < 70$
    $(14, 0), (0, 10)$

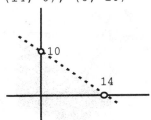

(b) $2x - 3y > 18$
    $(9, 0), (0, -6)$

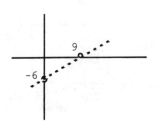

(c) $x + 9y \leq 21$
    $(21, 0), (0, 7/3)$

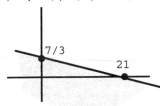

(d) $-2x + 12y \geq 26$
    $(-13, 0), (0, 13/6)$

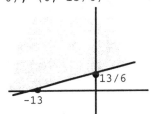

(e) $y \geq -6$

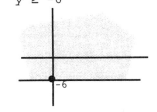

(f) $x \leq 3$

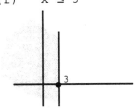

Review, Chapter 3

3. $x - 3y \geq 6$ (6, 0), (0, -2)
       $x - y \leq 4$ (4, 0), (0, -4)
       $y \geq -5$ (0, -5)
           Corners: A(-1, -5)
                       B(-9, -5)
                       C(3, -1)

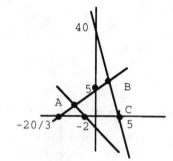

5. $-3x + 4y \leq 20$ (-20/3, 0), (0, 5)
        $x + y \geq -2$ (-2, 0), (0, -2)
       $8x + y \leq 40$ (5, 0), (0, 40)
           Corners: A(-4, 2)
                        B(4, 8)
                        C(5, 0)
                        D(-2, 0)

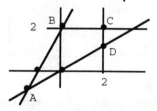

7. $x - 2y \leq 0$ (0, 0), (2, 1)
       $-2x + y \leq 2$ (-1, 0), (0, 2)
        $x \leq 2$ (2, 0)
        $y \leq 2$ (0, 2)
           Corners: A(-4/3, -2/3)
                        D(2, 1)
                        B(0, 2)
                        C(2, 2)

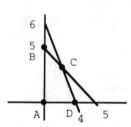

9. $3x + 2y \leq 12$ (4, 0), (0, 6)
        $x + y \leq 5$ (5, 0), (0, 5)

	5x + 4y
A(0, 0)	0
B(0, 5)	20
C(2, 3)	22
D(4, 0)	20

Maximum z is 22 at (2, 3)

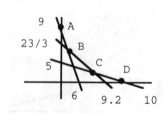

11. $3x + 2y \geq 18$ (6, 0), (0, 9)
        $x + 2y \geq 10$ (10, 0), (0, 5)
       $5x + 6y \geq 46$ (9.2, 0), (0, 23/3)

	5x + 4y	10x + 12y
A(0, 9)	36	108
B(2, 6)	34	92
C(8, 1)	44	92
D(10, 0)	50	100

   (a)   Min is 34 at (2, 6)
   (b)   Min is 92, at any point on line $5x + 6y = 46$
         from (2, 6) to (8, 1)

13. $2x + y \leq 90$ $(45, 0), (0, 90)$
     $x + 2y \leq 80$ $(80, 0), (0, 40)$
     $x + y \leq 50$ $(50, 0), (0, 50)$

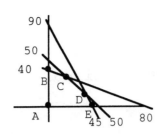

	$4x + 7y$
A(0, 0)	0
B(0, 40)	280
C(20, 30)	290
D(40, 10)	230
E(45, 0)	180

Maximum z is 290 at (20, 30)

15. Let x = number of hours Line A is used, y = number of hours Line B is used.
    (a) $65x + 105y \leq 1500$ (b)
           $x \geq 0, y \geq 0$

17. Let x = number of adult tickets, y = number of children tickets.
$$x + y \leq 275$$
$$4.5x + 3y \geq 1100$$
$$x \geq 0, y \geq 0$$

19. Let x = number of standard bars, y = number of premium bars.
    Maximize r = 90x + 100y subject to
   $(.9)(100)x + (.8)(100)y \leq 80,000$ $(888.9, 0), (0, 1000)$
   $(.1)(100)x + (.2)(100)y \leq 12,000$ $(1200, 0), (0, 600)$
        $x \geq 0, y \geq 0$

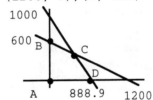

	$90x + 100y$
A(0, 0)	0
B(0, 600)	60,000
C(640, 280)	85,600
D(888.9, 0)	80,000

Maximum revenue is $85,600 when 640 bars of standard and 280 of premium are produced.

Chapter 4
Linear Programming: The Simplex Method

Section 4-1

1. Maximize $\begin{bmatrix} 50 & 80 \end{bmatrix} \begin{bmatrix} x_1 \\ x_2 \end{bmatrix}$

    Subject to $\begin{bmatrix} 7 & 15 \\ 3 & 14 \end{bmatrix} \begin{bmatrix} x_1 \\ x_2 \end{bmatrix} \leq \begin{bmatrix} 30 \\ 56 \end{bmatrix}$ and $\begin{bmatrix} x_1 \\ x_2 \end{bmatrix} \geq \begin{bmatrix} 0 \\ 0 \end{bmatrix}$

3. Maximize $\begin{bmatrix} 42 & 26 & 5 \end{bmatrix} \begin{bmatrix} x_1 \\ x_2 \\ x_3 \end{bmatrix}$

    Subject to $\begin{bmatrix} 13 & 4 & 23 \\ 4 & 15 & 7 \\ 3 & -2 & 32 \end{bmatrix} \begin{bmatrix} x_1 \\ x_2 \\ x_3 \end{bmatrix} \leq \begin{bmatrix} 88 \\ 92 \\ 155 \end{bmatrix}$ and $\begin{bmatrix} x_1 \\ x_2 \\ x_3 \end{bmatrix} \geq \begin{bmatrix} 0 \\ 0 \\ 0 \end{bmatrix}$

5. $2x_1 + 3x_2 + s_1 = 9$
    $x_1 + 5x_2 + s_2 = 16$

7. $x_1 + 7x_2 - 4x_3 + s_1 = 150$
    $5x_1 + 9x_2 + 2x_3 + s_2 = 435$
    $8x_1 - 3x_2 + 16x_3 + s_3 = 345$

9. $2x_1 + 6x_2 + s_1 = 9$
    $x_1 - 5x_2 + s_2 = 14$
    $-3x_1 + x_2 + s_3 = 8$
    $-3x_1 - 7x_2 + z = 0$

11. $6x_1 + 7x_2 + 12x_3 + s_1 = 50$
    $4x_1 + 18x_2 + 9x_3 + s_2 = 85$
    $x_1 - 2x_2 + 14x_3 + s_3 = 66$
    $-420x_1 - 260x_2 - 50x_3 + z = 0$

13. $\left[\begin{array}{ccccc|c} 4 & 5 & 1 & 0 & 0 & 10 \\ 3 & 1 & 0 & 1 & 0 & 25 \\ -3 & -17 & 0 & 0 & 1 & 0 \end{array} \right]$

15. $\left[\begin{array}{ccccccc|c} 16 & -4 & 9 & 1 & 0 & 0 & 0 & 128 \\ 8 & 13 & 22 & 0 & 1 & 0 & 0 & 144 \\ 5 & 6 & -15 & 0 & 0 & 1 & 0 & 225 \\ -20 & -45 & -40 & 0 & 0 & 0 & 1 & 0 \end{array} \right]$

17. Let x_1 = number of cartons of screwdrivers, x_2 = number of cartons
    of chisels, x_3 = number of cartons of putty knives.
    Maximize $z = 5x_1 + 6x_2 + 5x_3$
    Subject to $3x_1 + 4x_2 + 5x_3 \leq 2200$
    $15x_1 + 12x_2 + 11x_3 \leq 8500$
    $x_1 \geq 0, x_2 \geq 0, x_3 \geq 0$
    $\left[\begin{array}{cccccc|c} 3 & 4 & 5 & 1 & 0 & 0 & 2200 \\ 15 & 12 & 11 & 0 & 1 & 0 & 8500 \\ -5 & -6 & -5 & 0 & 0 & 1 & 0 \end{array} \right]$

19. Let x_1 = amount of salad, x_2 = amount of potatoes, x_3 = amount of steak.

Maximize $z = 0.5x_1 + 1x_2 + 9x_3$

Subject to $20x_1 + 50x_2 + 56x_3 \leq 1000$

$1.5x_1 + 3x_2 + 2x_3 \leq 35$

$x_1 \geq 0, \; x_2 \geq 0, \; x_3 \geq 0$

$$\left[\begin{array}{cccccc|c} 20 & 50 & 56 & 1 & 0 & 0 & 1000 \\ 1.5 & 3 & 2 & 0 & 1 & 0 & 35 \\ \hline -0.5 & -1 & -9 & 0 & 0 & 1 & 0 \end{array} \right]$$

21. Let x_1 = lbs of Lite, x_2 = lbs. of Trim, x_3 = lbs. of Health Fare.

Maximize $z = .25x_1 + .25x_2 + .32x_3$

Subject to $.75x_1 + .50x_2 + .15x_3 \leq 2320$

$.25x_1 + .25x_2 + .60x_3 \leq 1380$

$.25x_2 + .25x_3 \leq 700$

$x_1 \geq 0, \; x_2 \geq 0, \; x_3 \geq 0$

$$\left[\begin{array}{ccccccc|c} .75 & .50 & .15 & 1 & 0 & 0 & 0 & 2320 \\ .25 & .25 & .60 & 0 & 1 & 0 & 0 & 1380 \\ 0 & .25 & .25 & 0 & 0 & 1 & 0 & 700 \\ \hline -.25 & -.25 & -.32 & 0 & 0 & 0 & 1 & 0 \end{array} \right]$$

23. Let x_1 = number of military trunks, x_2 = number of commercial trunks, x_3 = number of decorative trunks.

Maximize $z = 6x_1 + 7x_2 + 9x_3$

Subject to $4x_1 + 3x_2 + 2x_3 \leq 4900$

$x_1 + 2x_2 + 4x_3 \leq 2200$

$.1x_1 + .2x_2 + .3x_3 \leq 210$

$x_1 \geq 0, \; x_2 \geq 0, \; x_3 \geq 0$

$$\left[\begin{array}{ccccccc|c} 4 & 3 & 2 & 1 & 0 & 0 & 0 & 4900 \\ 1 & 2 & 4 & 0 & 1 & 0 & 0 & 2200 \\ .1 & .2 & .3 & 0 & 0 & 1 & 0 & 210 \\ \hline -6 & -7 & -9 & 0 & 0 & 0 & 1 & 0 \end{array} \right]$$

25. Let x_1 = number of Majestic, x_2 = number of Traditional, x_3 = number of Wall clocks.

Maximize $z = 400x_1 + 250x_2 + 160x_3$

subject to

$4x_1 + 2x_2 + x_3 \leq 120$

$3x_1 + 2x_2 + x_3 \leq 80$

$x_1 + x_2 + .5x_3 \leq 40$

$x_1 \geq 0, \; x_2 \geq 0, \; x_3 \geq 0$

$$\left[\begin{array}{ccccccc|c} 4 & 2 & 1 & 1 & 0 & 0 & 0 & 120 \\ 3 & 2 & 1 & 0 & 1 & 0 & 0 & 80 \\ 1 & 1 & .5 & 0 & 0 & 1 & 0 & 40 \\ \hline -400 & -250 & -160 & 0 & 0 & 0 & 1 & 0 \end{array} \right]$$

Section 4-2

1. Basic: $x_1 = 8$, $s_2 = 10$, $z = 14$; nonbasic: $x_2 = 0$, $s_1 = 0$

3. Basic: $x_2 = 86$, $s_1 = 54$, $s_3 = 39$, $z = 148$;
   nonbasic: $x_1 = x_3 = \quad s_2 = 0$

5.
$$\begin{bmatrix} 5 & 4 & 3 & 1 & 0 & 0 & 0 & 8 \\ 2 & 7 & 1 & 0 & 1 & 0 & 0 & 15 \\ \underline{6} & \underline{8} & \underline{5} & \underline{0} & \underline{0} & \underline{1} & \underline{0} & \underline{24} \\ -8 & -10 & -4 & 0 & 0 & 0 & 1 & 0 \end{bmatrix} \begin{array}{l} 8/4 = 2 \\ 15/7 = 2.14 \\ 24/8 = 3 \end{array}$$
   4 in row 1, column 2

7.
$$\begin{bmatrix} 2 & 5 & 3 & 1 & 0 & 0 & 0 & 15 \\ 4 & 1 & 4 & 0 & 1 & 0 & 0 & 12 \\ \underline{7} & \underline{3} & \underline{-5} & \underline{0} & \underline{0} & \underline{1} & \underline{0} & \underline{10} \\ -25 & -30 & -50 & 0 & 0 & 0 & 1 & 0 \end{bmatrix} \begin{array}{l} 15/3 = 5 \\ 12/4 = 3 \\ 10/-5 = -2 \end{array}$$
   4 in row 2, column 3

9.
$$\begin{bmatrix} 2 & 1 & 1 & 0 & 0 & 0 & 7 \\ 3 & 4 & 0 & 1 & 0 & 0 & 12 \\ \underline{2} & \underline{5} & \underline{0} & \underline{0} & \underline{1} & \underline{0} & \underline{15} \\ -5 & -8 & 0 & 0 & 0 & 1 & 0 \end{bmatrix} \begin{array}{l} 7/1 = 7 \\ 12/4 = 3 \\ 15/5 = 3 \end{array}$$
   Either the 4 in row 2, column 2 or the 5 in row 3, column 2.

11.
$$\begin{bmatrix} 3 & 5 & 6 & 1 & 0 & 0 & 0 & 9 \\ 2 & 8 & 2 & 0 & 1 & 0 & 0 & 6 \\ \underline{5} & \underline{4} & \underline{3} & \underline{0} & \underline{0} & \underline{1} & \underline{0} & \underline{15} \\ -6 & -12 & -12 & 0 & 0 & 0 & 1 & 0 \end{bmatrix} \begin{array}{l} 9/6 \text{ or } 9/5 \\ 6/2 \text{ or } 6/8 \\ 15/3 \text{ or } 15/4 \end{array}$$
   Either the 8 in row 2, column 2 or the 6 in row 1, column 3.

13.
$$\begin{bmatrix} 6 & 2 & 1 & 0 & 0 & 0 & 3 \\ 4 & 3 & 0 & 1 & 0 & 0 & 0 \\ \underline{3} & \underline{5} & \underline{0} & \underline{0} & \underline{1} & \underline{0} & \underline{8} \\ -12 & -3 & 0 & 0 & 0 & 1 & 0 \end{bmatrix} \begin{array}{l} 3/6 = 1/2 \\ 0/4 = 0 \\ 8/3 \end{array}$$
   4 in row 2, column 1

15.
$$\begin{bmatrix} 2 & 3 & 1 & 0 & 0 & 0 & 12 \\ 1 & 2 & 0 & 1 & 0 & 0 & 6 \\ \underline{2} & \underline{5} & \underline{0} & \underline{0} & \underline{1} & \underline{0} & \underline{20} \\ -4 & -3 & 0 & 0 & 0 & 1 & 0 \end{bmatrix} \quad \begin{bmatrix} 0 & -1 & 1 & -2 & 0 & 0 & 0 \\ 1 & 2 & 0 & 1 & 0 & 0 & 6 \\ \underline{0} & \underline{1} & \underline{0} & \underline{-2} & \underline{1} & \underline{0} & \underline{8} \\ 0 & 5 & 0 & 4 & 0 & 1 & 24 \end{bmatrix}$$

17.
$$\begin{bmatrix} 6 & 11 & 4 & 1 & 0 & 0 & 0 & 250 \\ -5 & -14 & -8 & 0 & 1 & 0 & 0 & -460 \\ \underline{-1} & \underline{-1} & \underline{-3} & \underline{0} & \underline{0} & \underline{1} & \underline{0} & \underline{-390} \\ -10 & -50 & -30 & 0 & 0 & 0 & 1 & 0 \end{bmatrix}$$
$$\begin{bmatrix} 14/3 & 29/3 & 0 & 1 & 0 & 4/3 & 0 & -270 \\ -7/3 & -34/3 & 0 & 0 & 1 & -8/3 & 0 & 580 \\ \underline{1/3} & \underline{1/3} & \underline{1} & \underline{0} & \underline{0} & \underline{-1/3} & \underline{0} & \underline{130} \\ 0 & -40 & 0 & 0 & 0 & -10 & 1 & 3900 \end{bmatrix}$$

19. $\begin{bmatrix} 3 & 1 & 1 & 0 & 0 & 22 \\ 3 & 4 & 0 & 1 & 0 & 34 \\ -2 & -1 & 0 & 0 & 1 & 0 \end{bmatrix}$ $\begin{matrix} 22/3 \\ 34/3 \end{matrix}$ $\begin{bmatrix} 1 & 1/3 & 1/3 & 0 & 0 & 22/3 \\ 0 & 3 & -1 & 1 & 0 & 12 \\ 0 & -1/3 & 2/3 & 0 & 1 & 44/3 \end{bmatrix}$

$\begin{bmatrix} 1 & 0 & 4/9 & -1/9 & 0 & 6 \\ 0 & 1 & -1/3 & 1/3 & 0 & 4 \\ 0 & 0 & 5/9 & 1/9 & 1 & 16 \end{bmatrix}$ $\quad x_1 = 6, \ x_2 = 4, \ z = 16$

21. $\begin{bmatrix} 1 & 4 & 1 & 0 & 0 & 9 \\ 4 & 1 & 0 & 1 & 0 & 6 \\ -4 & -5 & 0 & 0 & 1 & 0 \end{bmatrix}$ $\begin{matrix} 9/4 = 2.25 \\ 6/1 = 6 \end{matrix}$ $\begin{bmatrix} 1/4 & 1 & 1/4 & 0 & 0 & 9/4 \\ 15/4 & 0 & -1/4 & 1 & 0 & 15/4 \\ -11/4 & 0 & 5/4 & 0 & 1 & 45/4 \end{bmatrix}$

$\begin{bmatrix} 0 & 1 & 4/15 & -1/15 & 0 & 2 \\ 1 & 0 & -1/15 & 4/15 & 0 & 1 \\ 0 & 0 & 16/15 & 11/15 & 1 & 14 \end{bmatrix}$ $\quad x_1 = 1, \ x_2 = 2, \ z = 14$

23. $\begin{bmatrix} 1 & 1 & 1 & 0 & 0 & 240 \\ 4 & 3 & 0 & 1 & 0 & 720 \\ -8 & -4 & 0 & 0 & 1 & 0 \end{bmatrix}$ $\begin{matrix} 240 \\ 180 \end{matrix}$ $\begin{bmatrix} 0 & 1/4 & 1 & -1/4 & 0 & 60 \\ 1 & 3/4 & 0 & 1/4 & 0 & 180 \\ 0 & 2 & 0 & 2 & 1 & 1440 \end{bmatrix}$

$x_1 = 180, \ x_2 = 0, \ z = 1440$

25. $\begin{bmatrix} 5 & 5 & 10 & 1 & 0 & 0 & 0 & 1000 \\ 10 & 8 & 5 & 0 & 1 & 0 & 0 & 2000 \\ 10 & 5 & 0 & 0 & 0 & 1 & 0 & 500 \\ -100 & -200 & -50 & 0 & 0 & 0 & 1 & 0 \end{bmatrix}$

$\begin{bmatrix} -5 & 0 & 10 & 1 & 0 & -1 & 0 & 500 \\ -6 & 0 & 5 & 0 & 1 & -8/5 & 0 & 1200 \\ 2 & 1 & 0 & 0 & 0 & 1/5 & 0 & 100 \\ 300 & 0 & -50 & 0 & 0 & 40 & 1 & 20000 \end{bmatrix}$

$\begin{bmatrix} -1/2 & 0 & 1 & 1/10 & 0 & -1/10 & 0 & 50 \\ -7/2 & 0 & 0 & -1/2 & 1 & -11/10 & 0 & 950 \\ 2 & 1 & 0 & 0 & 0 & 1/5 & 0 & 100 \\ 275 & 0 & 0 & 5 & 0 & 35 & 1 & 22500 \end{bmatrix}$

$x_1 = 0, \ x_2 = 100, \ x_3 = 50, \ z = 22,500$

27. $\begin{bmatrix} 1 & 1 & 1 & 1 & 0 & 0 & 0 & 100 \\ 3 & 2 & 4 & 0 & 1 & 0 & 0 & 210 \\ 1 & 2 & 0 & 0 & 0 & 1 & 0 & 150 \\ -3 & -5 & -5 & 0 & 0 & 0 & 1 & 0 \end{bmatrix}$

$\begin{bmatrix} 1/4 & 1/2 & 0 & 1 & -1/4 & 0 & 0 & 47.5 \\ 3/4 & 1/2 & 1 & 0 & 1/4 & 0 & 0 & 52.5 \\ 1 & 2 & 0 & 0 & 0 & 1 & 0 & 150 \\ 3/4 & -5/2 & 0 & 0 & 5/4 & 0 & 1 & 262.5 \end{bmatrix}$

$\begin{bmatrix} 0 & 0 & 0 & 1 & -1/4 & -1/4 & 0 & 10 \\ 1/2 & 0 & 1 & 0 & 1/4 & -1/4 & 0 & 15 \\ 1/2 & 1 & 0 & 0 & 0 & 1/2 & 0 & 75 \\ 2 & 0 & 0 & 0 & 5/4 & 5/4 & 1 & 450 \end{bmatrix}$

$x_1 = 0, \ x_2 = 75, \ x_3 = 15, \ z = 450$

29.

$$\begin{bmatrix} 2 & 1 & 4 & 1 & 0 & 0 & 0 & 360 \\ 2 & 5 & 10 & 0 & 1 & 0 & 0 & 850 \\ 3 & 3 & 1 & 0 & 0 & 1 & 0 & 510 \\ -15 & -9 & -15 & 0 & 0 & 0 & 1 & 0 \end{bmatrix}$$

$$\begin{bmatrix} 0 & -1 & 10/3 & 1 & 0 & -2/3 & 0 & 20 \\ 0 & 3 & 28/3 & 0 & 1 & -2/3 & 0 & 510 \\ 1 & 1 & 1/3 & 0 & 0 & 1/3 & 0 & \cdot 170 \\ 0 & 6 & -10 & 0 & 0 & 5 & 1 & 2550 \end{bmatrix}$$

$$\begin{bmatrix} 0 & -3/10 & 1 & 3/10 & 0 & -1/5 & 0 & 6 \\ 0 & 29/5 & 0 & -14/5 & 1 & 18/15 & 0 & 454 \\ 1 & 11/10 & 0 & -1/10 & 0 & 2/5 & 0 & 168 \\ 0 & 3 & 0 & 3 & 0 & 3 & 1 & 2610 \end{bmatrix}$$

$$x_1 = 168, \quad x_2 = 0, \quad x_3 = 6, \quad z = 2610$$

31.

$$\begin{bmatrix} 1 & 8 & 1 & 0 & 0 & 0 & 66 \\ 3 & 9 & 0 & 1 & 0 & 0 & 72 \\ 2 & 6 & 0 & 0 & 1 & 0 & 48 \\ -33 & -9 & 0 & 0 & 0 & 1 & 0 \end{bmatrix} \qquad \begin{bmatrix} 0 & 5 & 1 & 0 & -1/2 & 0 & 42 \\ 0 & 0 & 0 & 1 & -3/2 & 0 & 0 \\ 1 & 3 & 0 & 0 & 1/2 & 0 & 24 \\ 0 & 90 & 0 & 0 & 33/2 & 1 & 792 \end{bmatrix}$$

$$x_1 = 24, \quad x_2 = 0, \quad z = 792$$

33.

$$\begin{bmatrix} 2 & 1 & 2 & 1 & 0 & 0 & 0 & 100 \\ 1 & 2 & 2 & 0 & 1 & 0 & 0 & 100 \\ 2 & 2 & 1 & 0 & 0 & 1 & 0 & 100 \\ -22 & -20 & -18 & 0 & 0 & 0 & 1 & 0 \end{bmatrix}$$

$$\begin{bmatrix} 1 & 1/2 & 1 & 1/2 & 0 & 0 & 0 & 50 \\ 0 & 3/2 & 1 & -1/2 & 1 & 0 & 50 & 50 \\ 0 & 1 & -1 & -1 & 0 & 1 & 0 & 0 \\ 0 & -9 & 4 & 11 & 0 & 0 & 1 & 1100 \end{bmatrix}$$

$$\begin{bmatrix} 1 & 0 & 3/2 & 1 & 0 & -1/2 & 0 & 50 \\ 0 & 0 & 5/2 & 1 & 1 & -3/2 & 0 & 50 \\ 0 & 1 & -1 & -1 & 0 & 1 & 0 & 0 \\ 0 & 0 & -5 & 2 & 0 & 9 & 1 & 1100 \end{bmatrix}$$

$$\begin{bmatrix} 1 & 0 & 0 & 2/5 & -3/5 & 2/5 & 0 & 20 \\ 0 & 0 & 1 & 2/5 & 2/5 & -3/5 & 0 & 20 \\ 0 & 1 & 0 & -3/5 & 2/5 & 2/5 & 0 & 20 \\ 0 & 0 & 0 & 4 & 2 & 6 & 1 & 1200 \end{bmatrix}$$

$$x_1 = 20, \quad x_2 = 20, \quad x_3 = 20, \quad z = 1200$$

35. Let x_1 = number cartons of screwdrivers, x_2 = number cartons of chisels, x_3 = number cartons of putty knives.

$$\begin{bmatrix} 3 & 4 & 5 & 1 & 0 & 0 & 2200 \\ 15 & 12 & 11 & 0 & 1 & 0 & 8500 \\ -5 & -6 & -5 & 0 & 0 & 1 & 0 \end{bmatrix}$$

$$\begin{bmatrix} 3/4 & 1 & 5/4 & 1/4 & 0 & 0 & 550 \\ 6 & 0 & -4 & -3 & 1 & 0 & 1900 \\ -1/2 & 0 & 5/2 & 3/2 & 0 & 1 & 3300 \end{bmatrix}$$

$$\begin{bmatrix} 0 & 1 & 7/4 & 5/8 & -1/8 & 0 & 312.5 \\ 1 & 0 & -2/3 & -1/2 & 1/6 & 0 & 950/3 \\ 0 & 0 & 13/6 & 5/4 & 1/12 & 1 & 10375/3 \end{bmatrix}$$

316.7 cartons of screwdrivers, 312.5 of chisels, and no putty knives, for profit of $3458.33. It is reasonable to round this to 317 cartons of screwdrivers, 312 cartons of chisels, and no putty knives.

37.
$$\begin{bmatrix} 2 & 3 & 1 & 1 & 0 & 0 & 0 & | & 360 \\ 4 & 0 & 2 & 0 & 1 & 0 & 0 & | & 360 \\ 0 & 6 & 3 & 0 & 0 & 1 & 0 & | & 360 \\ -10 & -8 & -12 & 0 & 0 & 0 & 1 & | & 0 \end{bmatrix}$$

$$\begin{bmatrix} 2 & 1 & 0 & 1 & 0 & -1/3 & 0 & | & 240 \\ 4 & -4 & 0 & 0 & 1 & -2/3 & 0 & | & 120 \\ 0 & 2 & 1 & 0 & 0 & 1/3 & 0 & | & 120 \\ -10 & 16 & 0 & 0 & 0 & 4 & 1 & | & 1440 \end{bmatrix}$$

$$\begin{bmatrix} 0 & 3 & 0 & 1 & -1/2 & 0 & 0 & | & 180 \\ 1 & -1 & 0 & 0 & 1/4 & -1/6 & 0 & | & 30 \\ 0 & 2 & 1 & 0 & 0 & 1/3 & 0 & | & 120 \\ 0 & 6 & 0 & 0 & 5/2 & 7/3 & 1 & | & 1740 \end{bmatrix}$$

30 cartons of notepads, no loose-leaf paper, and 120 cartons of spiral notebooks

39. Let x_1 = lbs of Early Riser, x_2 = lbs of After Dinner, x_3 = lbs of Deluxe.

Maximize $z = x_1 + 1.1x_2 + 1.2x_3$, subject to

$$.80x_1 + .75x_2 + .50x_3 \leq 255$$
$$.20x_1 + .20x_2 + .40x_3 \leq 80$$
$$.05x_2 + .10x_3 \leq 15$$
$$x_1 \geq 0, \ x_2 \geq 0, \ x_3 \geq 0$$

$$\begin{bmatrix} .80 & .75 & .50 & 1 & 0 & 0 & 0 & | & 255 \\ .20 & .20 & .40 & 0 & 1 & 0 & 0 & | & 80 \\ 0 & .05 & .10 & 0 & 0 & 1 & 0 & | & 15 \\ -1 & -1.1 & -1.2 & 0 & 0 & 0 & 1 & | & 0 \end{bmatrix}$$

$$\begin{bmatrix} 4/5 & 1/2 & 0 & 1 & 0 & -5 & 0 & | & 180 \\ 1/5 & 0 & 0 & 0 & 1 & -4 & 0 & | & 20 \\ 0 & 1/2 & 1 & 0 & 0 & 10 & 0 & | & 150 \\ -1 & -1/2 & 0 & 0 & 0 & 12 & 1 & | & 180 \end{bmatrix}$$

$$\begin{bmatrix} 0 & 1/2 & 0 & 1 & -4 & 11 & 0 & | & 100 \\ 1 & 0 & 0 & 0 & 5 & -20 & 0 & | & 100 \\ 0 & 1/2 & 1 & 0 & 0 & 10 & 0 & | & 150 \\ 0 & -1/2 & 0 & 0 & 5 & -8 & 1 & | & 280 \end{bmatrix}$$

$$\begin{bmatrix} 0 & 1 & 0 & 2 & -8 & 22 & 0 & | & 200 \\ 1 & 0 & 0 & 0 & 5 & -20 & 0 & | & 100 \\ 0 & 0 & 1 & -1 & 4 & -1 & 0 & | & 50 \\ 0 & 0 & 0 & 1 & 1 & 3 & 1 & | & 380 \end{bmatrix}$$

Maximum profit is $380 using 100 lbs Early Riser, 200 lbs After Dinner, and 50 lbs Deluxe.

Section 4-2

41. Let x_1 = number of packages of TV mix, x_2 = number of packages of Party Mix, x_3 = number of packages of Dinner Mix.
    Maximize $z = 4.4x_1 + 4.8x_2 + 5.2x_3$, subject to
    $$600x_1 + 500x_2 + 300x_3 \leq 39{,}500$$
    $$300x_1 + 300x_2 + 200x_3 \leq 22{,}500$$
    $$100x_1 + 200x_2 + 400x_3 \leq 16{,}500$$
    $$x_1 \geq 0, \ x_2 \geq 0, \ x_3 \geq 0$$

    $$\begin{bmatrix} 600 & 500 & 300 & 1 & 0 & 0 & 0 & 39500 \\ 300 & 300 & 200 & 0 & 1 & 0 & 0 & 22500 \\ 100 & 200 & 400 & 0 & 0 & 1 & 0 & 16500 \\ -4.4 & -4.8 & -5.2 & 0 & 0 & 0 & 1 & 0 \end{bmatrix}$$

    $$\begin{bmatrix} 525 & 350 & 0 & 1 & 0 & -3/4 & & 27125 \\ 250 & 200 & 0 & 0 & 1 & -1/2 & & 14250 \\ 1/4 & 1/2 & 1 & 0 & 0 & 1/400 & & 165/4 \\ -31/10 & -11/5 & 0 & 0 & 0 & 13/1000 & & 429/2 \end{bmatrix}$$

    $$\begin{bmatrix} 1 & 2/3 & 0 & 1/525 & 0 & -1/700 & 0 & 155/3 \\ 0 & 100/3 & 0 & -10/21 & 1 & -1/7 & 0 & 4000/3 \\ 0 & 1/3 & 1 & -1/2100 & 0 & 1/350 & 0 & 85/3 \\ 0 & -2/15 & 0 & 31/5250 & 0 & 3/350 & 1 & 1124/3 \end{bmatrix}$$

    $$\begin{bmatrix} 1 & 0 & 0 & 2/175 & -1/50 & 1/700 & 0 & 25 \\ 0 & 1 & 0 & -1/70 & 3/100 & -3/700 & 0 & 40 \\ 0 & 0 & 1 & 3/700 & -1/100 & 3/700 & 0 & 15 \\ 0 & 0 & 0 & 1/250 & 1/250 & 1/125 & 1 & 380 \end{bmatrix}$$

    Maximum revenue is $380 making 25 packages of TV Mix, 40 packages of Party Mix, and 15 packages of Dinner Mix.

43. Let x = number of Majestic, y = number of Traditional, z = number of Wall clocks.
    Maximize $R = 400x + 250y + 160z$, subject to
    $$4x + 2y + z \leq 124$$
    $$3x + y + z \leq 81$$
    $$x + y + .5z \leq 46$$

    $$\begin{bmatrix} 4 & 2 & 1 & 1 & 0 & 0 & 0 & 124 \\ 3 & 1 & 1 & 0 & 1 & 0 & 0 & 81 \\ 1 & 1 & .5 & 0 & 0 & 1 & 0 & 46 \\ -400 & -250 & -160 & 0 & 0 & 0 & 1 & 0 \end{bmatrix}$$

    $$\begin{bmatrix} 0 & 2/3 & -1/3 & 1 & -4/3 & 0 & 0 & 16 \\ 1 & 1/3 & 1/3 & 0 & 1/3 & 0 & 0 & 27 \\ 0 & 2/3 & 1/6 & 0 & -1/3 & 1 & 0 & 19 \\ 0 & -350/3 & -80/3 & 0 & 400/3 & 0 & 1 & 10800 \end{bmatrix}$$

    $$\begin{bmatrix} 0 & 1 & -1/2 & 3/2 & -2 & 0 & 0 & 24 \\ 1 & 0 & 1/2 & -1/2 & 1 & 0 & 0 & 19 \\ 0 & 0 & 1/2 & -1 & 1 & 1 & 0 & 3 \\ 0 & 0 & -85 & 175 & -100 & 0 & 1 & 13600 \end{bmatrix}$$

    $$\begin{bmatrix} 0 & 1 & 0 & 1/2 & -1 & 1 & 0 & 27 \\ 1 & 0 & 0 & 1/2 & 0 & -1 & 0 & 16 \\ 0 & 0 & 1 & -2 & 2 & 2 & 0 & 6 \\ 0 & 0 & 0 & 5 & 70 & 170 & 1 & 14110 \end{bmatrix}$$

    Maximum revenue is $14,110 for 16 Majestic, 27 Traditional, and 6 Wall clocks.

Section 4-3

1. (a) For $(0, 0)$ $s_1 = 17$. For $(2, 2)$ $s_1 = 3$. For $(5, 10)$ $s_1 = -33$. For $(2, 1)$ $s_1 = 6$. For $(2, 3)$ $s_1 = 0$.

   (b) $(0, 0)$, $(2, 2)$, $(2, 1)$, and $(2, 3)$ are in the feasible region.

   (c) $(2, 3)$ is on the line.

3. Let $x_1 = 0$, $s_2 = 0$ in the second constraint to obtain $2x_2 = 30$, $x_2 = 15$. Thus, the corner point is $(0, 15)$.

5. For $(0, 0, 0)$, $s_1 = 40$. For $(1, 2, 3)$, $s_1 = 26$. For $(0, 10, 0)$, $s_1 = 0$. For $(4, 2, 7)$, $s_1 = 13$.

7.

Point	s_1	s_2	s_3	Is point on boundary?	Is point in feasible region?
$(5, 10)$	15	32	18	No	Yes
$(8, 10)$	12	14	-3	No	No
$(5, 13)$	0	29	0	Yes	Yes
$(11, 13)$	-6	-7	-42	No	No
$(10, 12)$	0	0	-29	No	No
$(15, 11)$	0	-29	-58	No	No

9. (i) (a) $x_1 = 0$, $x_2 = 0$, $s_1 = 900$, $s_2 = 2800$, $z = 0$

   (b) Intersection of $x_1 = 0$ and $x_2 = 0$

   (ii) (a) $x_1 = 180$, $x_2 = 0$, $s_1 = 0$, $s_2 = 1360$, $z = 540$

   (b) Intersection of $5x_1 + 2x_2 = 900$ and $x_2 = 0$

   (iii) (a) $x_1 = 100$, $x_2 = 200$, $s_1 = 0$, $s_2 = 0$, $z = 700$

   (b) Intersection of $5x_1 + 2x_2 = 900$ and $8x_1 + 10x_2 = 2800$

11. (a) For $(3, 5)$ to be on the boundary line $s_1 = 0$ and $6(3) + 4(5) = 24$. Since the latter is false, $(3, 5)$ is not on the boundary line.

    (b) For $(3, 5)$ to be in the feasible region, $6(3) + 4(5) + s_1 = 24$ for some nonnegative value of s_1. However, the equation is true only when $s_1 = -14$ so $(3, 5)$ cannot be in the feasible region.

13. (a) Both $x_2 \leq 36/7$ and $x_2 \leq 32/5$ must hold, so x_2 must be the smaller, $36/7$.

    (b) $x_1 \leq 6$ and $x_1 \leq 16$, so x_1 is the smaller, 6.

Section 4-4

1. $\begin{bmatrix} 4 & 3 & 1 & 0 & 0 & | & 120 \\ 2 & 1 & 0 & 1 & 0 & | & 50 \\ 2 & -5 & 0 & 0 & 1 & | & 0 \end{bmatrix}$ $\begin{bmatrix} 4/3 & 1 & 1/3 & 0 & 0 & | & 40 \\ 2/3 & 0 & -1/3 & 1 & 0 & | & 10 \\ 26/3 & 0 & 5/3 & 0 & 1 & | & 200 \end{bmatrix}$

Minimum z is -200 at $x_1 = 0$, $x_2 = 40$

3. $\begin{bmatrix} 3 & 2 & -12 & 1 & 0 & 0 & 0 & | & 120 \\ 2 & 4 & 6 & 0 & 1 & 0 & 0 & | & 120 \\ 1 & -2 & 3 & 0 & 0 & 1 & 0 & | & 52 \\ 4 & 5 & -9 & 0 & 0 & 0 & 1 & | & 0 \end{bmatrix}$

$\begin{bmatrix} 7 & -6 & 0 & 1 & 0 & 4 & 0 & | & 328 \\ 0 & 8 & 0 & 0 & 1 & -2 & 0 & | & 16 \\ 1/3 & -2/3 & 1 & 0 & 0 & 1/3 & 0 & | & 52/3 \\ 7 & -1 & 0 & 0 & 0 & 3 & 1 & | & 156 \end{bmatrix}$

$\begin{bmatrix} 7 & 0 & 0 & 1 & 3/4 & 5/2 & 0 & | & 340 \\ 0 & 1 & 0 & 0 & 1/8 & -1/4 & 0 & | & 2 \\ 1/3 & 0 & 1 & 0 & 1/12 & 1/6 & 0 & | & 56/3 \\ 7 & 0 & 0 & 0 & 1/8 & 11/4 & 1 & | & 158 \end{bmatrix}$

Minimum $z = -158$ at $x_1 = 0$, $x_2 = 2$, $x_3 = 56/3$

5. $\begin{bmatrix} 3 & 2 & 1 & 0 & 0 & | & 36 \\ -2 & 1 & 0 & 1 & 0 & | & -3 \\ -5 & -2 & 0 & 0 & 1 & | & 0 \end{bmatrix}$ $\begin{bmatrix} 0 & 7/2 & 1 & 3/2 & 0 & | & 63/2 \\ 1 & -1/2 & 0 & -1/2 & 0 & | & 3/2 \\ 0 & -9/2 & 0 & -5/2 & 1 & | & 15/2 \end{bmatrix}$

$\begin{bmatrix} 0 & 1 & 2/7 & 3/7 & 0 & | & 9 \\ 1 & 0 & 1/7 & -2/7 & 0 & | & 6 \\ 0 & 0 & 9/7 & -4/7 & 1 & | & 48 \end{bmatrix}$ $\begin{bmatrix} 0 & 7/3 & 2/3 & 1 & 0 & | & 21 \\ 1 & 2/3 & 1/3 & 0 & 0 & | & 12 \\ 0 & 4/3 & 5/3 & 0 & 1 & | & 60 \end{bmatrix}$

Maximum $z = 60$ at $(12, 0)$

7. $\begin{bmatrix} 2 & 4 & 7 & 1 & 0 & 0 & | & 42 \\ 1 & -3 & 1 & 0 & 1 & 0 & | & -14 \\ -3 & 2 & -9 & 0 & 0 & 1 & | & 0 \end{bmatrix}$

$\begin{bmatrix} 10/3 & 0 & 25/3 & 1 & 4/3 & 0 & | & 70/3 \\ -1/3 & 1 & -1/3 & 0 & -1/3 & 0 & | & 14/3 \\ -7/3 & 0 & -25/3 & 0 & 2/3 & 1 & | & -28/3 \end{bmatrix}$

$\begin{bmatrix} 2/5 & 0 & 1 & 3/25 & 4/25 & 0 & | & 14/5 \\ -1/5 & 1 & 0 & 1/25 & -7/25 & 0 & | & 28/5 \\ 1 & 0 & 0 & 1 & 2 & 1 & | & 14 \end{bmatrix}$

Maximum $z = 14$ at $(0, 28/5, 14/5)$

9. $\begin{bmatrix} 8 & 12 & 7 & 1 & 0 & 0 & 0 & | & 171 \\ -5 & -14 & -8 & 0 & 1 & 0 & 0 & | & -172 \\ 2 & 9 & 13 & 0 & 0 & 1 & 0 & | & 174 \\ -20 & -35 & -28 & 0 & 0 & 0 & 1 & | & 0 \end{bmatrix}$

11. $\begin{bmatrix} 5 & 11 & 1 & 0 & 0 & | & 350 \\ -15 & -8 & 0 & 1 & 0 & | & -300 \\ -15 & -22 & 0 & 0 & 1 & | & 0 \end{bmatrix}$ $\begin{bmatrix} 0 & 25/3 & 1 & 1/3 & 0 & | & 250 \\ 1 & 8/15 & 0 & -1/15 & 0 & | & 20 \\ 0 & -14 & 0 & -1 & 1 & | & 300 \end{bmatrix}$

$\begin{bmatrix} 0 & 1 & 3/25 & 1/25 & 0 & | & 30 \\ 1 & 0 & -8/125 & -11/125 & 0 & | & 4 \\ 0 & 0 & 42/25 & -11/25 & 1 & | & 720 \end{bmatrix}$ $\begin{bmatrix} 0 & 25 & 3 & 1 & 0 & | & 750 \\ 1 & 11/5 & 1/5 & 0 & 0 & | & 70 \\ 0 & 11 & 3 & 0 & 1 & | & 1050 \end{bmatrix}$

Maximum is $z = 1050$ at $x_1 = 70$, $x_2 = 0$

13.
$$\left[\begin{array}{ccccc|c} -1 & 3 & 1 & 0 & 0 & 12 \\ 1 & -1 & 0 & 1 & 0 & -2 \\ -2 & -3 & 0 & 0 & 1 & 0 \end{array}\right] \qquad \left[\begin{array}{ccccc|c} 2 & 0 & 1 & 3 & 0 & 6 \\ -1 & 1 & 0 & -1 & 0 & 2 \\ -5 & 0 & 0 & -3 & 1 & 6 \end{array}\right]$$

$$\left[\begin{array}{ccccc|c} 1 & 0 & 1/2 & 3/2 & 0 & 3 \\ 0 & 1 & 1/2 & 1/2 & 0 & 5 \\ 0 & 0 & 5/2 & 9/2 & 1 & 21 \end{array}\right]$$

Maximum z = 21 at (3, 5)

15.
$$\left[\begin{array}{ccccccc|c} 6 & 12 & 4 & 1 & 0 & 0 & 0 & 900 \\ -5 & -16 & -8 & 0 & 1 & 0 & 0 & -120 \\ -3 & -1 & -1 & 0 & 0 & 1 & 0 & -300 \\ -10 & -50 & -30 & 0 & 0 & 0 & 1 & 0 \end{array}\right]$$

$$\left[\begin{array}{ccccccc|c} 0 & 10 & 2 & 1 & 0 & 2 & 0 & 300 \\ 0 & -43/3 & -19/3 & 0 & 1 & -5/3 & 0 & 380 \\ 1 & 1/3 & 1/3 & 0 & 0 & -1/3 & 0 & 100 \\ 0 & -140/3 & -80/3 & 0 & 0 & -10/3 & 1 & 1000 \end{array}\right]$$

$$\left[\begin{array}{ccccccc|c} 0 & 1 & 1/5 & 1/10 & 0 & 1/5 & 0 & 30 \\ 0 & -0 & -52/15 & 43/30 & 1 & 6/5 & 0 & 810 \\ 1 & 0 & 4/15 & -1/30 & 0 & -2/5 & 0 & 90 \\ 0 & 0 & -52/3 & 14/3 & 0 & 6 & 1 & 2400 \end{array}\right]$$

$$\left[\begin{array}{ccccccc|c} 0 & 5 & 1 & 1/2 & 0 & 1 & 0 & 150 \\ 0 & 52/3 & 0 & 19/6 & 1 & 14/3 & 0 & 1330 \\ 1 & -4/3 & 0 & -1/6 & 0 & -2/3 & 0 & 50 \\ 0 & 260/3 & 0 & 40/3 & 0 & 70/3 & 1 & 5000 \end{array}\right]$$

Maximum z = 5000 at (50, 0, 150)

17.
$$\left[\begin{array}{ccccc|c} 5 & 8 & 1 & 0 & 0 & 180 \\ -3 & -6 & 0 & 1 & 0 & -127 \\ 11 & 20 & 0 & 0 & 1 & 0 \end{array}\right]$$

19.
$$\left[\begin{array}{ccccc|c} 1 & 3 & 1 & 0 & 0 & 75 \\ 2 & -3 & 0 & 1 & 0 & -30 \\ -3 & 4 & 0 & 0 & 1 & 0 \end{array}\right] \qquad \left[\begin{array}{ccccc|c} 3 & 0 & 1 & 1 & 0 & 45 \\ -2/3 & 1 & 0 & -1/3 & 0 & 10 \\ -1/3 & 0 & 0 & 4/3 & 1 & -40 \end{array}\right]$$

$$\left[\begin{array}{ccccc|c} 1 & 0 & 1/3 & 1/3 & 0 & 15 \\ 0 & 1 & 2/9 & -1/9 & 0 & 20 \\ 0 & 0 & 1/9 & 13/9 & 1 & -35 \end{array}\right]$$

Minimum z = 35 at (15, 20)

21.
$$\left[\begin{array}{cccccc|c} -10 & -12 & -5 & 1 & 0 & 0 & -100 \\ 5 & 7 & 5 & 0 & 1 & 0 & 75 \\ 4 & 5 & 1 & 0 & 0 & 1 & 0 \end{array}\right]$$

$$\left[\begin{array}{cccccc|c} 5/6 & 1 & 5/12 & -1/12 & 0 & 0 & 25/3 \\ -5/6 & 0 & 25/12 & 7/12 & 1 & 0 & 50/3 \\ -1/6 & 0 & -13/12 & 5/12 & 0 & 1 & -125/3 \end{array}\right]$$

$$\left[\begin{array}{cccccc|c} 1 & 1 & 0 & -1/5 & -1/5 & 0 & 5 \\ -2/5 & 0 & 1 & 7/25 & 12/25 & 0 & 8 \\ -3/5 & 0 & 0 & 18/25 & 13/25 & 1 & -33 \end{array}\right]$$

$$\left[\begin{array}{cccccc|c} 1 & 1 & 0 & -1/5 & -1/5 & 0 & 5 \\ 0 & 2/5 & 1 & 1/5 & 2/5 & 0 & 10 \\ 0 & 3/5 & 0 & 3/5 & 2/5 & 1 & -30 \end{array}\right]$$

Minimum z = 30 at (5, 0, 10)

23.
$$\left[\begin{array}{cccccc|c} 8 & 10 & 1 & 0 & 0 & 0 & 80 \\ -2 & 5 & 0 & 1 & 0 & 0 & 10 \\ 2 & -5 & 0 & 0 & 1 & 0 & -10 \\ -3 & 1 & 0 & 0 & 0 & 1 & 0 \end{array}\right]$$

Section 4-4

25.
$$\left[\begin{array}{ccccccc|c}
3 & 2 & 1 & 0 & 0 & 0 & 0 & 48 \\
2 & 4 & 0 & 1 & 0 & 0 & 0 & 64 \\
5 & 6 & 0 & 0 & 1 & 0 & 0 & 104 \\
\underline{-5} & \underline{-6} & \underline{0} & \underline{0} & \underline{0} & \underline{1} & \underline{0} & \underline{-104} \\
-5 & -20 & 0 & 0 & 0 & 0 & 1 & 0
\end{array}\right]$$

$$\left[\begin{array}{ccccccc|c}
4/3 & 0 & 1 & 0 & 0 & 1/3 & 0 & 40/3 \\
-4/3 & 0 & 0 & 1 & 0 & 2/3 & 0 & -16/3 \\
0 & 0 & 0 & 0 & 1 & 1 & 0 & 0 \\
\underline{5/6} & \underline{1} & \underline{0} & \underline{0} & \underline{0} & \underline{-1/6} & \underline{0} & \underline{52/3} \\
35/3 & 0 & 0 & 0 & 0 & -10/3 & 1 & 1040/3
\end{array}\right]$$

$$\left[\begin{array}{ccccccc|c}
0 & 0 & 1 & 1 & 0 & 1 & 0 & 8 \\
1 & 0 & 0 & -3/4 & 0 & -1/2 & 0 & 4 \\
0 & 0 & 0 & 0 & 1 & 1 & 0 & 0 \\
\underline{0} & \underline{1} & \underline{0} & \underline{5/8} & \underline{0} & \underline{1/4} & \underline{0} & \underline{14} \\
0 & 0 & 0 & 35/4 & 0 & 5/2 & 1 & 300
\end{array}\right]$$

Maximum $z = 300$ at $x_1 = 4$, $x_2 = 14$

27.
$$\left[\begin{array}{cccccccc|c}
2 & 1 & 4 & 1 & 0 & 0 & 0 & 0 & 86 \\
1 & 3 & 2 & 0 & 1 & 0 & 0 & 0 & 103 \\
3 & 1 & 3 & 0 & 0 & 1 & 0 & 0 & 90 \\
\underline{-3} & \underline{-1} & \underline{-3} & \underline{0} & \underline{0} & \underline{0} & \underline{1} & \underline{0} & \underline{-90} \\
-5 & -5 & -9 & 0 & 0 & 0 & 0 & 1 & 0
\end{array}\right]$$

$$\left[\begin{array}{cccccccc|c}
-2 & -1/3 & 0 & 1 & 0 & 0 & 4/3 & 0 & -34 \\
-1 & 7/3 & 0 & 0 & 1 & 0 & 2/3 & 0 & 43 \\
0 & 0 & 0 & 0 & 0 & 1 & 1 & 0 & 0 \\
\underline{1} & \underline{1/3} & \underline{1} & \underline{0} & \underline{0} & \underline{0} & \underline{-1/3} & \underline{0} & \underline{30} \\
4 & -2 & 0 & 0 & 0 & 0 & -3 & 1 & 270
\end{array}\right]$$

$$\left[\begin{array}{cccccccc|c}
1 & 1/6 & 0 & -1/2 & 0 & 0 & -2/3 & 0 & 17 \\
0 & 5/2 & 0 & -1/2 & 1 & 0 & 0 & 0 & 60 \\
0 & 0 & 0 & 0 & 0 & 1 & 1 & 0 & 0 \\
\underline{0} & \underline{1/6} & \underline{1} & \underline{1/2} & \underline{0} & \underline{0} & \underline{1/3} & \underline{0} & \underline{13} \\
0 & -8/3 & 0 & 2 & 0 & 0 & -1/3 & 1 & 202
\end{array}\right]$$

$$\left[\begin{array}{cccccccc|c}
1 & 0 & 0 & -7/15 & -1/15 & 0 & -2/3 & 0 & 13 \\
0 & 1 & 0 & -1/5 & 2/5 & 0 & 0 & 0 & 24 \\
0 & 0 & 0 & 0 & 0 & 1 & 1 & 0 & 0 \\
\underline{0} & \underline{0} & \underline{1} & \underline{8/15} & \underline{-1/15} & \underline{0} & \underline{1/3} & \underline{0} & \underline{9} \\
0 & 0 & 0 & 22/15 & 16/15 & 0 & -1/3 & 1 & 266
\end{array}\right]$$

$$\left[\begin{array}{cccccccc|c}
1 & 0 & 0 & -7/15 & -1/15 & 2/3 & 0 & 0 & 13 \\
0 & 1 & 0 & -1/5 & 2/5 & 0 & 0 & 0 & 24 \\
0 & 0 & 0 & 0 & 0 & 0 & 1 & 0 & 0 \\
\underline{0} & \underline{0} & \underline{1} & \underline{8/15} & \underline{-1/15} & \underline{-1/3} & \underline{0} & \underline{0} & \underline{9} \\
0 & 0 & 0 & 22/15 & 16/15 & 1/3 & 0 & 1 & 266
\end{array}\right]$$

Maximum is $z = 266$ at $(13, 24, 9)$

29. $$\begin{bmatrix} 3 & 8 & 1 & 0 & 0 & 0 & 0 & | & 120 \\ 2 & 1 & 0 & 1 & 0 & 0 & 0 & | & 50 \\ 1 & 1 & 0 & 0 & 1 & 0 & 0 & | & 20 \\ \underline{-1} & \underline{-1} & \underline{0} & \underline{0} & \underline{0} & \underline{1} & \underline{0} & | & \underline{-20} \\ 30 & 10 & 0 & 0 & 0 & 0 & 1 & | & 0 \end{bmatrix}$$

$$\begin{bmatrix} -5 & 0 & 1 & 0 & 0 & 8 & 0 & | & -40 \\ 1 & 0 & 0 & 1 & 0 & 1 & 0 & | & 30 \\ 0 & 0 & 0 & 0 & 1 & 1 & 0 & | & 0 \\ \underline{1} & \underline{1} & \underline{0} & \underline{0} & \underline{0} & \underline{-1} & \underline{0} & | & \underline{20} \\ 20 & 0 & 0 & 0 & 0 & 10 & 1 & | & -200 \end{bmatrix}$$

$$\begin{bmatrix} 1 & 0 & -1/5 & 0 & 0 & -8/5 & 0 & | & 8 \\ 0 & 0 & 1/5 & 1 & 0 & 13/5 & 0 & | & 22 \\ 0 & 0 & 0 & 0 & 1 & 1 & 0 & | & 0 \\ \underline{0} & \underline{1} & \underline{1/5} & \underline{0} & \underline{0} & \underline{3/5} & \underline{0} & | & \underline{12} \\ 0 & 0 & 4 & 0 & 0 & 42 & 1 & | & -360 \end{bmatrix}$$ Minimum $z = 360$ at $(8, 12)$

31. $$\begin{bmatrix} 20 & 3 & 25 & 1 & 0 & 0 & 0 & 0 & | & 620 \\ 20 & 11 & 10 & 0 & 1 & 0 & 0 & 0 & | & 440 \\ 120 & 94 & 105 & 0 & 0 & 1 & 0 & 0 & | & 2820 \\ \underline{-120} & \underline{-94} & \underline{-105} & \underline{0} & \underline{0} & \underline{0} & \underline{1} & \underline{0} & | & \underline{-2820} \\ 10 & 10 & 10 & 0 & 0 & 0 & 0 & 1 & | & 0 \end{bmatrix}$$

$$\begin{bmatrix} 0 & -38/3 & 15/2 & 1 & 0 & 0 & 1/6 & 0 & | & 150 \\ 0 & -14/3 & -15/2 & 0 & 1 & 0 & 1/6 & 0 & | & -30 \\ 0 & 0 & 0 & 0 & 0 & 1 & 1 & 0 & | & 0 \\ \underline{1} & \underline{47/60} & \underline{7/8} & \underline{0} & \underline{0} & \underline{0} & \underline{-1/120} & \underline{0} & | & \underline{23.5} \\ 0 & 13/6 & 5/4 & 0 & 0 & 0 & 1/12 & 1 & | & -235 \end{bmatrix}$$

$$\begin{bmatrix} 0 & -52/3 & 0 & 1 & 1 & 0 & 1/3 & 0 & | & 120 \\ 0 & 28/45 & 1 & 0 & -2/15 & 0 & -1/45 & 0 & | & 4 \\ 0 & 0 & 0 & 0 & 0 & 1 & 1 & 0 & | & 0 \\ \underline{1} & \underline{43/180} & \underline{0} & \underline{0} & \underline{7/60} & \underline{0} & \underline{1/90} & \underline{0} & | & \underline{20} \\ 0 & 25/18 & 0 & 0 & 1/6 & 0 & 1/9 & 1 & | & -240 \end{bmatrix}$$

Minimum $z = 240$ at $x_1 = 20$, $x_2 = 0$, $x_3 = 4$

33. $$\begin{bmatrix} 1 & 4 & 3 & 1 & 0 & 0 & 0 & 0 & | & 124 \\ -2 & -10 & -5 & 0 & 1 & 0 & 0 & 0 & | & -295 \\ 6 & 1 & 3 & 0 & 0 & 1 & 0 & 0 & | & 100 \\ \underline{-6} & \underline{-1} & \underline{-3} & \underline{0} & \underline{0} & \underline{0} & \underline{1} & \underline{0} & | & \underline{-100} \\ -7 & -7 & -3 & 0 & 0 & 0 & 0 & 1 & | & 0 \end{bmatrix}$$

35. $$\begin{bmatrix} 3 & 2 & 1 & 0 & 0 & 0 & 0 & | & 60 \\ -2 & -3 & 0 & 1 & 0 & 0 & 0 & | & -24 \\ 1 & 1 & 0 & 0 & 1 & 0 & 0 & | & 25 \\ \underline{-1} & \underline{-1} & \underline{0} & \underline{0} & \underline{0} & \underline{1} & \underline{0} & | & \underline{-25} \\ -6 & -4 & 0 & 0 & 0 & 0 & 1 & | & 0 \end{bmatrix}$$

$$\begin{bmatrix} 0 & -1 & 1 & 0 & 0 & 3 & 0 & | & -15 \\ 0 & -1 & 0 & 1 & 0 & -2 & 0 & | & 26 \\ 0 & 0 & 0 & 0 & 1 & 1 & 0 & | & 0 \\ \underline{1} & \underline{1} & \underline{0} & \underline{0} & \underline{0} & \underline{-1} & \underline{0} & | & \underline{25} \\ 0 & 2 & 0 & 0 & 0 & -6 & 1 & | & 150 \end{bmatrix}$$

$$\begin{bmatrix} 0 & 1 & -1 & 0 & 0 & -3 & 0 & | & 15 \\ 0 & 0 & -1 & 1 & 0 & -5 & 0 & | & 41 \\ 0 & 0 & 0 & 0 & 1 & 1 & 0 & | & 0 \\ \underline{1} & \underline{0} & \underline{1} & \underline{0} & \underline{0} & \underline{2} & \underline{0} & | & \underline{10} \\ 0 & 0 & 2 & 0 & 0 & 0 & 1 & | & 120 \end{bmatrix}$$ Maximum $z = 120$ at $x_1 = 10$, $x_2 = 15$

37.
$$\left[\begin{array}{cccccccc|c}
7 & 12 & 12 & 1 & 0 & 0 & 0 & 0 & 312 \\
-13 & -20 & -12 & 0 & 1 & 0 & 0 & 0 & -384 \\
5 & 4 & 12 & 0 & 0 & 1 & 0 & 0 & 168 \\
\underline{-5} & \underline{-4} & \underline{-12} & \underline{0} & \underline{0} & \underline{0} & \underline{1} & \underline{0} & \underline{-168} \\
-10 & -24 & -26 & 0 & 0 & 0 & 0 & 1 & 0
\end{array}\right]$$

$$\left[\begin{array}{cccccccc|c}
-4/5 & 0 & 24/5 & 1 & 3/5 & 0 & 0 & 0 & 408/5 \\
13/20 & 1 & 3/5 & 0 & -1/20 & 0 & 0 & 0 & 96/5 \\
12/5 & 0 & 48/5 & 0 & 1/5 & 1 & 0 & 0 & 456/5 \\
\underline{-12/5} & \underline{0} & \underline{-48/5} & \underline{0} & \underline{-1/5} & \underline{0} & \underline{1} & \underline{0} & \underline{-456/5} \\
28/5 & 0 & -58/5 & 0 & -6/5 & 0 & 0 & 1 & 2304/5
\end{array}\right]$$

$$\left[\begin{array}{cccccccc|c}
-2 & 0 & 0 & 1 & 1/2 & 0 & 1/2 & 0 & 36 \\
1/2 & 1 & 0 & 0 & -1/16 & 0 & 1/16 & 0 & 27/2 \\
0 & 0 & 0 & 0 & 0 & 1 & 1 & 0 & 0 \\
\underline{1/4} & \underline{0} & \underline{1} & \underline{0} & \underline{1/48} & \underline{0} & \underline{-5/48} & \underline{0} & \underline{19/2} \\
17/2 & 0 & 0 & 0 & -23/24 & 0 & -29/24 & 1 & 571
\end{array}\right]$$

$$\left[\begin{array}{cccccccc|c}
-2 & 0 & 0 & 1 & 1/2 & -1/2 & 0 & 0 & 36 \\
1/2 & 1 & 0 & 0 & -1/16 & -1/16 & 0 & 0 & 27/2 \\
0 & 0 & 0 & 0 & 0 & 1 & 1 & 0 & 0 \\
\underline{1/4} & \underline{0} & \underline{1} & \underline{0} & \underline{1/48} & \underline{5/48} & \underline{0} & \underline{0} & \underline{19/2} \\
17/2 & 0 & 0 & 0 & -23/24 & 29/24 & 0 & 1 & 571
\end{array}\right]$$

$$\left[\begin{array}{cccccccc|c}
-4 & 0 & 0 & 2 & 1 & -1 & 0 & 0 & 72 \\
1/4 & 1 & 0 & 1/8 & 0 & -1/8 & 0 & 0 & 18 \\
0 & 0 & 0 & 0 & 0 & 1 & 1 & 0 & 0 \\
\underline{1/3} & \underline{0} & \underline{1} & \underline{-1/24} & \underline{0} & \underline{1/8} & \underline{0} & \underline{0} & \underline{8} \\
14/3 & 0 & 0 & 23/12 & 0 & 1/4 & 0 & 1 & 640
\end{array}\right]$$
Maximum z = 640 at (0,18,8)

39.
$$\left[\begin{array}{ccccccc|c}
-2 & 5 & 1 & 0 & 0 & 0 & 0 & 90 \\
4 & 3 & 0 & 1 & 0 & 0 & 0 & 80 \\
-4 & -3 & 0 & 0 & 1 & 0 & 0 & -80 \\
\underline{-2} & \underline{1} & \underline{0} & \underline{0} & \underline{0} & \underline{1} & \underline{0} & \underline{-20} \\
9 & 5 & 0 & 0 & 0 & 0 & 1 & 0
\end{array}\right]$$

$$\left[\begin{array}{ccccccc|c}
0 & 13/2 & 1 & 0 & -1/2 & 0 & 0 & 130 \\
0 & 0 & 0 & 1 & 1 & 0 & 0 & 0 \\
1 & 3/4 & 0 & 0 & -1/4 & 0 & 0 & 20 \\
\underline{0} & \underline{5/2} & \underline{0} & \underline{0} & \underline{-1/2} & \underline{1} & \underline{0} & \underline{20} \\
0 & -7/4 & 0 & 0 & 9/4 & 0 & 1 & -180
\end{array}\right]$$

$$\left[\begin{array}{ccccccc|c}
0 & 0 & 1 & 0 & 4/5 & -13/5 & 0 & 78 \\
0 & 0 & 0 & 1 & 1 & 0 & 0 & 0 \\
1 & 0 & 0 & 0 & -1/10 & -3/10 & 0 & 14 \\
\underline{0} & \underline{1} & \underline{0} & \underline{0} & \underline{-1/5} & \underline{2/5} & \underline{0} & \underline{8} \\
0 & 0 & 0 & 0 & 19/10 & 7/10 & 1 & -166
\end{array}\right]$$
Minimum z is 166 at $x_1 = 14$, $x_2 = 8$

41.
$$\left[\begin{array}{cccccccc|c}
-10 & -12 & -5 & 1 & 0 & 0 & 0 & 0 & -100 \\
5 & 7 & 5 & 0 & 1 & 0 & 0 & 0 & 75 \\
-10 & -2 & -10 & 0 & 0 & 1 & 0 & 0 & -120 \\
\underline{10} & \underline{2} & \underline{10} & \underline{0} & \underline{0} & \underline{0} & \underline{1} & \underline{0} & \underline{120} \\
8 & 10 & 2 & 0 & 0 & 0 & 0 & 1 & 0
\end{array}\right]$$

$$\left[\begin{array}{cccccccc|c}
-5 & -11 & 0 & 1 & 0 & -1/2 & 0 & 0 & -40 \\
0 & 6 & 0 & 0 & 1 & 1/2 & 0 & 0 & 15 \\
1 & 1/5 & 1 & 0 & 0 & -1/10 & 0 & 0 & 12 \\
\underline{0} & \underline{0} & \underline{0} & \underline{0} & \underline{0} & \underline{1} & \underline{1} & \underline{0} & \underline{0} \\
6 & 48/5 & 0 & 0 & 0 & 1/5 & 0 & 1 & -24
\end{array}\right]$$

$$\begin{bmatrix} 1 & 11/5 & 0 & -1/5 & 0 & 1/10 & 0 & 0 & | & 8 \\ 0 & 6 & 0 & 0 & 1 & 1/2 & 0 & 0 & | & 15 \\ 0 & -2 & 1 & 1/5 & 0 & -1/5 & 0 & 0 & | & 4 \\ 0 & 0 & 0 & 0 & 0 & 1 & 1 & 0 & | & 0 \\ \hline 0 & -18/5 & 0 & 6/5 & 0 & -2/5 & 0 & 1 & | & -72 \end{bmatrix}$$

$$\begin{bmatrix} 1 & 0 & 0 & -1/5 & -11/30 & -1/12 & 0 & 0 & | & 5/2 \\ 0 & 1 & 0 & 0 & 1/6 & 1/12 & 0 & 0 & | & 5/2 \\ 0 & 0 & 1 & 1/5 & 1/3 & -1/30 & 0 & 0 & | & 9 \\ 0 & 0 & 0 & 0 & 0 & 1 & 1 & 0 & | & 0 \\ \hline 0 & 0 & 0 & 6/5 & 3/5 & -1/10 & 0 & 1 & | & -63 \end{bmatrix}$$

$$\begin{bmatrix} 1 & 0 & 0 & -1/5 & -11/30 & 0 & 1/12 & 0 & | & 5/2 \\ 0 & 1 & 0 & 0 & 1/6 & 0 & -1/12 & 0 & | & 5/2 \\ 0 & 0 & 1 & 1/5 & 1/3 & 0 & 1/30 & 0 & | & 9 \\ 0 & 0 & 0 & 0 & 0 & 1 & 1 & 0 & | & 0 \\ \hline 0 & 0 & 0 & 6/5 & 3/5 & 0 & 1/10 & 1 & | & -63 \end{bmatrix}$$

Minimum $z = 63$ at $x_1 = 5/2$, $x_2 = 5/2$, $x_3 = 9$

43.   Let x = number of Custom, y = number of Executive.
Minimize $C = 70x + 80y$
Subject to
$$\begin{aligned} x + \quad y &\geq 100 \\ 90x + 120y &\geq 10800 \\ 4x + \quad 5y &\leq 800 \\ x \geq 0,\ y &\geq 0 \end{aligned}$$

$$\begin{bmatrix} -1 & -1 & 1 & 0 & 0 & 0 & | & -100 \\ -90 & -120 & 0 & 1 & 0 & 0 & | & -10800 \\ 4 & 5 & 0 & 0 & 1 & 0 & | & 800 \\ \hline 70 & 80 & 0 & 0 & 0 & 1 & | & 0 \end{bmatrix}$$

45.   Let x = number of A, y = number of B, z = number of C.
Maximize $z = 6x + 9y + 6z$
Subject to
$$\begin{aligned} x + \quad y + \quad z &\geq 6600 \\ 20x + 25y + 15z &\leq 133000 \\ x + \quad 3y + \quad 2z &\leq 13600 \\ 8x + 10y + 15z &\leq 73000 \\ x \geq 0,\ y \geq 0,\ z &\geq 0 \end{aligned}$$

$$\begin{bmatrix} -1 & -1 & -1 & 1 & 0 & 0 & 0 & 0 & | & -6600 \\ 20 & 25 & 15 & 0 & 1 & 0 & 0 & 0 & | & 133000 \\ 1 & 3 & 2 & 0 & 0 & 1 & 0 & 0 & | & 13600 \\ 8 & 10 & 15 & 0 & 0 & 0 & 1 & 0 & | & 73000 \\ \hline -6 & -9 & -6 & 0 & 0 & 0 & 0 & 1 & | & 0 \end{bmatrix}$$

47.
$$\begin{bmatrix} -1 & -1 & -1 & 1 & 0 & 0 & 0 & 0 & 0 & | & -6800 \\ 20 & 25 & 15 & 0 & 1 & 0 & 0 & 0 & 0 & | & 133000 \\ 1 & 3 & 2 & 0 & 0 & 1 & 0 & 0 & 0 & | & 13600 \\ 8 & 10 & 15 & 0 & 0 & 0 & 1 & 0 & 0 & | & 80000 \\ 0 & -1 & 0 & 0 & 0 & 0 & 0 & 1 & 0 & | & -2000 \\ \hline -6 & -9 & -6 & 0 & 0 & 0 & 0 & 0 & 1 & | & 0 \end{bmatrix}$$

49.   Let x_1 = minutes jogging, x_2 = minutes playing handball,
x_3 = minutes swimming.

(a)   Minimize $z = x_1 + x_2 + x_3$
Subject to
$$\begin{aligned} 13x_1 + 11x_2 + 7x_3 &\geq 660 \\ x_1 - x_3 &= 0 \\ x_2 &\geq 2x_1 \\ x_1 \geq 0,\ x_2 \geq 0,\ x_3 &\geq 0 \end{aligned}$$

Section 4-4

$$\begin{bmatrix} -13 & -11 & -7 & 1 & 0 & 0 & 0 & 0 & -660 \\ 1 & 0 & -1 & 0 & 1 & 0 & 0 & 0 & 0 \\ -1 & 0 & 1 & 0 & 0 & 1 & 0 & 0 & 0 \\ 2 & -1 & 0 & 0 & 0 & 0 & 1 & 0 & 0 \\ 1 & 1 & 1 & 0 & 0 & 0 & 0 & 1 & 0 \end{bmatrix}$$

(b) Maximize $z = 13x_1 + 11x_2 + 7x_3$

Subject to $x_1 + x_2 + x_3 \le 90$

$x_1 - x_3 = 0$

$x_2 \ge 2x_1$

$x_1 \ge 0, \; x_2 \ge 0, \; x_3 \ge 0$

$$\begin{bmatrix} 1 & 1 & 1 & 1 & 0 & 0 & 0 & 0 & 90 \\ 1 & 0 & -1 & 0 & 1 & 0 & 0 & 0 & 0 \\ -1 & 0 & 1 & 0 & 0 & 1 & 0 & 0 & 0 \\ 2 & -1 & 0 & 0 & 0 & 0 & 1 & 0 & 0 \\ -13 & -11 & -7 & 0 & 0 & 0 & 0 & 1 & 0 \end{bmatrix}$$

51. Let x = number of Custom, y = number of Executive.
Minimize $C = 70x + 80y$
Subject to $x + y \ge 100$

$90x + 120y \ge 10800$

$4x + 5y \le 800$

$$\begin{bmatrix} -1 & -1 & 1 & 0 & 0 & 0 & -100 \\ -90 & -120 & 0 & 1 & 0 & 0 & -10800 \\ 4 & 5 & 0 & 0 & 1 & 0 & 800 \\ 70 & 80 & 0 & 0 & 0 & 1 & 0 \end{bmatrix}$$

$$\begin{bmatrix} -1/4 & 0 & 1 & -1/120 & 0 & 0 & -10 \\ 3/4 & 1 & 0 & -1/120 & 0 & 0 & 90 \\ 1/4 & 0 & 0 & 1/24 & 1 & 0 & 350 \\ 10 & 0 & 0 & 2/3 & 0 & 1 & -7200 \end{bmatrix}$$

$$\begin{bmatrix} 1 & 0 & -4 & 1/30 & 0 & 0 & 40 \\ 0 & 1 & 3 & -1/30 & 0 & 0 & 60 \\ 0 & 0 & 1 & 1/30 & 1 & 0 & 340 \\ 0 & 0 & 40 & 1/3 & 0 & 1 & -7600 \end{bmatrix}$$

The manager should order 40 Custom and 60 Executive for a minimum cost of \$7600.

53. Let x = number of A, y = number of B, z = number of C.
Maximize $z = 6x + 9y + 6z$
Subject to $x + y + z \ge 6600$

$20x + 25y + 15z \le 133000$

$x + 3y + 2z \le 13600$

$8x + 10y + 15z \le 73000$

$x \ge 0, \; y \ge 0, \; z \ge 0$

$$\begin{bmatrix} -1 & -1 & -1 & 1 & 0 & 0 & 0 & 0 & -6600 \\ 20 & 25 & 15 & 0 & 1 & 0 & 0 & 0 & 133000 \\ 1 & 3 & 2 & 0 & 0 & 1 & 0 & 0 & 13600 \\ 8 & 10 & 15 & 0 & 0 & 0 & 1 & 0 & 73000 \\ -6 & -9 & -6 & 0 & 0 & 0 & 0 & 1 & 0 \end{bmatrix}$$

$$\begin{bmatrix} 1 & 1 & 1 & -1 & 0 & 0 & 0 & 0 & 6600 \\ -5 & 0 & -10 & 25 & 1 & 0 & 0 & 0 & -32000 \\ -2 & 0 & -1 & 3 & 0 & 1 & 0 & 0 & -6200 \\ -2 & 0 & 5 & 10 & 0 & 0 & 1 & 0 & 7000 \\ 3 & 0 & 3 & -9 & 0 & 0 & 0 & 1 & 59400 \end{bmatrix}$$

$$
\begin{bmatrix}
0 & 1 & 1/2 & 1/2 & 0 & 1/2 & 0 & 0 & 3500 \\
0 & 0 & -15/2 & 35/2 & 1 & -5/2 & 0 & 0 & -16500 \\
1 & 0 & 1/2 & -3/2 & 0 & -1/2 & 0 & 0 & 3100 \\
\underline{0} & \underline{0} & \underline{6} & \underline{7} & \underline{0} & \underline{-1} & \underline{1} & \underline{0} & \underline{13200} \\
0 & 0 & 3/2 & -9/2 & 0 & 3/2 & 0 & 1 & 50100
\end{bmatrix}
$$

$$
\begin{bmatrix}
0 & 1 & 0 & 5/3 & 1/15 & 1/3 & 0 & 0 & 2400 \\
0 & 0 & 1 & -7/3 & -2/15 & 1/3 & 0 & 0 & 2200 \\
1 & 0 & 0 & -1/3 & 1/15 & -2/3 & 0 & 0 & 2000 \\
\underline{0} & \underline{0} & \underline{0} & \underline{21} & \underline{4/5} & \underline{-3} & \underline{1} & \underline{0} & \underline{0} \\
0 & 0 & 0 & -1 & 1/5 & 1 & 0 & 1 & 46800
\end{bmatrix}
$$

$$
\begin{bmatrix}
0 & 1 & 0 & 0 & 1/315 & 4/7 & -5/63 & 0 & 2400 \\
0 & 0 & 1 & 0 & -2/45 & 0 & 1/9 & 0 & 2200 \\
1 & 0 & 0 & 0 & 5/63 & -5/7 & 1/63 & 0 & 2000 \\
\underline{0} & \underline{0} & \underline{0} & \underline{1} & \underline{4/105} & \underline{-1/7} & \underline{1/21} & \underline{0} & \underline{0} \\
0 & 0 & 0 & 0 & 5/21 & 6/7 & 1/21 & 1 & 46800
\end{bmatrix}
$$

Maximum profit is \$46,800 when 2000 of A, 2400 of B, and 2200 of C are ordered.

55.
$$
\begin{bmatrix}
-1 & -1 & -1 & 1 & 0 & 0 & 0 & 0 & 0 & -6800 \\
20 & 25 & 15 & 0 & 1 & 0 & 0 & 0 & 0 & 133000 \\
1 & 3 & 2 & 0 & 0 & 1 & 0 & 0 & 0 & 13600 \\
8 & 10 & 15 & 0 & 0 & 0 & 1 & 0 & 0 & 80000 \\
\underline{0} & \underline{-1} & \underline{0} & \underline{0} & \underline{0} & \underline{0} & \underline{0} & \underline{1} & \underline{0} & \underline{-2000} \\
-6 & -9 & -6 & 0 & 0 & 0 & 0 & 0 & 1 & 0
\end{bmatrix}
$$

$$
\begin{bmatrix}
1 & 1 & 1 & -1 & 0 & 0 & 0 & 0 & 6800 \\
-5 & 0 & -10 & 25 & 1 & 0 & 0 & 0 & -37000 \\
-2 & 0 & -1 & 3 & 0 & 1 & 0 & 0 & -6800 \\
-2 & 0 & 5 & 10 & 0 & 0 & 1 & 0 & 12000 \\
\underline{1} & \underline{0} & \underline{1} & \underline{-1} & \underline{0} & \underline{0} & \underline{0} & \underline{1} & \underline{0} & \underline{4800} \\
3 & 0 & 3 & -9 & 0 & 0 & 0 & 1 & 61200
\end{bmatrix}
$$

$$
\begin{bmatrix}
0 & 1 & 1/2 & 1/2 & 0 & 1/2 & 0 & 0 & 0 & 3400 \\
0 & 0 & -15/2 & 35/2 & 1 & -5/2 & 0 & 0 & 0 & -20000 \\
1 & 0 & 1/2 & -3/2 & 0 & -1/2 & 0 & 0 & 0 & 3400 \\
0 & 0 & 6 & 7 & 0 & -1 & 1 & 0 & 0 & 18800 \\
\underline{0} & \underline{0} & \underline{1/2} & \underline{1/2} & \underline{0} & \underline{1/2} & \underline{0} & \underline{1} & \underline{0} & \underline{1400} \\
0 & 0 & 3/2 & -9/2 & 0 & 3/2 & 0 & 0 & 1 & 51000
\end{bmatrix}
$$

$$
\begin{bmatrix}
0 & 1 & 0 & 5/3 & 1/15 & 1/3 & 0 & 0 & 0 & 6200/3 \\
0 & 0 & 1 & -7/3 & -2/15 & 1/3 & 0 & 0 & 0 & 8000/3 \\
1 & 0 & 0 & -1/3 & 1/15 & -2/3 & 0 & 0 & 0 & 6200/3 \\
0 & 0 & 0 & 21 & 4/5 & -3 & 1 & 0 & 0 & 2800 \\
\underline{0} & \underline{0} & \underline{0} & \underline{5/3} & \underline{1/15} & \underline{1/3} & \underline{0} & \underline{1} & \underline{0} & \underline{200/3} \\
0 & 0 & 0 & -1 & 1/5 & 1 & 0 & 0 & 1 & 47000
\end{bmatrix}
$$

$$
\begin{bmatrix}
0 & 1 & 0 & 0 & 0 & 0 & 0 & -1 & 0 & 2000 \\
0 & 0 & 1 & 0 & -1/25 & 4/5 & 0 & 7/5 & 0 & 2760 \\
1 & 0 & 0 & 0 & 2/25 & -3/5 & 0 & 1/5 & 0 & 2080 \\
0 & 0 & 0 & 0 & -1/25 & -36/5 & 1 & -63/5 & 0 & 1960 \\
\underline{0} & \underline{0} & \underline{0} & \underline{1} & \underline{1/25} & \underline{1/5} & \underline{0} & \underline{3/5} & \underline{0} & \underline{40} \\
0 & 0 & 0 & 0 & 6/25 & 6/5 & 0 & 3/5 & 1 & 47040
\end{bmatrix}
$$

Maximum profit is \$47,040 when ordering 2080 of A, 2000 of B, and 2760 of C.

Section 4-4

57.   Let x_1 = minutes jogging, x_2 = minutes playing handball,
    x_3 = minutes swimming.

    (a)   Minimize $z = x_1 + x_2 + x_3$

           Subject to $13x_1 + 11x_2 + 7x_3 \geq 660$

$$x_1 - x_3 = 0$$
$$x_2 \geq 2x_1$$
$$x_1 \geq 0, \ x_2 \geq 0, \ x_3 \geq 0$$

$$\left[\begin{array}{cccccccc|c}
-13 & -11 & -7 & 1 & 0 & 0 & 0 & 0 & -660 \\
1 & 0 & -1 & 0 & 1 & 0 & 0 & 0 & 0 \\
-1 & 0 & 1 & 0 & 0 & 1 & 0 & 0 & 0 \\
2 & -1 & 0 & 0 & 0 & 0 & 1 & 0 & 0 \\
\hline
1 & 1 & 1 & 0 & 0 & 0 & 0 & 1 & 0
\end{array}\right]$$

$$\left[\begin{array}{cccccccc|c}
13/11 & 1 & 7/11 & -1/11 & 0 & 0 & 0 & 0 & 60 \\
1 & 0 & -1 & 0 & 1 & 0 & 0 & 0 & 0 \\
-1 & 0 & 1 & 0 & 0 & 1 & 0 & 0 & 0 \\
35/11 & 0 & 7/11 & -1/11 & 0 & 0 & 1 & 0 & 60 \\
\hline
-2/11 & 0 & 4/11 & 1/11 & 0 & 0 & 0 & 1 & -60
\end{array}\right]$$

$$\left[\begin{array}{cccccccc|c}
0 & 1 & 20/11 & -1/11 & -13/11 & 0 & 0 & 0 & 60 \\
1 & 0 & -1 & 0 & 1 & 0 & 0 & 0 & 0 \\
0 & 0 & 0 & 0 & 1 & 1 & 0 & 0 & 0 \\
0 & 0 & 42/11 & -1/11 & -35/11 & 0 & 1 & 0 & 60 \\
\hline
0 & 0 & 2/11 & 1/11 & 2/11 & 0 & 0 & 1 & -60
\end{array}\right]$$

0 minutes jogging, 60 minutes playing handball, 0 minutes swimming.

    (b)   Maximize $z = 13x_1 + 11x_2 + 7x_3$

           Subject to $x_1 + x_2 + x_3 \leq 90$

$$x_1 - x_3 = 0$$
$$x_2 \geq 2x_1$$
$$x_1 \geq 0, \ x_2 \geq 0, \ x_3 \geq 0$$

$$\left[\begin{array}{cccccccc|c}
1 & 1 & 1 & 1 & 0 & 0 & 0 & 0 & 90 \\
1 & 0 & -1 & 0 & 1 & 0 & 0 & 0 & 0 \\
-1 & 0 & 1 & 0 & 0 & 1 & 0 & 0 & 0 \\
2 & -1 & 0 & 0 & 0 & 0 & 1 & 0 & 0 \\
\hline
-13 & -11 & -7 & 0 & 0 & 0 & 0 & 1 & 0
\end{array}\right]$$

$$\left[\begin{array}{cccccccc|c}
0 & 1 & 2 & 1 & -1 & 0 & 0 & 0 & 90 \\
1 & 0 & -1 & 0 & 1 & 0 & 0 & 0 & 0 \\
0 & 0 & 0 & 0 & 1 & 1 & 0 & 0 & 0 \\
0 & -1 & 2 & 0 & -2 & 0 & 1 & 0 & 0 \\
\hline
0 & -11 & -20 & 0 & 13 & 0 & 0 & 1 & 0
\end{array}\right]$$

$$\left[\begin{array}{cccccccc|c}
0 & 2 & 0 & 1 & 1 & 0 & -1 & 0 & 90 \\
1 & -1/2 & 0 & 0 & 0 & 0 & 1/2 & 0 & 0 \\
0 & 0 & 0 & 0 & 1 & 1 & 0 & 0 & 0 \\
0 & -1/2 & 1 & 0 & -1 & 0 & 1/2 & 0 & 0 \\
\hline
0 & -21 & 0 & 0 & -7 & 0 & 10 & 1 & 0
\end{array}\right]$$

$$\left[\begin{array}{cccccccc|c}
0 & 1 & 0 & 1/2 & 1/2 & 0 & -1/2 & 0 & 45 \\
1 & 0 & 0 & 1/4 & 1/4 & 0 & 1/4 & 0 & 45/2 \\
0 & 0 & 0 & 0 & 1 & 1 & 0 & 0 & 0 \\
0 & 0 & 1 & 1/4 & -3/4 & 0 & 1/4 & 0 & 45/2 \\
\hline
0 & 0 & 0 & 21/2 & 7/2 & 0 & -1/2 & 1 & 945
\end{array}\right]$$

$$\begin{bmatrix} 2 & 1 & 0 & 1 & 1 & 0 & 0 & 0 & 90 \\ 4 & 0 & 0 & 1 & 1 & 0 & 1 & 0 & 90 \\ 0 & 0 & 0 & 0 & 1 & 1 & 0 & 0 & 0 \\ -1 & 0 & 1 & 0 & -1 & 0 & 0 & 0 & 0 \\ 2 & 0 & 0 & 11 & 4 & 0 & 0 & 1 & 990 \end{bmatrix}$$

No time jogging or swimming - all 90 minutes playing handball

Section 4-5

1. The -20 in the last column with nonnegative entries in the rest of the first row indicates no feasible solutions.

3. There is an unbounded feasible region, so no solution, because all entries in column 4 are negative.

5. $$\begin{bmatrix} 3 & 5 & 1 & 0 & 0 & 0 & 60 \\ 1 & 1 & 0 & 1 & 0 & 0 & 14 \\ 2 & 1 & 0 & 0 & 1 & 0 & 24 \\ -15 & -15 & 0 & 0 & 0 & 1 & 0 \end{bmatrix}$$ $$\begin{bmatrix} 3/5 & 1 & 1/5 & 0 & 0 & 0 & 12 \\ 2/5 & 0 & -1/5 & 1 & 0 & 0 & 2 \\ 7/5 & 0 & -1/5 & 0 & 1 & 0 & 12 \\ -6 & 0 & 3 & 0 & 0 & 1 & 180 \end{bmatrix}$$

$$\begin{bmatrix} 0 & 1 & 1/2 & -3/2 & 0 & 0 & 9 \\ 1 & 0 & -1/2 & 5/2 & 0 & 0 & 5 \\ 0 & 0 & 1/2 & -7/2 & 1 & 0 & 5 \\ 0 & 0 & 0 & 15 & 0 & 1 & 210 \end{bmatrix}$$

This gives maximum of 210 at (5, 9)

$$\begin{bmatrix} 0 & 1 & 0 & 2 & -1 & 0 & 4 \\ 1 & 0 & 0 & -1 & 1 & 0 & 10 \\ 0 & 0 & 1 & -7 & 2 & 0 & 10 \\ 0 & 0 & 0 & 15 & 0 & 1 & 210 \end{bmatrix}$$

Maximum = 210 also at (10, 4)

7. $$\begin{bmatrix} 2 & 1 & 2 & 1 & 0 & 0 & 0 & 20 \\ 1 & 2 & 2 & 0 & 1 & 0 & 0 & 20 \\ 1 & 1 & 4 & 0 & 0 & 1 & 0 & 20 \\ -3 & -3 & -4 & 0 & 0 & 0 & 1 & 0 \end{bmatrix}$$ $$\begin{bmatrix} 3/2 & 1/2 & 0 & 1 & 0 & -1/2 & 0 & 10 \\ 1/2 & 3/2 & 0 & 0 & 1 & -1/2 & 0 & 10 \\ 1/4 & 1/4 & 1 & 0 & 0 & 1/4 & 0 & 5 \\ -2 & -2 & 0 & 0 & 0 & 1 & 1 & 20 \end{bmatrix}$$

$$\begin{bmatrix} 1 & 1/3 & 0 & 2/3 & 0 & -1/3 & 0 & 20/3 \\ 0 & 4/3 & 0 & -1/3 & 1 & -1/3 & 0 & 20/3 \\ 0 & 1/6 & 1 & -1/6 & 0 & 1/3 & 0 & 10/3 \\ 0 & -4/3 & 0 & 4/3 & 0 & 1/3 & 1 & 100/3 \end{bmatrix}$$

$$\begin{bmatrix} 1 & 0 & 0 & 3/4 & -1/4 & -1/4 & 0 & 5 \\ 0 & 1 & 0 & -1/4 & 3/4 & -1/4 & 0 & 5 \\ 0 & 0 & 1 & -1/8 & -1/8 & 3/8 & 0 & 5/2 \\ 0 & 0 & 0 & 1 & 1 & 0 & 1 & 40 \end{bmatrix}$$

Maximum = 40 at (5, 5, 2.5)

$$\begin{bmatrix} 1 & 0 & 2/3 & 2/3 & -1/3 & 0 & 0 & 20/3 \\ 0 & 1 & 2/3 & -1/3 & 2/3 & 0 & 0 & 20/3 \\ 0 & 0 & 8/3 & -1/3 & -1/3 & 1 & 0 & 20/3 \\ 0 & 0 & 0 & 1 & 1 & 0 & 1 & 40 \end{bmatrix}$$

Maximum = 40 also at (20/3, 20/3, 0)

Section 4-5

9. $\begin{bmatrix} 2 & -5 & 1 & 0 & 0 & | & 10 \\ \underline{2} & -1 & 0 & 1 & 0 & | & \underline{-2} \\ -8 & -3 & 0 & 0 & 1 & | & 0 \end{bmatrix}$ $\begin{bmatrix} -8 & 0 & 1 & -5 & 0 & | & 20 \\ \underline{-2} & 1 & 0 & -1 & 0 & | & \underline{2} \\ -14 & 0 & 0 & -3 & 1 & | & 6 \end{bmatrix}$

Unbounded feasible region

11. $\begin{bmatrix} 1 & -3 & 2 & 1 & 0 & 0 & | & 50 \\ \underline{-2} & 4 & 5 & 0 & 1 & 0 & | & \underline{40} \\ -8 & -6 & -2 & 0 & 0 & 1 & | & 0 \end{bmatrix}$ $\begin{bmatrix} 1 & -3 & 2 & 1 & 0 & 0 & | & 50 \\ \underline{0} & -2 & 9 & 2 & 1 & 0 & | & \underline{140} \\ 0 & -30 & 14 & 8 & 0 & 1 & | & 400 \end{bmatrix}$

Unbounded feasible region

13. $\begin{bmatrix} 1 & -1 & 1 & 0 & | & -13 \\ \underline{2} & 9 & 0 & 1 & | & \underline{72} \\ -12 & -20 & 0 & 0 & | & 0 \end{bmatrix}$ $\begin{bmatrix} -1 & 1 & -1 & 0 & | & 13 \\ \underline{11} & 0 & 9 & 1 & | & \underline{-45} \\ -32 & 0 & -20 & 0 & | & 260 \end{bmatrix}$

No feasible solution

15. $\begin{bmatrix} 6 & 4 & 3 & 1 & 0 & 0 & 0 & | & 60 \\ 3 & 6 & 4 & 0 & 1 & 0 & 0 & | & 48 \\ \underline{1} & \underline{1} & -2 & 0 & 0 & 1 & 0 & | & \underline{-60} \\ -20 & -30 & -15 & 0 & 0 & 0 & 1 & | & 0 \end{bmatrix}$

$\begin{bmatrix} 15/2 & 11/2 & 0 & 1 & 0 & 3/2 & 0 & | & -30 \\ 5 & 8 & 0 & 0 & 1 & 2 & 0 & | & -72 \\ \underline{-1/2} & \underline{-1/2} & 1 & 0 & 0 & -1/2 & 0 & | & \underline{30} \\ -55/2 & -75/2 & 0 & 0 & 0 & -15/2 & 1 & | & 450 \end{bmatrix}$ No feasible solution

17. $\begin{bmatrix} -4 & 1 & 1 & 0 & 0 & | & 2 \\ \underline{2} & -1 & 0 & 1 & 0 & | & \underline{1} \\ -1 & -4 & 0 & 0 & 1 & | & 0 \end{bmatrix}$ $\begin{bmatrix} -4 & 1 & 1 & 0 & 0 & | & 2 \\ \underline{-2} & 0 & 1 & 1 & 0 & | & \underline{3} \\ -17 & 0 & 4 & 0 & 1 & | & 8 \end{bmatrix}$

Unbounded feasible region

19. $\begin{bmatrix} 9 & -4 & -6 & 1 & 0 & 0 & 0 & | & -36 \\ 4 & 5 & 8 & 0 & 1 & 0 & 0 & | & 40 \\ \underline{6} & \underline{-2} & 1 & 0 & 0 & 1 & 0 & | & \underline{18} \\ -18 & -15 & -8 & 0 & 0 & 0 & 1 & | & 0 \end{bmatrix}$

$\begin{bmatrix} -3/2 & 2/3 & 1 & -1/6 & 0 & 0 & 0 & | & 6 \\ 16 & -1/3 & 0 & 4/3 & 1 & 0 & 0 & | & -8 \\ \underline{15/2} & \underline{-8/3} & 0 & 1/6 & 0 & 1 & 0 & | & \underline{12} \\ -30 & -29/3 & 0 & -4/3 & 0 & 0 & 1 & | & 48 \end{bmatrix}$

$\begin{bmatrix} 61/2 & 0 & 1 & 5/2 & 2 & 0 & 0 & | & -10 \\ -48 & 1 & 0 & -4 & -3 & 0 & 0 & | & 24 \\ \underline{-241/2} & 0 & 0 & -21/2 & -8 & 1 & 0 & | & \underline{76} \\ -494 & 0 & 0 & -40 & -29 & 0 & 1 & | & 280 \end{bmatrix}$ No feasible solution

21. $\begin{bmatrix} 5 & 3 & 1 & 0 & 0 & | & 30 \\ \underline{-2} & -1 & 0 & 1 & 0 & | & \underline{-20} \\ -15 & -9 & 0 & 0 & 1 & | & 0 \end{bmatrix}$ $\begin{bmatrix} 0 & 1/2 & 1 & 5/2 & 0 & | & -20 \\ \underline{1} & 1/2 & 0 & -1/2 & 0 & | & \underline{10} \\ 0 & -3/2 & 0 & -15/2 & 1 & | & 150 \end{bmatrix}$

No feasible solution

23. $\begin{bmatrix} 10 & 15 & 1 & 0 & 0 & | & 150 \\ \underline{-6} & -3 & 0 & 1 & 0 & | & \underline{-180} \\ -4 & -12 & 0 & 0 & 1 & | & 0 \end{bmatrix}$ $\begin{bmatrix} 0 & 10 & 1 & 5/3 & 0 & | & -150 \\ \underline{1} & 1/2 & 0 & -1/6 & 0 & | & \underline{30} \\ 0 & -10 & 0 & -2/3 & 1 & | & 120 \end{bmatrix}$

No feasible solution

25.

$$\left[\begin{array}{ccccccc|c} -2 & -3 & -4 & 1 & 0 & 0 & 0 & -60 \\ -2 & -3 & 6 & 0 & 1 & 0 & 0 & -30 \\ 0 & 6 & -5 & 0 & 0 & 1 & 0 & 30 \\ \hline 2 & 3 & 1 & 0 & 0 & 0 & 1 & 0 \end{array}\right]$$

$$\left[\begin{array}{ccccccc|c} 1/2 & 3/4 & 1 & -1/4 & 0 & 0 & 0 & 5 \\ -5 & -15/2 & 0 & 3/2 & 1 & 0 & 0 & -120 \\ 5/2 & 39/4 & 0 & -5/4 & 0 & 1 & 0 & 105 \\ \hline 3/2 & 9/4 & 0 & 1/4 & 0 & 0 & 1 & -15 \end{array}\right]$$

$$\left[\begin{array}{ccccccc|c} 0 & 0 & 1 & -1/10 & 1/10 & 0 & 0 & 3 \\ 2/3 & 1 & 0 & -1/5 & -2/15 & 0 & 0 & 16 \\ -4 & 0 & 0 & 7/10 & 13/10 & 1 & 0 & -51 \\ \hline 0 & 0 & 0 & 7/10 & 3/10 & 0 & 1 & -51 \end{array}\right]$$

$$\left[\begin{array}{ccccccc|c} 0 & 0 & 1 & -1/10 & 1/10 & 0 & 0 & 3 \\ 0 & 1 & 0 & -1/12 & 1/12 & 1/6 & 0 & 15/2 \\ 1 & 0 & 0 & -7/40 & -13/40 & -1/4 & 0 & 51/4 \\ \hline 0 & 0 & 0 & 7/10 & 3/10 & 0 & 1 & -51 \end{array}\right]$$

$$\left[\begin{array}{ccccccc|c} 0 & 0 & 1 & -1/10 & 1/10 & 0 & 0 & 3 \\ 0 & 6 & 0 & -1/2 & 1/2 & 1 & 0 & 45 \\ 1 & 3/2 & 0 & -3/10 & -1/5 & 0 & 0 & 24 \\ \hline 0 & 0 & 0 & 7/10 & 3/10 & 0 & 1 & -51 \end{array}\right]$$

Multiple solutions, minimum z = 51 at (51/4, 15/2, 3)
and (24, 0, 3)

27.

$$\left[\begin{array}{ccccccc|c} 3 & -10 & 6 & 1 & 0 & 0 & 0 & 60 \\ -15 & 4 & 6 & 0 & 1 & 0 & 0 & 60 \\ 4 & 5 & -20 & 0 & 0 & 1 & 0 & 100 \\ \hline -8 & -5 & -8 & 0 & 0 & 0 & 1 & 0 \end{array}\right]$$

$$\left[\begin{array}{ccccccc|c} 1/2 & -5/3 & 1 & 1/6 & 0 & 0 & 0 & 10 \\ -18 & 14 & 0 & -1 & 1 & 0 & 0 & 0 \\ 14 & -85/3 & 0 & 10/3 & 0 & 1 & 0 & 300 \\ \hline -4 & -55/3 & 0 & 4/3 & 0 & 0 & 1 & 80 \end{array}\right]$$

$$\left[\begin{array}{ccccccc|c} -23/14 & 0 & 1 & 1/21 & 5/42 & 0 & 0 & 10 \\ -9/7 & 1 & 0 & -1/14 & 1/14 & 0 & 0 & 0 \\ -157/7 & 0 & 0 & 55/42 & 85/42 & 1 & 0 & 300 \\ \hline -193/7 & 0 & 0 & 1/42 & 55/42 & 0 & 1 & 80 \end{array}\right]$$

Unbounded feasible region

29. Let x = number of Petite, y = number of Deluxe.
Maximize z = 5x + 6y
subject to
$$x + 2y \le 3950$$
$$4x + 3y \le 9575$$
$$y \ge 2000$$
$$x \ge 0, \ y \ge 0$$

$$\left[\begin{array}{cccccc|c} 1 & 2 & 1 & 0 & 0 & 0 & 3950 \\ 4 & 3 & 0 & 1 & 0 & 0 & 9575 \\ 0 & -1 & 0 & 0 & 1 & 0 & -2000 \\ \hline -5 & -6 & 0 & 0 & 0 & 1 & 0 \end{array}\right]$$

$$\left[\begin{array}{cccccc|c} 1 & 0 & 1 & 0 & 2 & 0 & -50 \\ 4 & 0 & 0 & 1 & 3 & 0 & 3575 \\ 0 & 1 & 0 & 0 & -1 & 0 & 2000 \\ \hline -5 & 0 & 0 & 0 & -6 & 1 & 12000 \end{array}\right]$$

No feasible solution

70

Section 4-6

1. $\begin{bmatrix} 2 & 4 \\ 1 & 0 \\ 3 & 2 \end{bmatrix}$
   3. $\begin{bmatrix} 4 & 1 & 6 & 2 \\ 3 & 8 & -7 & 4 \\ 2 & -2 & 1 & 6 \end{bmatrix}$

5. (a) $\left[\begin{array}{cc|c} 6 & 5 & 30 \\ 8 & 3 & 42 \\ \hline 25 & 30 & 1 \end{array}\right]$
   (b) $\left[\begin{array}{cc|c} 6 & 8 & 25 \\ 5 & 3 & 30 \\ \hline 30 & 42 & 1 \end{array}\right]$

   (c) $\left[\begin{array}{ccccc|c} 6 & 8 & 1 & 0 & 0 & 25 \\ 5 & 3 & 0 & 1 & 0 & 30 \\ \hline -30 & -42 & 0 & 0 & 1 & 0 \end{array}\right]$

7. (a) $\left[\begin{array}{cc|c} 22 & 30 & 110 \\ 15 & 40 & 95 \\ 20 & 35 & 68 \\ \hline 500 & 700 & 1 \end{array}\right]$
   (b) $\left[\begin{array}{ccc|c} 22 & 15 & 20 & 500 \\ 30 & 40 & 35 & 700 \\ \hline 110 & 95 & 68 & 1 \end{array}\right]$

   (c) $\left[\begin{array}{cccccc|c} 22 & 15 & 20 & 1 & 0 & 0 & 500 \\ 30 & 40 & 35 & 0 & 1 & 0 & 700 \\ \hline -110 & -95 & -68 & 0 & 0 & 1 & 0 \end{array}\right]$

9.
$$\begin{array}{ccccc} y_1 & y_2 & x_1 & x_2 & w \\ \end{array}$$
$$\left[\begin{array}{ccccc|c} 0 & 1 & 1 & -1 & 0 & 1 \\ 1 & 0 & -1 & 2 & 0 & 2 \\ \hline 0 & 0 & 6 & 4 & 1 & 40 \end{array}\right]$$
From the last row $x_1 = 6$, $x_2 = 4$, $z = 40$.

11.
$$\begin{array}{ccccccc} y_1 & y_2 & y_3 & x_1 & x_2 & x_3 & w \\ \end{array}$$
$$\left[\begin{array}{ccccccc|c} 1/6 & 0 & 1 & 1/5 & -1/8 & 0 & 0 & 7/6 \\ 1/3 & 1 & 0 & -1/5 & 1/4 & 0 & 0 & 4/3 \\ -1 & 0 & 0 & -2/5 & -1 & 1 & 0 & 1 \\ \hline 45 & 0 & 0 & 12 & 10 & 0 & 1 & 510 \end{array}\right]$$
Minimum $z = 510$ at $(12, 10, 0)$

13.
$$\begin{array}{ccccc} y_1 & y_2 & x_1 & x_2 & w \\ \end{array}$$
$$\left[\begin{array}{ccccc|c} 1 & 2 & 1 & 0 & 0 & 4 \\ 1 & 1 & 0 & 1 & 0 & 3 \\ \hline -8 & -14 & 0 & 0 & 1 & 0 \end{array}\right]$$
$$\left[\begin{array}{ccccc|c} 1/2 & 1 & 1/2 & 0 & 0 & 2 \\ 1/2 & 0 & -1/2 & 1 & 0 & 1 \\ \hline -1 & 0 & 7 & 0 & 1 & 28 \end{array}\right]$$

$$\begin{array}{ccccc} y_1 & y_2 & x_1 & x_2 & w \\ \end{array}$$
$$\left[\begin{array}{ccccc|c} 0 & 1 & 1 & -1 & 0 & 1 \\ 1 & 0 & -1 & 2 & 0 & 2 \\ \hline 0 & 0 & 6 & 2 & 1 & 30 \end{array}\right]$$
Minimum $z = 30$ at $(6, 2)$

15.
$$\begin{array}{ccccccc} y_1 & y_2 & y_3 & x_1 & x_2 & x_3 & w \\ \end{array}$$
$$\left[\begin{array}{ccccccc|c} 3 & 1 & 0 & 1 & 0 & 0 & 0 & 10 \\ 1 & 1 & 4 & 0 & 1 & 0 & 0 & 16 \\ 6 & 0 & 1 & 0 & 0 & 1 & 0 & 20 \\ \hline -9 & -9 & -12 & 0 & 0 & 0 & 1 & 0 \end{array}\right]$$
$$\left[\begin{array}{ccccccc|c} 3 & 1 & 0 & 1 & 0 & 0 & 0 & 10 \\ 1/4 & 1/4 & 1 & 0 & 1/4 & 0 & 0 & 4 \\ 23/4 & -1/4 & 0 & 0 & -1/4 & 1 & 0 & 16 \\ \hline -6 & -6 & 0 & 0 & 3 & 0 & 1 & 48 \end{array}\right]$$

$$\begin{array}{ccccccc} y_1 & y_2 & y_3 & x_1 & x_2 & x_3 & w \\ \end{array}$$
$$\left[\begin{array}{ccccccc|c} 3 & 1 & 0 & 1 & 0 & 0 & 0 & 10 \\ -1/2 & 0 & 1 & -1/4 & 1/4 & 0 & 0 & 3/2 \\ 13/2 & 0 & 0 & 1/4 & -1/4 & 1 & 0 & 37/2 \\ \hline 12 & 0 & 0 & 6 & 3 & 0 & 1 & 108 \end{array}\right]$$
Minimum $z = 108$ at $(6, 3, 0)$

17.

$$\begin{array}{ccccccc} Y_1 & Y_2 & Y_3 & x_1 & x_2 & x_3 & w \end{array}$$

$$\left[\begin{array}{ccccccc|c} 1 & 3 & 3 & 1 & 0 & 0 & 0 & 8 \\ 1 & 1 & 6 & 0 & 1 & 0 & 0 & 5 \\ 1 & 3 & 8 & 0 & 0 & 1 & 0 & 12 \\ -37 & -81 & -216 & 0 & 0 & 0 & 1 & 0 \end{array}\right]$$

$$\begin{array}{ccccccc} Y_1 & Y_2 & Y_3 & x_1 & x_2 & x_3 & w \end{array}$$

$$\left[\begin{array}{ccccccc|c} 1/2 & 5/2 & 0 & 1 & -1/2 & 0 & 0 & 11/2 \\ 1/6 & 1/6 & 1 & 0 & 1/6 & 0 & 0 & 5/6 \\ -1/3 & 5/3 & 0 & 0 & -4/3 & 1 & 0 & 16/3 \\ -1 & -45 & 0 & 0 & 36 & 0 & 1 & 180 \end{array}\right]$$

$$\begin{array}{ccccccc} Y_1 & Y_2 & Y_3 & x_1 & x_2 & x_3 & w \end{array}$$

$$\left[\begin{array}{ccccccc|c} 1/5 & 1 & 0 & 2/5 & -1/5 & 0 & 0 & 11/5 \\ 2/15 & 0 & 1 & -1/15 & 1/5 & 0 & 0 & 7/5 \\ -2/3 & 0 & 0 & -2/3 & -1 & 1 & 0 & 5/3 \\ 8 & 0 & 0 & 18 & 27 & 0 & 1 & 279 \end{array}\right]$$

Minimum z = 279 at (18, 27, 0)

19. Let x_1 = number at Dallas, x_2 = number at New Orleans.
Minimize $z = 22{,}000x_1 + 12{,}000x_2$
subject to $800x_1 + 500x_2 \geq 28{,}000$
$$280x_1 + 150x_2 \geq 9{,}000$$
$$x_1 \geq 0, \; x_2 \geq 0$$

$$\left[\begin{array}{ccccc|c} 800 & 280 & 1 & 0 & 0 & 22000 \\ 500 & 150 & 0 & 1 & 0 & 12000 \\ -28000 & -9000 & 0 & 0 & 1 & 0 \end{array}\right] \quad \left[\begin{array}{ccccc|c} 0 & 40 & 1 & -8/5 & 0 & 2800 \\ 1 & 3/10 & 0 & 1/500 & 0 & 24 \\ 0 & -600 & 0 & 56 & 1 & 672000 \end{array}\right]$$

$$\left[\begin{array}{ccccc|c} 0 & 1 & 1/40 & -1/25 & 0 & 70 \\ 1 & 0 & -3/400 & 7/500 & 0 & 3 \\ 0 & 0 & 15 & 32 & 1 & 714000 \end{array}\right]$$

15 at Dallas, 32 at New Orleans for cost of \$714,000

21. Let x_1 = number of days the Chicago plant operates
x_2 = number of days the Detroit plant operates.
Minimize $z = 20{,}000x_1 + 15{,}000x_2$
subject to $600x_1 + 300x_2 \geq 24{,}000$
$$100x_1 + 100x_2 \geq 5{,}000$$
$$x_1 \geq 0, \; x_2 \geq 0$$
This is a standard minimization problem so we solve it using its dual problem. The augmented matrix of the problem is

The transpose of A is

$$\left[\begin{array}{cc|c} 600 & 300 & 24000 \\ 100 & 100 & 5000 \\ 20000 & 15000 & 1 \end{array}\right] \quad \left[\begin{array}{ccc} 600 & 100 & 20000 \\ 300 & 100 & 15000 \\ 24000 & 5000 & 1 \end{array}\right]$$

This matrix represents the dual problem.
The tableaux that solve this dual problem are:

$$\left[\begin{array}{ccccc|c} 600 & 100 & 1 & 0 & 0 & 20000 \\ 300 & 100 & 0 & 1 & 0 & 15000 \\ -24000 & -5000 & 0 & 0 & 1 & 0 \end{array}\right]$$

$$\left[\begin{array}{ccccc|c} 1 & 1/6 & 1/600 & 0 & 0 & 200/6 \\ 300 & 100 & 0 & 1 & 0 & 15000 \\ -24000 & -5000 & 0 & 0 & 1 & 0 \end{array}\right]$$

$$\begin{bmatrix} 1 & 1/6 & 1/600 & 0 & 0 & | & 200/6 \\ 0 & 50 & -1/2 & 1 & 0 & | & 5000 \\ 0 & -1000 & 40 & 0 & 1 & | & 800000 \end{bmatrix}$$

$$\begin{bmatrix} 1 & 1/6 & 1/600 & 0 & 0 & | & 200/6 \\ 0 & 1 & -1/100 & 1/50 & 0 & | & 100 \\ 0 & -1000 & 40 & 0 & 1 & | & 800000 \end{bmatrix}$$

$$\begin{bmatrix} 1 & 0 & 1/300 & -1/300 & 0 & | & 100/6 \\ 0 & 1 & -1/100 & 1/50 & 0 & | & 100 \\ 0 & 0 & 30 & 20 & 1 & | & 900000 \end{bmatrix}$$

The last row gives the solution to the original problem
$$x_1 = 30, \quad x_2 = 20, \quad z = 900,000.$$
The minimum operating costs are \$900,000 when the Chicago plant operates 30 days and the Detroit plant 20 days.

Review Exercises, Chapter 4

1. $6x_1 + 4x_2 + 3x_3 + s_1 = 220$
    $x_1 + 5x_2 + x_3 + s_2 = 162$
    $7x_1 + 2x_2 + 5x_3 + s_3 = 139$

3. $6x_1 + 5x_2 + 3x_3 + 3x_4 + s_1 = 89$
    $7x_1 + 4x_2 + 6x_3 + 2x_4 + s_2 = 72$

5. $10x_1 + 12x_2 + 8x_3 + s_1 = 24$
    $7x_1 + 13x_2 + 5x_3 + s_2 = 35$
    $-20x_1 - 36x_2 - 19x_3 + z = 0$

7. $3x_1 + 7x_2 + s_1 = 14$
    $9x_1 + 5x_2 + s_2 = 18$
    $x_1 - x_2 + s_3 = 21$
    $-9x_1 - 2x_2 + z = 0$

9. $x_1 + x_2 + x_3 + s_1 = 15$
    $2x_1 + 4x_2 + x_3 + s_2 = 44$
    $-6x_1 - 8x_2 - 4x_3 + z = 0$

11. (a) $\begin{bmatrix} 1 & 4 & 0 & 3 & 0 & -2 & 0 & | & 60 \\ 0 & 6 & 1 & 5 & 0 & 4 & 0 & | & 60 \\ 0 & -3 & 0 & 1 & 1 & 2 & 0 & | & 60 \\ 0 & -1 & 0 & -2 & 0 & 3 & 1 & | & 0 \end{bmatrix}$ $\begin{array}{l} 60/3 = 20 \\ 60/5 = 12 \quad \text{Pivot Row} \\ 60/1 = 60 \end{array}$

Column 4 is pivot column.
The 5 in row 2, column 4 is the pivot element.

(b) $\begin{bmatrix} 5 & 0 & 1 & 1 & -6 & 0 & 0 & | & 75 \\ 4 & 1 & 3 & 0 & 3 & 0 & 0 & | & 150 \\ 2 & 0 & -2 & 0 & 2 & 1 & 0 & | & 80 \\ -3 & 0 & -5 & 0 & 4 & 0 & 1 & | & 98 \end{bmatrix}$ $\begin{array}{l} 75/1 = 75 \\ 150/3 = 50 \quad \text{Pivot Row} \\ 80/-2 = -40 \end{array}$

Column 3 is the pivot column.
The 3 in row 2, column 3 is the pivot element.

13. (a) $x_1 = 0, \quad x_2 = 80, \quad s_1 = 0, \quad s_2 = 42, \quad z = 98$
     (b) $x_1 = 73, \quad x_2 = 42, \quad x_3 = 15, \quad s_1 = 0, \quad s_2 = 0, \quad s_3 = 0,$
     $z = 138$

15. (a) $\begin{bmatrix} 11 & 5 & 3 & 1 & 0 & 0 & 0 & | & 142 \\ -3 & -4 & -7 & 0 & 1 & 0 & 0 & | & -95 \\ 2 & 15 & 1 & 0 & 0 & 1 & 0 & | & 124 \\ -3 & -5 & -4 & 0 & 0 & 0 & 1 & | & 0 \end{bmatrix}$

     (b) $\begin{bmatrix} 7 & 4 & 1 & 0 & 0 & | & 28 \\ -1 & -3 & 0 & 1 & 0 & | & -6 \\ 14 & 22 & 0 & 0 & 1 & | & 0 \end{bmatrix}$

17. (a)
$$\begin{bmatrix} -15 & -8 & 1 & 0 & 0 & 0 & 0 & -120 \\ 10 & 12 & 0 & 1 & 0 & 0 & 0 & 120 \\ 15 & 5 & 0 & 0 & 1 & 0 & 0 & 75 \\ -15 & -5 & 0 & 0 & 0 & 1 & 0 & -75 \\ -5 & -12 & 0 & 0 & 0 & 0 & 1 & 0 \end{bmatrix}$$

(b)
$$\begin{bmatrix} 14 & 9 & 1 & 0 & 0 & 0 & 0 & 126 \\ -10 & -11 & 0 & 1 & 0 & 0 & 0 & -110 \\ -5 & 1 & 0 & 0 & 1 & 0 & 0 & 9 \\ 5 & -1 & 0 & 0 & 0 & 1 & 0 & -9 \\ 3 & 2 & 0 & 0 & 0 & 0 & 1 & 0 \end{bmatrix}$$

19.
$$\begin{bmatrix} 2 & 4 & 2 & 1 & 0 & 0 & 0 & 34 \\ 3 & 6 & 4 & 0 & 1 & 0 & 0 & 57 \\ 2 & 5 & 1 & 0 & 0 & 1 & 0 & 30 \\ -3 & -5 & -2 & 0 & 0 & 0 & 1 & 0 \end{bmatrix}$$

$$\begin{bmatrix} 2/5 & 0 & 6/5 & 1 & 0 & -4/5 & 0 & 10 \\ 3/5 & 0 & 14/5 & 0 & 1 & -6/5 & 0 & 21 \\ 2/5 & 1 & 1/5 & 0 & 0 & 1/5 & 0 & 6 \\ -1 & 0 & -1 & 0 & 0 & 1 & 1 & 30 \end{bmatrix}$$

$$\begin{bmatrix} 0 & -1 & 1 & 1 & 0 & -1 & 0 & 4 \\ 0 & -3/2 & 5/2 & 0 & 1 & -3/2 & 0 & 12 \\ 1 & 5/2 & 1/2 & 0 & 0 & 1/2 & 0 & 15 \\ 0 & 5/2 & -1/2 & 0 & 0 & 3/2 & 1 & 45 \end{bmatrix}$$

$$\begin{bmatrix} 0 & -1 & 1 & 1 & 0 & -1 & 0 & 4 \\ 0 & 1 & 0 & -5/2 & 1 & 1 & 0 & 2 \\ 1 & 3 & 0 & -1/2 & 0 & 1 & 0 & 13 \\ 0 & 2 & 0 & 1/2 & 0 & 1 & 1 & 47 \end{bmatrix}$$ Maximum z = 47 at (13, 0, 4)

21.
$$\begin{bmatrix} -4 & 1 & 1 & 0 & 0 & 3 \\ 1 & -2 & 0 & 1 & 0 & 12 \\ -10 & -15 & 0 & 0 & 1 & 0 \end{bmatrix} \qquad \begin{bmatrix} -4 & 1 & 1 & 0 & 0 & 3 \\ -7 & 0 & 2 & 1 & 0 & 18 \\ -70 & 0 & 15 & 0 & 1 & 45 \end{bmatrix}$$
Unbounded feasible region, no maximum.

23.
$$\begin{bmatrix} 4 & 1 & 1 & 1 & 0 & 0 & 372 \\ 1 & 8 & 6 & 0 & 1 & 0 & 1116 \\ -1 & -3 & -1 & 0 & 0 & 1 & 0 \end{bmatrix}$$

$$\begin{bmatrix} 31/8 & 0 & 1/4 & 1 & -1/8 & 0 & 465/2 \\ 1/8 & 1 & 3/4 & 0 & 1/8 & 0 & 279/2 \\ -5/8 & 0 & 5/4 & 0 & 3/8 & 1 & 837/2 \end{bmatrix}$$

$$\begin{bmatrix} 1 & 0 & 2/31 & 8/31 & -1/31 & 0 & 60 \\ 0 & 1 & 23/31 & -1/31 & 4/31 & 0 & 132 \\ 0 & 0 & 40/31 & 5/31 & 11/31 & 1 & 456 \end{bmatrix}$$
Maximum z = 456 at (60, 132, 0)

25. (a) x_3 (b) x_2 27.
$$\begin{bmatrix} 3 & 4 & 5 \\ 1 & 0 & 7 \\ -2 & 6 & 8 \end{bmatrix} \qquad \begin{bmatrix} 4 & -5 \\ 3 & 0 \\ 2 & 12 \\ 1 & 9 \end{bmatrix}$$

29.
$$\begin{bmatrix} -2 & -1 & 0 & 1 & 0 & 0 & -6 \\ 0 & -1 & -2 & 0 & 1 & 0 & -8 \\ 6 & 8 & 16 & 0 & 0 & 1 & 0 \end{bmatrix} \qquad \begin{bmatrix} 1 & 1/2 & 0 & -1/2 & 0 & 0 & 3 \\ 0 & -1 & -2 & 0 & 1 & 0 & -8 \\ 0 & 5 & 16 & 3 & 0 & 1 & -18 \end{bmatrix}$$

$$\begin{bmatrix} 1 & 1/2 & 0 & -1/2 & 0 & 0 & 3 \\ 0 & 1/2 & 1 & 0 & -1/2 & 0 & 4 \\ 0 & -3 & 0 & 3 & 8 & 1 & -82 \end{bmatrix}$$

$$\begin{bmatrix} 2 & 1 & 0 & -1 & 0 & 0 & 6 \\ -1 & 0 & 1 & 1/2 & -1/2 & 0 & 1 \\ 6 & 0 & 0 & 0 & 8 & 1 & -64 \end{bmatrix} \qquad \begin{bmatrix} 0 & 1 & 2 & 0 & -1 & 0 & 8 \\ -2 & 0 & 2 & 1 & -1 & 0 & 2 \\ 6 & 0 & 0 & 0 & 8 & 1 & -64 \end{bmatrix}$$

Multiple solutions, minimum z = 64 at (0, 6, 1) and (0, 8, 0).

31.
$$\begin{bmatrix} 2 & 5 & 4 & 1 & 0 & 0 & 0 & 40 \\ 40 & 45 & 30 & 0 & 1 & 0 & 0 & 430 \\ -6 & -3 & -4 & 0 & 0 & 1 & 0 & -48 \\ -6 & -11 & -8 & 0 & 0 & 0 & 1 & 0 \end{bmatrix}$$

$$\begin{bmatrix} 0 & 4 & 8/3 & 1 & 0 & 1/3 & 0 & 24 \\ 0 & 25 & 10/3 & 0 & 1 & 20/3 & 0 & 110 \\ 1 & 1/2 & 2/3 & 0 & 0 & -1/6 & 0 & 8 \\ 0 & -8 & -4 & 0 & 0 & -1 & 1 & 48 \end{bmatrix}$$

$$\begin{bmatrix} 0 & 0 & 32/15 & 1 & -4/25 & -11/15 & 0 & 32/5 \\ 0 & 1 & 2/15 & 0 & 1/25 & 4/15 & 0 & 22/5 \\ 1 & 0 & 3/5 & 0 & -1/50 & -3/10 & 0 & 29/5 \\ 0 & 0 & -44/15 & 0 & 8/25 & 17/15 & 1 & 416/5 \end{bmatrix}$$

$$\begin{bmatrix} 0 & 0 & 1 & 15/32 & -3/40 & -11/32 & 0 & 3 \\ 0 & 1 & 0 & -1/16 & 1/20 & 5/16 & 0 & 4 \\ 1 & 0 & 0 & -9/32 & 1/40 & -3/32 & 0 & 4 \\ 0 & 0 & 0 & 11/8 & 1/10 & 1/8 & 1 & 92 \end{bmatrix}$$
Maximum z = 92 at (4, 4, 3)

33.
$$\begin{bmatrix} -1 & -1 & -1 & 1 & 0 & 0 & 0 & -6 \\ 2 & 1 & 3 & 0 & 1 & 0 & 0 & 10 \\ 0 & 2 & -1 & 0 & 0 & 1 & 0 & 5 \\ -2 & -5 & -3 & 0 & 0 & 0 & 1 & 0 \end{bmatrix} \qquad \begin{bmatrix} 1 & 1 & 1 & -1 & 0 & 0 & 0 & 6 \\ 0 & -1 & 1 & 2 & 1 & 0 & 0 & -2 \\ 0 & 2 & -1 & 0 & 0 & 1 & 0 & 5 \\ 0 & -3 & -1 & -2 & 0 & 0 & 1 & 12 \end{bmatrix}$$

$$\begin{bmatrix} 1 & 0 & 2 & 1 & 1 & 0 & 0 & 4 \\ 0 & 1 & -1 & -2 & -1 & 0 & 0 & 2 \\ 0 & 0 & 1 & 4 & 2 & 1 & 0 & 1 \\ 0 & 0 & -4 & -8 & -3 & 0 & 1 & 18 \end{bmatrix}$$

$$\begin{bmatrix} 1 & 0 & 7/4 & 0 & 1/2 & -1/4 & 0 & 15/4 \\ 0 & 1 & -1/2 & 0 & 0 & 1/2 & 0 & 5/2 \\ 0 & 0 & 1/4 & 1 & 1/2 & 1/4 & 0 & 1/4 \\ 0 & 0 & -2 & 0 & 1 & 2 & 1 & 20 \end{bmatrix}$$

$$\begin{bmatrix} 1 & 0 & 0 & -7 & -3 & -2 & 0 & 2 \\ 0 & 1 & 0 & 2 & 1 & 1 & 0 & 3 \\ 0 & 0 & 1 & 4 & 2 & 1 & 0 & 1 \\ 0 & 0 & 0 & 8 & 5 & 4 & 1 & 22 \end{bmatrix}$$
Maximum z = 22 at (2, 3, 1)

35.
$$\begin{bmatrix} 1 & -3 & 1 & 0 & 0 & 24 \\ -5 & 4 & 0 & 1 & 0 & 20 \\ -20 & -32 & 0 & 0 & 1 & 0 \end{bmatrix} \qquad \begin{bmatrix} -11/4 & 0 & 1 & 3/4 & 0 & 39 \\ -5/4 & 1 & 0 & 1/4 & 0 & 5 \\ -60 & 0 & 0 & 8 & 1 & 160 \end{bmatrix}$$

Unbounded feasible region, no maximum.

37.
$$\begin{bmatrix} -3 & -2 & 1 & 0 & 0 & 0 & -24 \\ -5 & -4 & 0 & 1 & 0 & 0 & -46 \\ -4 & -9 & 0 & 0 & 1 & 0 & -60 \\ 18 & 36 & 0 & 0 & 0 & 1 & 0 \end{bmatrix} \qquad \begin{bmatrix} 1 & 2/3 & -1/3 & 0 & 0 & 0 & 8 \\ 0 & -2/3 & -5/3 & 1 & 0 & 0 & -6 \\ 0 & -19/3 & -4/3 & 0 & 1 & 0 & -28 \\ 0 & 24 & 6 & 0 & 0 & 1 & -144 \end{bmatrix}$$

$$\begin{bmatrix} 1 & 0 & -2 & 1 & 0 & 0 & 2 \\ 0 & 1 & 5/2 & -3/2 & 0 & 0 & 9 \\ 0 & 0 & 29/2 & -19/2 & 1 & 1 & 29 \\ 0 & 0 & -54 & 36 & 0 & 0 & -360 \end{bmatrix}$$

$$\begin{bmatrix} 1 & 0 & 0 & -9/29 & 4/29 & 0 & 6 \\ 0 & 1 & 0 & 4/29 & -5/29 & 0 & 4 \\ 0 & 0 & 1 & -19/29 & 2/29 & 0 & 2 \\ 0 & 0 & 0 & 18/29 & 108/29 & 1 & -252 \end{bmatrix}$$

Minimum $z = 252$ at $(6, 4, 2)$

39.

$$\begin{bmatrix} 4 & 1 & 1 & 0 & 0 & 0 & 0 & 180 \\ -1 & -3 & 0 & 1 & 0 & 0 & 0 & -120 \\ -1 & 3 & 0 & 0 & 1 & 0 & 0 & 150 \\ 1 & -3 & 0 & 0 & 0 & 1 & 0 & -150 \\ -5 & -15 & 0 & 0 & 0 & 0 & 1 & 0 \end{bmatrix}$$

$$\begin{bmatrix} 11/3 & 0 & 1 & 1/3 & 0 & 0 & 0 & 140 \\ 1/3 & 1 & 0 & -1/3 & 0 & 0 & 0 & 40 \\ -2 & 0 & 0 & 1 & 1 & 0 & 0 & 30 \\ 2 & 0 & 0 & -1 & 0 & 1 & 0 & -30 \\ 0 & 0 & 0 & -5 & 0 & 0 & 1 & 600 \end{bmatrix}$$

$$\begin{bmatrix} 13/3 & 0 & 1 & 0 & 0 & 1/3 & 0 & 130 \\ -1/3 & 1 & 0 & 0 & 0 & -1/3 & 0 & 50 \\ 0 & 0 & 0 & 0 & 1 & 1 & 0 & 0 \\ -2 & 0 & 0 & 1 & 0 & -1 & 0 & 30 \\ -10 & 0 & 0 & 0 & 0 & -5 & 1 & 750 \end{bmatrix}$$

$$\begin{bmatrix} 1 & 0 & 3/13 & 0 & 0 & 1/13 & 0 & 30 \\ 0 & 1 & 1/13 & 0 & 0 & -4/13 & 0 & 60 \\ 0 & 0 & 0 & 0 & 1 & 1 & 0 & 0 \\ 0 & 0 & 6/13 & 1 & 0 & -11/13 & 0 & 90 \\ 0 & 0 & 30/13 & 0 & 0 & -55/13 & 1 & 1050 \end{bmatrix}$$

$$\begin{bmatrix} 1 & 0 & 3/13 & 0 & -1/13 & 0 & 0 & 30 \\ 0 & 1 & 1/13 & 0 & 4/13 & 0 & 0 & 60 \\ 0 & 0 & 0 & 0 & 1 & 1 & 0 & 0 \\ 0 & 0 & 6/13 & 1 & 11/13 & 0 & 0 & 90 \\ 0 & 0 & 30/13 & 0 & 55/13 & 0 & 1 & 1050 \end{bmatrix}$$

Maximum $z = 1050$ at $(30, 60)$

41.

$$\begin{bmatrix} 1 & 3 & 1 & 0 & 0 & 9 \\ 1 & -1 & 0 & 1 & 0 & -2 \\ -2 & -1 & 0 & 0 & 1 & 0 \end{bmatrix} \qquad \begin{bmatrix} 4 & 0 & 1 & 3 & 0 & 3 \\ -1 & 1 & 0 & -1 & 0 & 2 \\ -3 & 0 & 0 & -1 & 1 & 2 \end{bmatrix}$$

$$\begin{bmatrix} 1 & 0 & 1/4 & 3/4 & 0 & 3/4 \\ 0 & 1 & 1/4 & -1/4 & 0 & 11/4 \\ 0 & 0 & 3/4 & 5/4 & 1 & 17/4 \end{bmatrix}$$

Maximum $z = 17/4$ at $x_1 = 3/4$, $x_2 = 11/4$

43. Let x_1 = number of hunting jackets, x_2 = number of
all-weather jackets, x_3 = number of ski jackets.

Maximize $z = 7.5x_1 + 9x_2 + 11x_3$

subject to $\quad 3x_1 + 2.5x_2 + 3.5x_3 \leq 3200$

$\qquad\qquad 26x_1 + 20x_2 + 22x_3 \leq 18000$

$\qquad\qquad x_1 \geq 0,\ x_2 \geq 0,\ x_3 \geq 0$

$$\begin{bmatrix} 3 & 2.5 & 3.5 & 1 & 0 & 0 & 3200 \\ 26 & 20 & 22 & 0 & 1 & 0 & 18000 \\ -7.5 & -9 & -11 & 0 & 0 & 1 & 0 \end{bmatrix}$$

Chapter 5
Sets and Counting

Section 5-1

1. (a) True   (b) False   (c) False   (d) False   (e) True
    (f) True   (g) False   (h) True   (i) False

3. B = {M, I, S, P}   5. C = {16, 18, 20, 22, ...}   7. Not equal

9. Equal   11. Not equal   13. A ⊂ B   15. A ⊄ B

17. A ⊂ B   19. A ⊂ B

21. (a) ∅, {-1}, {2}, {4}, {-1, 2}, {-1, 4}, {2, 4}, {-1, 2, 4}

    (b) ∅, {4}

    (c) ∅, {-3}, {5}, {6}, {8}, {-3, 5}, {-3, 6}, {-3, 8}, {5, 6},
        {5, 8}, {6, 8}, {-3, 5, 6}, {-3, 5, 8}, {-3, 6, 8}, {6, 5, 8},
        {-3, 5, 6, 8}

23. ∅   25. Not empty   27. ∅   29. ∅   31. ∅

33. {1, 2, 4, 6, 7}   35. {a, b, c, d, x, y, z}   37. {9, 12}

39. A ∩ B = {1, 2, 3}   41. A ∪ B = {1, 2, 3, 6, 9}

43. A ∩ B ∩ C = {2, 3}   45. A ∩ ∅ = ∅

47. (A ∩ C) ∪ B = {1, 2, 3, 6, 9}

49. {13, 22, 33, ...}   51. {1, 2, 3, 4}

53. (a) ⊂   (b) Neither   (c) =   (d) Neither   (e) ⊂

55. A ∩ B = {x|x is an integer that is a multiple of 35}

57. Disjoint

59. A ∩ B is the set of students at Miami Bay Univ. who are taking both
     finite math and American history.

Section 5-2

1. A' = {17, 18, 19}   3. A' = {11, 12, 13}

5. (a) A' = {-1, 0, 12}   (b) B' = {1, 12, 13}
    (c) (A ∪ B)' = {12}   (d) (A ∩ B)' = {-1, 0, 1, 12, 13}

7. (a) n(A) = 10   (b) n(B) = 5   (c) n(A ∩ B) = 4
    (d) n(A ∪ B) = 10 + 5 - 4 = 11

9. n(A ∪ B) = 120 + 100 - 40 = 180

11.   30 = 15 + 22 - n(A ∩ B)   n(A ∩ B) = 7

13.   n(B) = 28 - 14 + 5 = 19   15.   60 + 75 - 100 = 35

17.   (a)   42   (b)   60   (c)   84   (d) 57   (e) 39
      (f)   81   (g)   15   (h)   15   (i) 81

19.   (a)   35   (b)   9   (c)   6   (d)   38   (e)   38   (f)   12

21.   n(A ∪ B) = 27; n(A ∪ C) = 26; Since
      n(A ∪ B ∪ C) = 33, the number in C only is
      33-27 = 6. The number in B only is 33-26 = 7

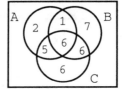

23. 460 = 240 + n(B) - 55, n(B) = 275 so n(B') = 500 - 275 = 225

25.   (a)   14   (b)   24
      (c)   14 + 24 = 38
      (d)   14 + 6 + 24 = 44

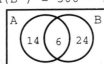

27.   (a)   8   (b)   27
      (c)   4   (d)   31

29.   (a)   21   (b)   10
      (c)   8   (d)   56
      (e)   29   (f)   62

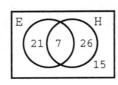

31.   (a)   28   (b)   9
      (c)   20   (d)   7

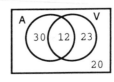

33.   69

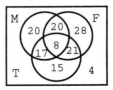

35.   It must be the case that n(A ∪ B) ≥ n(A), but it is not.

37.   (a)   30   (b)   20

39. Yes, since these numbers total only 133, not 135.

41.   (a)   n(A ∩ B) = 5 + 10 - 15 = 0   (b)   A ∩ B = ∅

Section 5-3

1.

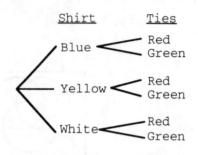

3.

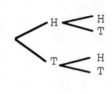

5. $12 \cdot 15 = 180$ 7. $5 \cdot 9 = 45$ 9. $6 \cdot 7 = 42$ 11. $4 \cdot 7 = 28$

13.   (a) $13 \cdot 13 = 169$ (b) $13 \cdot 13 \cdot 13 \cdot 13 = 28,561$

15. $2 \cdot 4 \cdot 3 = 24$ 17. $6 \cdot 5 \cdot 3 = 90$ 19. $4^6 = 4,096$

21. $8 \cdot 10^6 = 8,000,000$ 23.   (a) $5^4 = 625$ (b) $5 \cdot 4 \cdot 3 \cdot 2 = 120$

25.   (a) $26^3 \cdot 10^3 = 17,576,000$ (b) $26 \cdot 25 \cdot 24 \cdot 10 \cdot 9 \cdot 8 = 11,232,000$

27.

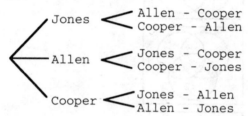

29.   (a) $7 \cdot 6 \cdot 5 = 210$ (b) $1 \cdot 6 \cdot 5 = 30$ (c) $2 \cdot 6 \cdot 5 = 60$
      (d) $6 \cdot 2 \cdot 5 = 60$ (e) $2 \cdot 5 \cdot 4 + 5 \cdot 2 \cdot 4 + 5 \cdot 4 \cdot 2 = 3 \cdot 40 = 120$

31. $8 \cdot 1 \cdot 6 \cdot 1 \cdot 4 \cdot 1 \cdot 2 \cdot 1 = 384$ 33.   1st is man: $4 \cdot 3 \cdot 3 \cdot 2 \cdot 2 \cdot 1 \cdot 1 = 144$

35.   (a) $6 \cdot 5 \cdot 4 \cdot 3 = 360$ (b) $6 \cdot 5 \cdot 5 \cdot 5 = 750$

37. $5 \cdot 4 \cdot 3 \cdot 2 \cdot 1 \cdot 3 \cdot 2 \cdot 1 + 3 \cdot 2 \cdot 1 \cdot 5 \cdot 4 \cdot 3 \cdot 2 \cdot 1 = 2 \cdot 720 = 1440$ 39. $2^7 = 128$

41.

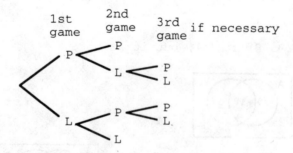

Section 5-4

1. $3! = 6$ 3. $5! = 120$ 5. $5!3! = (120)(6) = 720$

7. $\dfrac{7!}{3!} = 840$ 9. $\dfrac{12!}{7!} = 95,040$ 11. $P(6, 4) = 6 \cdot 5 \cdot 4 \cdot 3 = 360$

13. $P(100, 3) = 100 \cdot 99 \cdot 98 = 970,200$ 15. $P(7, 4) = 7 \cdot 6 \cdot 5 \cdot 4 = 840$

17. $P(6, 3) = 6 \cdot 5 \cdot 4 = 120$ 19. $P(7, 5) = 7 \cdot 6 \cdot 5 \cdot 4 \cdot 3 = 2,520$

21. $P(8, 3) = 8 \cdot 7 \cdot 6 = 336$

23. (a) $P(7, 7) = 7! = 5,040$ (b) $P(7, 3) = 7 \cdot 6 \cdot 5 = 210$

25. $P(3, 3) = 3! = 6$ 27. $P(22, 3) = 22 \cdot 21 \cdot 20 = 9,240$

29. (a) $P(4, 4) = 4! = 24$ (b) $P(7, 4) = 7 \cdot 6 \cdot 5 \cdot 4 = 840$

31. $P(7, 3) = 7 \cdot 6 \cdot 5 = 210$ 33. $P(5, 5) = 5! = 120$

35. $P(4, 4) = 4! = 24$

37. (a) $P(4, 3) = 4 \cdot 3 \cdot 2 = 24$ (b) $4^3 = 64$

39. $P(12, 2) \cdot P(11, 5) \cdot P(10, 2) = (12 \cdot 11)(11 \cdot 10 \cdot 9 \cdot 8 \cdot 7)(10 \cdot 9)$
$$= (132)(55440)(90) = 658,627,200$$

41. $\dfrac{8!}{2!} = 20,160$ 43. $\dfrac{6!}{3!} = 120$

45. (a) $\dfrac{8!}{2!2!} = 10,080$ (b) $\dfrac{11!}{4!4!2!} = 34,650$

(c) $\dfrac{10!}{2!2!3!} = 151,200$ (d) $\dfrac{10!}{3!2!2!} = 151,200$

47. (a) $\dfrac{7!}{4!3!} = 35$ (b) $\dfrac{7!}{5!2!} = 21$

49. (a) The series ends when team A wins 4 games so the total number of
games played may range from 4 to 7. However, assume that A wins 4
and B wins 3 games (B "wins" the unplayed games). The number of
sequences of games possible if A wins the series is the number of
sequences of 4 wins by A and 3 wins by B,

$\dfrac{7!}{4!3!} = 35$ (b)   35   (c) $35 + 35 = 70$

51. $P(10, 4) = 10 \cdot 9 \cdot 8 \cdot 7 = 5,040$ 53. $P(28, 3) = 28 \cdot 27 \cdot 26 = 19,656$

55. (a) $P(n, 2) = n(n - 1)$ (b) $P(n, 3) = n(n - 1)(n - 2)$
(c) $P(n, 1) = n$ (d) $P(n, 5) = n(n - 1)(n - 2)(n - 3)(n - 4)$

57. $26 \cdot 9 \cdot 26 \cdot 9 \cdot 26 = 1,423,656$ 59. $P(15, 4) = 15 \cdot 14 \cdot 13 \cdot 12 = 32,760$

61. (a) $\dfrac{7!}{(3!4!)} = 35$ (b) $\dfrac{8!}{(3!5!)} = 56$

Section 5-5

1. $C(6, 2) = \dfrac{6 \cdot 5}{2} = 15$ 3. $C(13, 3) = \dfrac{13 \cdot 12 \cdot 11}{3 \cdot 2} = 286$

5. $C(9, 5) = \dfrac{9 \cdot 8 \cdot 7 \cdot 6 \cdot 5}{5 \cdot 4 \cdot 3 \cdot 2} = 126$ 7. $C(4, 4) = \dfrac{4!}{4!} = 1$

9. $\{a, b\}, \{a, c\}, \{a, d\}, \{b, c\}, \{b, d\}, \{c, d\}$

11. $\{a, b, c, d\}, \{a, b, c, e\}, \{a, b, d, e\}, \{a, c, d, e\}, \{b, c, d, e\}$

13. $C(6, 2) = \dfrac{6 \cdot 5}{2 \cdot 1} = 15$ 15. $C(15, 3) = \dfrac{15 \cdot 14 \cdot 13}{3 \cdot 2} = 455$

17. (a) $C(7, 4) = \dfrac{7 \cdot 6 \cdot 5 \cdot 4}{4 \cdot 3 \cdot 2} = 35$ (b) $P(7, 4) = 7 \cdot 6 \cdot 5 \cdot 4 = 840$

19. $C(5, 2) \cdot C(6, 3) \cdot C(8, 2) = (10)(20)(28) = 5600$

Section 5-6

21. $C(6, 3) \cdot C(10, 4) = (20)(210) = 4200$

23. $C(9, 3) + C(11, 3) = 84 + 165 = 249$

25. $C(7, 3) + C(6, 3) = 35 + 20 = 55$

27. $C(5, 3) \cdot C(6, 2) + C(5, 4) \cdot C(6, 1) + C(5, 5) = 10 \cdot 15 + 5 \cdot 6 + 1 \cdot 1 = 181$

29. $C(8, 2) \cdot C(6, 2) + C(8, 3) \cdot C(6, 1) + C(8, 4) = 28 \cdot 15 + 56 \cdot 6 + 70 = 826$

31. $P(40, 2) \cdot C(10, 3) = 1560 \cdot 120 = 187,200$

33. $P(8, 2) \cdot C(12, 4) = 56 \cdot 495 = 27,720$ 35. $C(7, 3) = 35$

37. $C(20, 5) = 15,504$

39. (a) {Alice}, {Bianca}, {Cal}, {Dewayne}
    (b) {Alice, Bianca}, {Alice, Cal}, {Alice, Dewayne},
        {Bianca, Cal}, {Bianca, Dewayne}, {Cal, Dewayne}
    (c) {Alice, Bianca, Cal}, {Alice, Bianca, Dewayne},
        {Bianca, Cal, Dewayne}, {Alice, Cal, Dewayne},
        {Alice, Cal, Dewayne}
    (d) {Alice, Bianca, Cal, Dewayne}   (e) $\varnothing$ (f) 16

41. $C(4, 2) \cdot C(4, 3) = 6 \cdot 4 = 24$

43. (a) $C(10, 6) \cdot C(8, 5) = (210)(56) = 11,760$
    (b) $C(8, 6) \cdot C(10, 4) + C(8, 7) \cdot C(10, 3) + C(8, 8) \cdot C(10, 2)$
        $= 5880 + 960 + 45 = 6885$

Section 5-6

1. $\dfrac{12!}{(3!)^4} = 369,600$ 3. $\dfrac{7!}{3!4!} = 35$ 5. $\dfrac{9!}{2!3!4!} = 1260$

7. $\dfrac{6!}{2!4!} = 15$ 9. $\dfrac{9!}{(3!)^3} = 1680$ 11. $\dfrac{14!}{3!5!6!} = 168,168$

13. $\dfrac{18!}{(6!)^3} = 17,153,136$ 15. $\dfrac{15!}{6!4!5!} = 630,630$ 17. $\dfrac{10!}{4!4!2!} = 3,150$

19. $\dfrac{10!}{(5!)^2} = 252$ 21. $\dfrac{18!}{(6!)^3} = 17,153,136$ 23. $\dfrac{9!}{(3!)^4} = 280$

25. $\dfrac{12!}{3!(4!)^3} = 5,775$ 27. $\dfrac{15!}{2!(5!)^2 3!2!} = 3,783,780$

29. $\dfrac{22!}{3!(2!)^3 4!(4!)^4}$ 31. $\dfrac{50!}{10!(5!)^{10}}$

Review Exercises, Chapter 5

1. (a) True   (b) False   (c) False   (d) False
   (e) True   (f) False   (g) True   (h) False
   (i) True   (j) False   (k) True   (l) False
   (m) True   (n) False   (o) False

3. (a) Equal (b) Not equal (c) Equal, both are empty

5. $n(A \cap B) = 32 + 40 - 58 = 14$

7.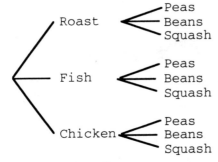

```
              ┌─ Peas
      Roast ──┼─ Beans
              └─ Squash

              ┌─ Peas
      Fish ───┼─ Beans
              └─ Squash

              ┌─ Peas
     Chicken ─┼─ Beans
              └─ Squash
```

9. (a) $10^4 \cdot 26^2 = 6,760,000$ (b) $10 \cdot 9 \cdot 8 \cdot 7 \cdot 26 \cdot 25 = 3,276,000$

11. $C(15, 5) = 3,003$ 13. $(40)(27)(85)(34) = 3,121,200$

15. $4 \cdot 5! \cdot 3 = 1,440$ 17. (a) $P(11, 3) = 990$ (b) $11^3 = 1,331$

19. $P(10, 2) \cdot C(8, 4) = (90)(70) = 6300$

21. This totals 58, not 60 23. (a) 20 (b) 6
(c) 23

25. $5 \cdot 8 \cdot 7 = 280$ 27. $C(5, 2) = 10$

29. (a) $(20)^3 = 8,000$ (b) $20 \cdot 19 \cdot 18 = 6,840$

31. $C(15, 4)C(20, 4)C(25, 3)C(11, 1)$ 33. $P(9, 5) = 15,120$

35. $C(22, 5) = 26,334$

37. (a) $P(8, 4) = 8 \cdot 7 \cdot 6 \cdot 5 = 1,680$ (b) $C(9, 5) = \dfrac{9 \cdot 8 \cdot 7 \cdot 6 \cdot 5}{6 \cdot 5 \cdot 4 \cdot 3} = 126$

(c) $P(7, 7) = 7! = 5,040$ (d) $C(5, 5) = 1$

(e) $4! = 24$ (f) $\dfrac{7!}{3!4!} = 35$ (g) $\dfrac{8!}{4!} = 1,680$

39. $P(20, 2)P(15, 1)P(25, 1) = (380)(15)(25) = 142,500$

41. $46 + 51 - 83 = 97 - 83 = 14$ 43. $C(10, 4) = 210$

45. $\varnothing$, {red}, {white}, {blue}, {red, white}, {red, blue}, {white, blue}, {red, white, blue}

47. $P(10, 2) \cdot C(8, 3) = (90)(56) = 5,040$

49. $C(6, 4) + C(8, 4) = 15 + 70 = 85$

51. (a) $5! = 120$ (b) $\dfrac{5!}{3!} = 20$ (c) $\dfrac{8!}{2!2!} = 10,080$

53. $\dfrac{18!}{2!(3!)^2 2!(6!)^2} = 85,765,680$ 55. $\dfrac{12!}{2!(3!)^2(2!)(3!)^2} = 92,400$

Chapter 6

Probability

Section 6-1

1. (a)   {True, False}
    (b)   {vowel, consonant} or the letters {a,b,c, . . . ,x,y,z}
    (c)   {1, 2, 3, 4, 5, 6}
    (d)   {HHH, HHT, HTH, THH, TTH, THT, HTT, TTT}
    (e)   {Mon, Tue, Wed, Thurs, Fri, Sat, Sun}
    (f)   {Grand Canyon wins, Bosque wins, tie}, or
          {Bosque wins, Bosque loses, tie}
    (g)   {pass, fail}, {A, B, C, D, F}
    (h)   {Susan & Leah, Susan & Dana, Susan & Julie, Leah &
          Dana, Leah & Julie, Dana and Julie}
    (i)   {Mon, Tue, Wed, Thur, Fri, Sat, Sun}, or {1, 2, 3, 4,...,31}
    (j)   {male, female}, {passing student, failing student}

3. (a)   Valid   (b)   Valid
    (c)   Invalid $P(T) + P(D) + P(H) = .95$
    (d)   Invalid $P(2) + P(4) + P(6) + P(8) + P(10) = 1.15$
    (e)   Valid   (f)   Invalid $P(Utah) = -.4 < 0$
    (g)   Valid   (h)   Invalid $P(maybe) = 1.1 > 1$
    (i)   Invalid $P(True) + P(False) = 0$

5. (a) $P(\{A, B\}) = .1 + .2 = .3$ (b) $P(\{B, D\}) = .2 + .4 = .6$
    (c) $P(\{A, C, D\}) = .1 + .3 + .4 = .8$ (d) $P(\{A, B, C, D\}) = 1$

7. (a) $.10 + .37 = .47$ (b) $.05 + .18 + .30 = .53$

9. (a) $.05 + .10 + .06 = .21$ (b) $.10 + .15 + .18 = .43$
    (c) $.21 + .11 + .18 + .14 = .64$ (d) $.12 + .15 = .27$

11. $P(A) + P(B) + P(C) + P(D)$
     $= 2 \cdot P(D) + 3 \cdot P(D) + 4 \cdot P(D) + P(D) = 1$
           $10 \cdot P(D) = 1 \Rightarrow P(D) = .1$
           $P(A) = .20, P(B) = .30, P(C) = .40, P(D) = .10$

13. $P(A) + P(B) + P(C) = 1$
     $P(A) + P(B)   = .75$
         $P(B) + P(C) = .45$
     Subtract second equation from the first
             $P(A) + P(B) + P(C) = 1$
             $\underline{P(A) + P(B)   = .75}$
                     $P(C) = .25$
     From third equation $P(B) + .25 = .45$ gives $P(B) = .20$, so $P(A) = .55$.

15. $P(Mini) = 140/800 = .175, P(Burger) = 345/800 = .43125,$
     $P(Big B) = 315/800 = .39375$

17. $P(below 40) = 160/1800 = .089,$
     $P(40-49) = 270/1800 = .15$
     $P(50-55) = 1025/1800 = .569,$
     $P(over 55) = 345/1800 = .192$

19. (a) $P(\{2, 4\}) = .16 + .30 = .46$
     (b) $P(\{1, 3, 5\}) = .15 + .19 + .20 = .54$
     (c) $P(prime) = .16 + .19 + .20 = .55$

21.   (a) $4/52 = 1/13$ (b) $(4 + 4)/52 = 2/13$
      (c) $13/52 = 1/4$ (d) $26/52 = 1/2$

Section 6-2

1. $4/15$ 3. $5/8$ 5. $6/36 = 1/6$

7. $\dfrac{C(10,\ 2)}{C(17,\ 2)} = \dfrac{45}{136} = .33$ 9. $\dfrac{C(4,\ 2)}{C(52,\ 2)} = \dfrac{6}{1326} = \dfrac{1}{221} = .0045$

11.   (a) $5/9$ (b) 0 (c) 1 13. $3/4$

15. $\dfrac{C(12,\ 2)\cdot C(9,\ 1)}{C(21,\ 3)} = \dfrac{594}{1330} = \dfrac{297}{665} = .447$

17.   (a) $\dfrac{C(4,\ 4)}{C(15,4)} = \dfrac{1}{1365} = .00073$

      (b) $\dfrac{C(4,\ 3)\cdot C(11,\ 1)}{C(15,\ 4)} = \dfrac{4\cdot 11}{1365} = \dfrac{44}{1365} = .0322$

      (c) $\dfrac{C(4,\ 2)\cdot C(11,\ 2)}{C(15,\ 4)} = \dfrac{6\cdot 55}{1365} = \dfrac{22}{91} = .242$

      (d) $\dfrac{C(11,\ 4)}{C(15,\ 4)} = \dfrac{330}{1365} = \dfrac{22}{91} = .242$

19.   (a) $\dfrac{P(10,\ 2)\cdot P(6,\ 3)}{P(16,\ 5)} = \dfrac{90\cdot 120}{524160} = \dfrac{90}{4368} = \dfrac{15}{728} = .0206$

      (b) $\dfrac{10\cdot 6\cdot 9\cdot 5\cdot 8}{P(16,\ 5)} = \dfrac{10\cdot 6\cdot 9\cdot 5\cdot 8}{524160} = \dfrac{15}{364} = .0412$

21.   (a) $\dfrac{P(4,\ 4)}{P(8,\ 4)} = \dfrac{24}{1680} = \dfrac{1}{70} = .0143$

      (b) $\dfrac{P(4,\ 2)\cdot P(4,\ 2)}{P(8,\ 4)} = \dfrac{12\cdot 12}{1680} = \dfrac{3}{35} = .0857$

23. $1 - (.6 + .3) = .1$

25.   Begins with a 5, 6, 7, 8 or 9:

      $\dfrac{5\cdot 8\cdot 7}{P(9,\ 3)} = \dfrac{280}{504} = \dfrac{5}{9} = .555$

27.   (a) $\dfrac{1}{P(5,\ 5)} = \dfrac{1}{5!} = \dfrac{1}{120}$ (b) $\dfrac{P(2,\ 2)\cdot P(3,\ 3)}{P(5,\ 5)} = \dfrac{2\cdot 6}{120} = \dfrac{1}{10}$

29. $\dfrac{C(8,\ 3)\cdot C(6,\ 1)}{C(14,\ 4)} = \dfrac{56\cdot 6}{1001} = \dfrac{48}{143} = .336$

31.   (a) $6/28 = 3/14$ (b) $3/28$ (c) $10/28 = 5/14$

33.   (a) $5/14$ (b) $(6 + 3)/14 = 9/14$

35.   (a) $400/500 = 4/5$ (b) $100/500 = 1/5$

Section 6-3

37. (a) $\dfrac{P(8,\ 3)}{P(15,\ 3)} = \dfrac{8\cdot7\cdot6}{15\cdot14\cdot13} = \dfrac{8}{65} = .123$

    (b) $\dfrac{8\cdot7\cdot7}{P(15,\ 3)} = \dfrac{8\cdot7\cdot7}{15\cdot14\cdot13} = \dfrac{28}{195} = .144$

    (c) $\dfrac{5\cdot4\cdot3}{P(15,\ 3)} = \dfrac{5\cdot4\cdot3}{15\cdot14\cdot13} = \dfrac{2}{91} = .022$

39. $324/570 = 54/95 = .568$

41. (a) $C(4,\ 3)/2^4 = 4/16 = 1/4$ (b) $1/2^4 = 1/16$

43. (a) $\dfrac{P(2,\ 2)\ P(2,\ 1)}{P(4,\ 3)} = \dfrac{1}{6}$ (b) $\dfrac{C(2,\ 2)\ C(2,\ 1)}{C(4,\ 3)} = \dfrac{1}{2}$

45. x = number of dimes dated before 1960
    $x/250 = .2 \Rightarrow x = .2(250) = 50$

47. $\dfrac{C(2,\ 2)}{C(6,\ 2)} = \dfrac{1}{15}$

49. (a) $\dfrac{3\cdot5\cdot2}{P(10,\ 3)} = \dfrac{3\cdot5\cdot2}{10\cdot9\cdot8} = \dfrac{1}{24}$ (b) $\dfrac{5\cdot4\cdot2}{P(10,\ 3)} = \dfrac{5\cdot4\cdot2}{10\cdot9\cdot8} = \dfrac{1}{18}$

    (c) $\dfrac{3\cdot2\cdot2}{P(10,\ 3)} = \dfrac{3\cdot2\cdot2}{10\cdot9\cdot8} = \dfrac{1}{60}$

Section 6-3

1. $E \cup F = \{1,\ 2,\ 3,\ 4,\ 5,\ 7,\ 9\}$ $E \cap F = \{1,\ 3\}$
   $E' = \{2,\ 4,\ 6,\ 8,\ 10\}$

3. $E \cup F$ = the set of students who are passing English or failing
   chemistry (or both)
   $E \cap F$ = the set of students who are passing English and failing
   chemistry
   E' = the set of students who are failing English

5. $1 - 3/5 = 2/5$ 7. $P(E) = 1 - 0.7 = 0.3$

9. $1 - 0.3 = 0.7$ 11. Mutually exclusive

13. Not mutually exclusive   15. Mutually exclusive

17. (a) $\dfrac{C(4,\ 4)}{C(52,\ 4)} = \dfrac{1}{270725}$ (b) $\dfrac{1}{270725} + \dfrac{1}{270725} = \dfrac{2}{270725}$

19. $1/10 + 3/10 = 4/10 = 2/5$

21. (a) Find 1 - probability all females.
    $1 - \dfrac{C(5,\ 3)}{C(12,\ 3)} = 1 - \dfrac{10}{220} = 1 - \dfrac{1}{22} = \dfrac{21}{22}$

    (b) Find 1 - probability all males.
    $1 - \dfrac{C(7,\ 3)}{C(12,\ 3)} = 1 - \dfrac{35}{220} = 1 - \dfrac{7}{44} = \dfrac{37}{44}$

23. $1 - \dfrac{C(46,\ 3)}{C(50,\ 3)} = 1 - \dfrac{15180}{19600} = \dfrac{4420}{19600} = \dfrac{221}{980}$ (1 - probability none of 4 wins)

25. (a) $120/400 = 3/10$ (b) $220/400 = 11/20$ (c) $55/400 = 11/80$
    (d) $\dfrac{120 + 220 - 55}{400} = \dfrac{285}{400} = \dfrac{57}{80} = .7125$

27. (a) $4/35$ (b) $\dfrac{10 + 14 - 4}{35} = \dfrac{20}{35} = \dfrac{4}{7}$

29. $.75 + .24 - .18 = 0.81$ 31. $.36 + .26 - .11 = .51$

33. (a) $.85 + .60 - .55 = .90$ (b) $1 - .90 = .10$

35. (a) $.75 + .63 - .54 = 0.84$ (b) $1 - .84 = 0.16$

37. (a) $3/6 = 1/2$ (b) $2/6 = 1/3$
    (c) $3/6 = 1/2$ (d) $4/6 = 2/3$

39. Mutually exclusive   41. Mutually exclusive

43. (a) $5/6$ (b) $1/6$ (c) $3/6 = 1/2$
    (d) $2/6 = 1/3$ (e) $2/6 = 1/3$

45. (a) $1/10$ (b) $1/10$ (c) $5/10 = 1/2$
    (d) $5/10 = 1/2$ (e) $5/10 = 1/2$
    (f) $(5 + 6 - 3)/10 = 8/10 = 4/5$ (g) $(5 + 7 - 3)/10 = 9/10$

47. $(4 + 13 - 1)/52 = 16/52 = 4/13$

49. $.89 = .76 + .62 - P(\text{passing both})$
    $P(\text{passing both}) = .49$

51. P(Female or Executive)
    = P(Female) + P(Executives) - P(Females and Executives)
    $.65 = .55 + P(\text{Executives}) - .05$, so
    P (Executives) = .15
    Since .05 are female executives, the remainder
    $.10 = 10\%$, are male executives.

53. $(3 + 1)/6 = 4/6 = 2/3$

55. (a) $P(E) = 4/10 = 2/5$ = probability he attends a small or large
       state university
       $P(F) = 6/10 = 3/5$ = probability he attends a small or large
       private university
       $P(G) = 5/10 = 1/2$ = probability he attends a large university
       $P(H) = 5/10 = 1/2$ = probability he attends a small state
       university or a small private university
    (b) $P(E') = 1 - 2/5 = 3/5$ = probability he does not attend a
       state university
    (c) $P(E \cup G) = (3 + 2 + 1)/10 = 6/10 = 3/5$ = probability he
       attends a large or state university
    (d) $P(F' \cap H) = 1/10$ = probability he attends a small state
       university

57. $.85 + .93 - .81 = 0.97$

Section 6-4

1. (a) 3/4 (b) 1/2

3. (a) 16/45 (b) P(correct|from Section 1) = 7/24
    (c) P(Section 2|correct) = 9/16

5. (a) 3/8 (b) 7/10 7. P(K|F) = 1/10, P(F|K) = 1

9. (a) 28/60 = 7/15 (b) 6/20 = 3/10 (c) 6/28 = 3/14

11. P(E|F) = .3/.7 = 3/7 P(F|E) = .3/.6 = 1/2

13. P(E|F) = .24/.40 = 3/5 P(F|E) = .24/.60 = 2/5 = .4

15. (a) .20/.45 = 4/9 (b) .20/.75 = 4/15

17. (a) 41/497 = .082 (b) 260/497 = .523
     (c) 145/497 = .292 (d) 46/260 = .177
     (e) 46/115 = .40 (f) (23 + 145)/(41 + 341) = 168/382 = .440

19. (4/52)(4/51) = 4/663

21. (a) $(4/52)(4/52) = (1/13)^2 = 1/169$

     (b) $(13/52)(13/52) = (1/4)^2 = 1/16$

     (c) $(26/52)(26/52) = (1/2)^2 = 1/4$

23. (4/12)(2/11)(6/10) = 2/55 25. (6/14)(5/13) = 15/91 = .165

27. (3/32)(3/32) = 9/1024 = .0088

29. (a) (4/15)(4/15) = 16/225 (b) (4/15)(3/15) = 4/75

31. (a) (6/15)(4/15)(6/15) = 16/375 (b) (5/15)(5/15)(5/15) = 1/27

33. If one die shows a 2, the other die can show five different faces.
     If the second die shows a 2, the first one can show five different
     faces. Thus, there are 10 possible ways one die shows a 2. Of
     these 10 ways, two of them total 6. The probability of a total of 6
     given one die shows a 2 is 2/10.

35. (a) 75/135 = 5/9 (b) .35 (c) .40
     (d) P(O|M)·P(M) + P(O|F)·P(F) = (.35)(4/9) + (.40)(5/9)
                                     = .156 + .222 = .378

     (e) $\dfrac{P(F|O) \cdot P(F)}{P(O)} = \dfrac{(.40)(5/9)}{.378} = \dfrac{2/9}{.378} = .588$

37. (a) $(\frac{2}{3})(\frac{1}{2}) = \frac{1}{3}$ (b) $(\frac{2}{3})(\frac{1}{2}) = \frac{1}{3}$ (c) $(\frac{2}{3})(\frac{1}{2}) + (\frac{1}{3})(\frac{2}{2}) = \frac{2}{3}$

39. P(forged) = 1/10,000 P(postdated) = .05
     P(postdated | forged) = .80

     Find P(forged | postdated) = $\dfrac{P(\text{forged and postdated})}{P(\text{postdated})}$

     Since P(postdated | forged) = $\dfrac{P(\text{forged and postdated})}{P(\text{forged})}$,

     then .80 = $\dfrac{P(\text{forged and postdated})}{.0001}$

     P(forged and postdated) = .00008

     P(forged | postdated) = $\dfrac{.00008}{.05}$ = .0016

41. P(scholarship and continues) =
          P(continues | scholarship)P(scholarship)
                                = (.90)(.30) = .27

43. (a) $(\frac{1}{5})(\frac{1}{4})(\frac{1}{3}) = \frac{1}{60}$ (b) $\frac{3!}{60} = \frac{1}{10}$ (c)   0

     (d) $\frac{C(3, 3)}{C(5, 3)} = \frac{1}{10}$ (e) $\frac{1}{10}$ (f) $\frac{C(3, 2)\ C(2, 1)}{C(5, 3)} = \frac{3}{5}$

45. (a)   1/10   (b) $(\frac{9}{10})(\frac{8}{9}) = \frac{8}{10} = \frac{4}{5}$

     (c) $\frac{1}{10}\frac{9}{9} + \frac{9}{10}\frac{8}{9} = \frac{9}{10}$

47. If $E \subset F$, then $E \cap F = E$, so that $P(E \cap F) = P(E)$. So as long as
     $P(F) \neq 0$, we have $P(E|F) = \frac{P(E \cap F)}{P(F)} = \frac{P(E)}{P(F)}$.

49. If $E \subset F$, then $F \cap E = E$, so that $P(F \cap E) = P(E)$. As long as
     $P(E) \neq 0$, we have $P(F|E) = \frac{P(F \cap E)}{P(E)} = \frac{P(E)}{P(E)} = 1$.

Section 6-5

1.   (a)   (i)   Not mutually exclusive
           (ii)   Independent, since P(E) = 40/160 = 1/4 and
                  P(E|F) = 10/40 = 1/4
     (b)   (i)   Not mutually exclusive
           (ii)   Dependent, since P(E) = 40/160 = 1/4
                  and P(E|F) = 10/50 = 1/5
     (c)   (i)   Not mutually exclusive
           (ii)   Independent, since P(E) = 50/100 = 1/2
                  and P(E|F) = 30/60 = 1/2
     (d)   (i)   Mutually exclusive
           (ii)   Dependent, since $P(E \cap F) = 0 \neq P(E)P(F) = \frac{1}{16}$
     (e)   (i)   Mutually exclusive
           (ii)   Dependent, since P(E) = 30/120 = 1/4
                  and P(E|F) = 0/40 = 0
     (f)   (i)   Mutually exclusive
           (ii)   Independent, since P(E) = 0/80 = 0
                  and P(E|F) = 0/20 = 0

3.   Independent, since (.3)(.5) = .15

5.   Dependent, since (.3)(.7) ≠ .20

7.   (a)   Not mutually exclusive
     (b)   Independent since P(E) = 2/4 = 1/2 and P(E|F) = 1/2

9.   Dependent, since $P(A \cap S) = 10/100 = 1/10$
     and $P(A) \cdot P(S) = (15/100)(20/100) = 3/100$

11. (6/14)(12/21) = (3/7)(4/7) = 12/49   13.   (1/4)(1/5) = 1/20

Section 6-6

15.　(a)　$(.2)(.3) = .06$ (b)　$(.8)(.7) = .56$
　　(c)　$(.2)(.7) + (.8)(.3) = .14 + .24 = .38$

17.　(a)　$(.5)(.6)(.8) = .24$ (b)　$(.5)(.4)(.2) = .04$

19.　(a)　$.3 + .5 - (.3)(.5) = .8 - .15 = .65$
　　(b)　$.2 + .6 - (.2)(.6) = .8 - .12 = .68$
　　(c)　$.4 + .6 - (.4)(.6) = 1 - .24 = .76$

21.　(a)　$1 - (.4)(.2) = 1 - .08 = .92$
　　(b)　$1 - (.6)(.8) = 1 - .48 = .52$

23.　$1 - (.7)(.1) = 1 - .07 = .93$

25.　$P(F) = 12/52 = 3/13$, $P(G) = 4/52 = 1/13$,
　　$P(G|F) = 4/12 = 1/3$, $P(F|G) = 1$, dependent since $P(G) \neq P(G|F)$

27.　$(1/6)(1/6)(1/6)(3/6)(3/6) = 1/864$

29.　(a)

　　(b)　$(120/300)(.36) + (180/300)(.52) = 0.456$
　　(c)　$(120/300)(.44) = 0.176$
　　(d)　$P(F) = 0.456$, $P(F|W) = .52$, so dependent

31.　$P(F) \cdot P(G) = (1/2)(3/13) = 3/26$, $P(F \cap G) = 6/52 = 3/26$,
　　so independent

33.　(a)　$(.5)^{12} = .00024414$ (b)　$(.90)^{12} = 0.2824$

35.　$(3/5)(1/3)(1/3) + (2/5)(1/3) = 1/15 + 2/15 = 3/15 = 1/5$

37.　If E & F are mutually exclusive, then $P(E \cap F) = 0$, but if neither
　　E nor F has probability 0, then $P(E) \cdot P(F) \neq 0$.
　　So $P(E \cap F) \neq P(E) \cdot P(F)$ implies they are dependent.

Section 6-6

1.

3.　(a)　$P(E_1|F) = .7/.9 = 7/9$

　　(b)　$P(E_1|F) = \dfrac{(.75)(.40)}{(.75)(.40) + (.25)(.10)}$

　　　　$= \dfrac{.3}{.3 + .025} = 0.923$

5.   (a) $P(E_1 \cap F) = (5/12)(2/5) = 1/6,$
                 $P(E_2 \cap F) = (4/12)(1/4) = 1/12,$
                 $P(E_3 \cap F) = (3/12)(1/3) = 1/12$

    (b) $P(F) = 1/6 + 1/12 + 1/12 = 1/3$

    (c) $P(E_1|F) = \dfrac{\frac{1}{6}}{\frac{1}{3}} = \dfrac{1}{2} \qquad P(E_3|F) = \dfrac{\frac{1}{12}}{\frac{1}{3}} = \dfrac{1}{4}$

7. $P(II|D) = \dfrac{P(II)\ P(D|II)}{P(I)\ P(D|I) + P(II)\ P(D|II)} =$
                      $\dfrac{(.45)(.04)}{(.55)(.03) + (.45)(.04)} = 0.5217$

9. $P(H|W) = \dfrac{P(H)\ P(W|H)}{P(H)\ P(W|H) + P(Away)\ P(W|Away)} =$
                      $\dfrac{(.60)(.80)}{(.60)(.80) + (.40)(.55)} = 0.6857$

11.   (a) $P(I|D) = \dfrac{P(I)\ P(D|I)}{P(I)P(D|I) + P(II)P(D|II) + P(III)P(D|III)}$
             $= \dfrac{(.15)(.01)}{(.15)(.01) + (.45)(.02) + (.40)(.04)} = \dfrac{.0015}{.0265} = .0566$

    (b) $P(II|D) = \dfrac{(.45)(.02)}{(.15)(.01) + (.45)(.02) + (.40)(.04)} = \dfrac{.0090}{.0265} = .3396$

    (c) $P(III|D) = \dfrac{(.40)(.04)}{(.15)(.01) + (.45)(.02) + (.40)(.04)} = \dfrac{.0160}{.0265} = .6038$

13.   (a)

    (b) $P(red|Box\ I) = 2/5$
        $P(red\ and\ Box\ I) = (3/5)(2/5) = 6/25$
        $P(red) = (3/5)(2/5) + (2/5)(5/12)$
             $= 6/25 + 1/6 = 61/150$

    (c) $P(Box\ I|red) = \dfrac{P(Box\ I\ and\ red)}{P(red)} = (6/25)/(61/150)$
                      $= (6)(150)/((61)(25)) = 36/61$

15. $P(grad|earn\ more) =$
        $\dfrac{P(grad)\ P(earn\ more|grad)}{P(grad)P(earn\ more|grad) + P(not\ grad)P(earn\ more|not\ grad)}$
        $= \dfrac{(.12)(.6)}{(.12)(.6) + (.88)(.2)} = \dfrac{.072}{.248} = 0.2903$

Section 6-7

17. (a)

      W from I P = 5/90

      W not from I   P = 15/90

      Black   P = 30/90

      W not from I P = 12/90

      Black   P = 28/90

(b)

$$P(I|W) = \frac{P(I \text{ and } W)}{P(W)}$$

From diagram $P(I \text{ and } W) = 5/90$

$$P(W) = \frac{5}{90} + \frac{15}{90} + \frac{12}{90} = \frac{32}{90}$$

so $P(I|W) = \frac{5}{90} / \frac{32}{90} = \frac{5}{32}$

19. $P(\text{hep}|\text{react}) = \dfrac{(.70)(.95)}{(.70)(.95) + (.30)(.02)} = \dfrac{.665}{.671} = 0.991$

21.   (a) $P(\text{under } 25|\text{accident}) = 0.18$

      (b) $P(\text{over } 50|\text{accident}) = .25 + .05 = 0.30$

      (c) $P(\text{accident}|\text{under } 25)$

$$= \frac{P(\text{under } 25|\text{accident}) \cdot P(\text{accident})}{P(\text{under } 25)}$$

$$= \frac{(.18)(.15)}{(.12)} = \frac{0.027}{0.12} = 0.225$$

23.   (a) $P(\text{fraud}) = (.11)(.20) + (.89)(.03) = 0.0487 = 4.87\%$

      (b) $P(\text{exceed}|\text{fraud}) = \dfrac{P(\text{exceed} \cap \text{fraud})}{P(\text{fraud})} = \dfrac{(.11)(.20)}{.0487} = .4517$

25. $P(A|\text{def}) =$

$$\frac{(.10)(.03)}{(.10)(.03) + (.15)(.01) + (.55)(.02) + (.20)(.01)}$$

$$= \frac{.003}{.0175} = 0.1714$$

      $P(B|\text{def}) = (.15)(.01)/.0175 = 0.0857$

      $P(C|\text{def}) = (.55)(.02)/.0175 = 0.6286$

      $P(D|\text{def}) = (.20)(.01)/.0175 = 0.1143$

27. $P(\text{disease}|\text{test } +) = \dfrac{(.01)(.95)}{(.01)(.95) + (.99)(.02)}$

$$= \frac{.0095}{.0293} = 0.324$$

29. $P(Y|\text{def}) = \dfrac{(.35)(5/350)}{(.40)(1/40) + (.35)(5/350) + (.25)(2/250)} = \dfrac{.005}{.017} = .294$

Section 6-7

1. $(15)(.0016)(.64) = 0.0154$ 3. $(6)(.01)(.81) = 0.0486$

5. $(8)(.0002187)(.7) = 0.00122$ 7. $(330)(.1296)(.0016384) = 0.0701$

9. $C(6, 2)(0.5)^2(0.5)^4 = 0.234$ 11. $C(5, 4)(0.1)^4(0.9)^1 = 0.00045$

13. $P(X = 3) = C(5, 3)(.25)^3(.75)^2 = 0.0879$

15. P(two hits in 3 attempts) $= 3(.7)(.7)(.3) = 0.44$

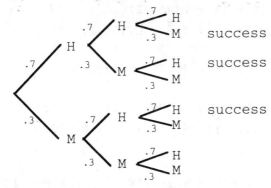

17. $n = 5$, $p = .8$, $x = 3$

$P(x = 3) = C(5, 3)(.8)^3(.2)^2 = 0.2048$

19. $n = 3$, $P = 1/4$, $x = 2$

$P(x = 2) = C(3, 2)(1/4)^2(3/4)^1 = 0.141$

21. $n = 6$, $P = 1/6$ $P(x = 4) = C(6, 4)(1/6)^4(5/6)^2 = 0.0080$

23. (a) $n = 4$, $p = 1/6$, $P(x = 0) = C(4, 0)(1/6)^0(5/6)^4 = 0.482$

(b) $n = 4$, $p = 1/6$, $P(x = 1) = C(4, 1)(1/6)^1(5/6)^3 = 0.386$

(c) $n = 4$, $p = 1/6$, $P(x = 2) = C(4, 2)(1/6)^2(5/6)^2 = 0.116$

(d) $n = 4$, $p = 1/6$, $P(x = 3) = C(4, 3)(1/6)^3(5/6)^1 = 0.0154$

(e) $n = 4$, $p = 1/6$, $P(x = 4) = C(4, 4)(1/6)^4(5/6)^0 = 0.00077$

25. $n = 6$, $p = 1/2$, $P(x = 4) = C(6, 4)(1/2)^4(1/2)^2 = 0.234$

27. $n = 6$, $p = .8$ $P(x = 4) = C(6, 4)(.8)^4(.2)^2 = 0.2458$

29. $n = 6$, $p = .4$, $P(x = 3) = C(6, 3)(.4)^3(.6)^3 = 0.27648$

31. $n = 10$, $p = .4$, $P(x = 7) = C(10, 7)(.4)^7(.6)^3 = 0.0425$

33. $n = 10$, $p = .6$, $P(x = 8) = C(10, 8)(.6)^8(.4)^2 = 0.1209$

35. $n = 5$, $p = 1/6$

$P(x \geq 3) = P(x = 3) + P(x = 4) + P(x = 5) =$

$C(5, 3)(1/6)^3(5/6)^2 + C(5, 4)(1/6)^4(5/6)^1 + C(5, 5)(1/6)^5(5/6)^0$

$= 0.0355$

37. $n = 8$, $p = 1/2$, $P(x \geq 5)$

$= P(x = 5) + P(x = 6) + P(x = 7) + P(x = 8)$

$= C(8, 5)(1/2)^5(1/2)^3 + C(8, 6)(1/2)^6(1/2)^2$

$+ C(8, 7)(1/2)^7(1/2) + C(8, 8)(1/2)^8 = 0.3633$

Section 6-8

39.   (a) $n = 10$, $p = .5$, $P(x = 8) = C(10, 8)(.5)^8(.5)^2 = 0.0439$
      (b) $n = 10$, $p = .5$,
            $P(\geq 8) = P(x = 8) + P(x = 9) + P(x = 10)$
      $= C(10, 8)(.5)^8(.5)^2 + C(10, 9)(.5)^9(.5)^1 + C(10, 10)(.5)^0 = 0.0547$
      (c) $n = 10$, $p = .5$,
            $P(x \leq 2) = P(x = 0) + P(x = 1) + P(x = 2)$
      $= C(10, 0)(.5)^0(.5)^{10} + C(10, 1)(.5)^1(.5)^9 + C(10, 2)(.5)^2(.5)^8$
      $= 0.0547$

41. $n = 6$, $p = 1/6$ $P(x = 4) = C(6, 4)(1/6)^4(5/6)^2 = 0.0080$

43. $n = 5$, $p = .36$
      $P(x \geq 2) = 1 - P(x < 2) = 1 - [P(x = 0) + P(x = 1)]$
      $= 1 - [C(5, 0)(.36)^0(.64)^5 + C(5, 1)(.36)^1(.64)^4] = 0.5906$

45.   Let someone in favor of repeal be a "success."
      $n = 10$, $p = .40$
      $P(x \geq 6) = P(x = 6) + P(x = 7) + P(x = 8) + P(x = 9) + P(x = 10)$
      $= C(10, 6)(.4)^6(.6)^4 + C(10, 7)(.4)^7(.6)^3 + C(10, 8)(.4)^8(.6)^2$
      $\qquad + C(10, 9)(.4)^9(.6)^1 + C(10, 10)(.4)^{10}(.6)^0$
      $= .1115 + .0425 + .0106 + .0016 + .0001 = 0.166$

Section 6-8

1.   (a)   Is a transition matrix.
      (b)   Not a transition matrix because row 2 does not add to 1.
      (c)   Not a transition matrix because it is not square.
      (d)   A transition matrix.

3.   (a)   10%   (b)   .60   (c)   .90   (d)   40%

5.   (a)   .4   (b)   .8   (c)   .3   7.   ST = [.675   .325]

9. $M_1 = M_0 T = [.282 \quad .718]$ $M_2 = M_1 T = [.282 \quad .718]T = [.32616 \quad .67384]$

11. $M_1 = M_0 T = [.175 \quad .375 \quad .45]$ $M_2 = M_1 T = [.18 \quad .4075 \quad .4125]$

13. $ST = [2/3 \quad 1/3] \begin{bmatrix} .6 & .4 \\ .8 & .2 \end{bmatrix} = S$

15. $ST = [.464286 \quad .535714] \begin{bmatrix} .25 & .75 \\ .65 & .35 \end{bmatrix} = [13/28 \quad 15/28] = S$

17. $MT = [.25 \quad .33 \quad .42]$
      $(MT)T = [.259 \quad .323 \quad .418]$
      $((MT)T)T = [.2577 \quad .3233 \quad .419]$
      $MT^3 = [.2577 \quad .3233 \quad .419]$

19. $x = .4$

21. $[.45 \quad .55] \begin{bmatrix} .75 & .25 \\ .15 & .85 \end{bmatrix} = [.42 \quad .58]$
                     $\Rightarrow$ 42% will contribute next year
      $[.42 \quad .58] \begin{bmatrix} .75 & .25 \\ .15 & .85 \end{bmatrix} = [.402 \quad .598]$
                     $\Rightarrow$ 40.2% will contribute in two years

23. $[.6 \quad .4] \begin{bmatrix} .5 & .5 \\ .2 & .8 \end{bmatrix} = [.38 \quad .62]$

$[.38 \quad .62] \begin{bmatrix} .5 & .5 \\ .2 & .8 \end{bmatrix} = [.314 \quad .686]$

$[.314 \quad .686] \begin{bmatrix} .5 & .5 \\ .2 & .8 \end{bmatrix} = [.2942 \quad .7058]$

$[.2942 \quad .7058] \begin{bmatrix} .5 & .5 \\ .2 & .8 \end{bmatrix} = [.28826 \quad .71174]$

$[.28826 \quad .71174] \begin{bmatrix} .5 & .5 \\ .2 & .8 \end{bmatrix} = [.286478 \quad .713522]$

$[.286478 \quad .713522] \begin{bmatrix} .5 & .5 \\ .2 & .8 \end{bmatrix} = [.2859434 \quad .7140566]$

It appears that [.285   .714] is the steady-state matrix.
The steady-state matrix is actually [2/7   5/7].

25.   Find [x y z] such that
$[x \quad y \quad z] \begin{bmatrix} .6 & .2 & .2 \\ .1 & .8 & .1 \\ .2 & .4 & .4 \end{bmatrix} = [x \quad y \quad z]$

This with x + y + z = 1 gives
$$x + \quad y + \quad z = 1$$
$$-.4x + .1y + .2z = 0$$
$$.2x - .2y + .4z = 0$$
$$.2x + .1y - .6z = 0$$

$\begin{bmatrix} 1 & 1 & 1 & 1 \\ -.4 & .1 & .2 & 0 \\ .2 & -.2 & .4 & 0 \\ .2 & .1 & -.6 & 0 \end{bmatrix}$ $\begin{bmatrix} 1 & 1 & 1 & 1 \\ 0 & .5 & .6 & .4 \\ 0 & -.4 & .2 & -.2 \\ 0 & -.1 & -.8 & -.2 \end{bmatrix}$

$\begin{bmatrix} 1 & 0 & -7 & -1 \\ 0 & 0 & -3.4 & -.6 \\ 0 & 0 & 3.4 & .6 \\ 0 & 1 & 8 & 2 \end{bmatrix}$ $\begin{bmatrix} 1 & 0 & 0 & 4/17 \\ 0 & 1 & 0 & 10/17 \\ 0 & 0 & 1 & 3/17 \\ 0 & 0 & 0 & 0 \end{bmatrix}$

so [4/17 10/17 3/17] is the steady-state matrix.

27. $[x \quad y \quad z] \begin{bmatrix} .3 & .2 & .5 \\ .4 & .6 & 0 \\ .1 & .8 & .1 \end{bmatrix} = [x \quad y \quad z]$

and x + y + z = 1 gives the augmented matrix

$\begin{bmatrix} 1 & 1 & 1 & 1 \\ -.7 & .4 & .1 & 0 \\ .2 & -.4 & .8 & 0 \\ .5 & 0 & -.9 & 0 \end{bmatrix}$ $\begin{bmatrix} 1 & 1 & 1 & 1 \\ 0 & 1.1 & .8 & .7 \\ 0 & -.6 & .6 & -.2 \\ 0 & -.5 & -1.4 & -.5 \end{bmatrix}$

Divide row 3 by -.6 and then interchange rows 2 and 3.

$\begin{bmatrix} 1 & 1 & 1 & 1 \\ 0 & 1 & -1 & 1/3 \\ 0 & 1.1 & .8 & .7 \\ 0 & -.5 & -1.4 & -.5 \end{bmatrix}$ $\begin{bmatrix} 1 & 0 & 2 & 2/3 \\ 0 & 1 & -1 & 1/3 \\ 0 & 0 & 1.9 & 1/3 \\ 0 & 0 & -1.9 & -1/3 \end{bmatrix}$

$\begin{bmatrix} 1 & 0 & 0 & 18/57 \\ 0 & 1 & 0 & 29/57 \\ 0 & 0 & 1 & 10/57 \\ 0 & 0 & 0 & 0 \end{bmatrix}$

so [18/57 29/57 10/57] is the steady-state matrix

29. $[x \quad y \quad z] \begin{bmatrix} .6 & .2 & .2 \\ .1 & .8 & .1 \\ .2 & .3 & .5 \end{bmatrix} = [x \quad y \quad z]$ and $x + y + z = 1$ gives

$$\left[\begin{array}{ccc|c} 1 & 1 & 1 & 1 \\ -.4 & .1 & .2 & 0 \\ .2 & -.2 & .3 & 0 \\ .2 & .1 & -.5 & 0 \end{array}\right] \qquad \left[\begin{array}{ccc|c} 1 & 1 & 1 & 1 \\ 0 & .5 & .6 & .4 \\ 0 & -.4 & .1 & -.2 \\ 0 & -.1 & -.7 & -.2 \end{array}\right]$$

$$\left[\begin{array}{ccc|c} 1 & 0 & -1/5 & 1/5 \\ 0 & 1 & 6/5 & 4/5 \\ 0 & 0 & 29/50 & 3/25 \\ 0 & 0 & -29/50 & -3/25 \end{array}\right] \qquad \left[\begin{array}{ccc|c} 1 & 0 & 0 & 7/29 \\ 0 & 1 & 0 & 16/29 \\ 0 & 0 & 1 & 6/29 \\ 0 & 0 & 0 & 0 \end{array}\right]$$

So at steady-state 24.14% are at I, 55.17% are at II, 20.69% are at III

31. $[x \quad y] \begin{bmatrix} .9 & .1 \\ .1 & 0 \end{bmatrix} = [x \quad y]$ and $x + y = 1$ gives

$$\left[\begin{array}{cc|c} .1 & 1 & 1 \\ -.1 & 1 & 0 \\ .1 & -1 & 0 \end{array}\right] \qquad \left[\begin{array}{cc|c} 1 & 1 & 1 \\ 0 & 1.1 & .1 \\ 0 & -1.1 & -.1 \end{array}\right]$$

$$\left[\begin{array}{cc|c} 1 & 0 & 10/11 \\ 0 & 1 & 1/11 \\ 0 & 0 & 0 \end{array}\right] \qquad \text{so } [10/11 \quad 1/11] \text{ is the steady-state matrix.}$$

33. $[x \quad y \quad z] \begin{bmatrix} 1/3 & 1/3 & 1/3 \\ 1/2 & 1/2 & 0 \\ 0 & 1/4 & 3/4 \end{bmatrix} = [x \quad y \quad z]$ and $x + y + z = 1$ gives

$$\left[\begin{array}{ccc|c} 1 & 1 & 1 & 1 \\ -2/3 & 1/2 & 0 & 0 \\ 1/3 & -1/2 & 1/4 & 0 \\ 1/3 & 0 & -1/4 & 0 \end{array}\right] \qquad \left[\begin{array}{ccc|c} 1 & 1 & 1 & 1 \\ 0 & 7/6 & 2/3 & 2/3 \\ 0 & -5/6 & -1/12 & -1/3 \\ 0 & -1/3 & -7/12 & -1/3 \end{array}\right]$$

$$\left[\begin{array}{ccc|c} 1 & 0 & 3/7 & 3/7 \\ 0 & 1 & 4/7 & 4/7 \\ 0 & 0 & 11/28 & 1/7 \\ 0 & 0 & -11/28 & -1/7 \end{array}\right] \qquad \left[\begin{array}{ccc|c} 1 & 0 & 0 & 3/11 \\ 0 & 1 & 0 & 4/11 \\ 0 & 0 & 1 & 4/11 \\ 0 & 0 & 0 & 0 \end{array}\right]$$

The steady-state matrix is $[3/11 \quad 4/11 \quad 4/11]$

35.

$$\begin{array}{c} \\ \\ \text{From} \end{array} \begin{array}{c} \\ 1 \\ 2 \\ 3 \\ 4 \\ 5 \end{array} \overset{\displaystyle \begin{array}{ccccc} \quad & \text{To} & & & \\ 1 & 2 & 3 & 4 & 5 \end{array}}{\left[\begin{array}{ccccc} 0 & 1/2 & 0 & 0 & 1/2 \\ 1/2 & 0 & 1/2 & 0 & 0 \\ 0 & 1/2 & 0 & 1/2 & 0 \\ 0 & 0 & 1/2 & 0 & 1/2 \\ 1/2 & 0 & 0 & 1/2 & 0 \end{array}\right]}$$

37. $$\left[\begin{array}{ccc|c} 1 & 1 & 1 & 1 \\ -1/2 & 1/4 & 0 & 0 \\ 1/2 & -1/2 & 1/2 & 0 \\ 0 & 1/4 & -1/2 & 0 \end{array}\right] \qquad \left[\begin{array}{ccc|c} 1 & 1 & 1 & 1 \\ 0 & 3/4 & 1/2 & 1/2 \\ 0 & -1 & 0 & -1/2 \\ 0 & 1/4 & -1/2 & 0 \end{array}\right]$$

$$\left[\begin{array}{cc|cc} 1 & 1 & 1 & 1 \\ 0 & -1 & 0 & -1/2 \\ 0 & 3/4 & 1/2 & 1/2 \\ 0 & 1/4 & -1/2 & 0 \end{array}\right] \qquad \left[\begin{array}{ccc|c} 1 & 0 & 1 & 1/2 \\ 0 & 1 & 0 & 1/2 \\ 0 & 0 & 1/2 & 1/8 \\ 0 & 0 & -1/2 & -1/8 \end{array}\right]$$

$$\begin{bmatrix} 1 & 0 & 0 & | & 1/4 \\ 0 & 1 & 0 & | & 1/2 \\ 0 & 0 & 1 & | & 1/4 \\ 0 & 0 & 0 & | & 0 \end{bmatrix}$$

When the process reaches a steady-state 25% of the flowers will be red, 50% of the flowers will be pink, and 25% of the flowers will be white.

39.   (a)   .06   (b)   .05   (c)   .80   (d)   .04

Review Exercises, Chapter 6

1.   No, because the probability assignments do not sum to 1.

3.   P(medium-sized soft drink) = 146/360 = .41 since a total of 360 soft drinks were sold.

5.   P(sports or band) = P(sports) + P(band) - P(both)
                          = 1/3 + 2/5 - 1/6 = 17/30 = 0.57

7.   P(Mrs. Thomas and Ms. Ramirez) = $\dfrac{C(2, 2) \times C(10, 1)}{C(12, 3)}$ = 10/220 = 1/22

9.   P(king or spade) = P(king) + P(spade) - P(king of spades)
                         = 4/52 + 13/52 - 1/52 = 4/13

11.   Let heads be considered a success. This is a Bernoulli experiment with n = 5, p = 1/2, and x = 5
           $P(x = 5) = C(5, 5)(1/2)^5 (1/2)^0 = 1/32$

13.   (a)   P(red or white ball) = P(red) + P(white)
                                    = 5/12 + 4/12 = 9/12 = 3/4
      (b)   P(2 black or 2 red) = P(2 black) + P(2 red)
                                  = (3/12)(2/11) + (5/12)(4/11)
                                  = (1/22) + (5/33) = 13/66 = 0.20

15.   (a)   P(same kind) = $\dfrac{C(10, 2)}{C(40, 2)}$ + $\dfrac{C(10, 2)}{C(40, 2)}$ + $\dfrac{C(10, 2)}{C(40, 2)}$ + $\dfrac{C(10, 2)}{C(40, 2)}$
                           = 4(45/780) = 0.23
      (b)   P(different kinds) = 1 - P(same kinds) = 1 - 0.23 = 0.77

17. $C(4, 2)(.4)^2 (.6)^2$ = (6)(.16)(.36) = .3456

19.   P(Even) = 20/52   P(Ten) = 4/52
      P(Even) P(Ten) = (20/52)(4/52) = 5/169   P(Even ∩ Ten) = 4/52
      Since P(Even) P(Ten) ≠ P(Even ∩ Ten), Even and Ten are not independent events

21.   (a)   P(1, 2, 3, 4, in that order) = (1/6)(1/6)(1/6)(1/6) = 1/1296
      (b)   P(1, 2, 3, 4, in any order) = Any one of the four on the first roll, any of the 3 remaining on second roll, etc. = (4/6)(3/6)(2/6)(1/6) = 24/1296 = 1/54
      (c)   P(two even, then a 5, then a number less than 3)
             = (3/6)(3/6)(1/6)(2/6) = 18/1296 = 1/72

Review, Chapter 6

23.   (a) P(passing math, history, and English, and failing chemistry)
        = P(passing math) $\times$ P(passing history)
               $\times$ P(passing English) $\times$ P(failing chemistry)
        = (.8)(.3)(.5)(.3) = 0.036

  (b) P(passing math and chemistry and failing history and English)
        = P(passing math) $\times$ P(passing chemistry)
               $\times$ P(failing history) $\times$ P(failing English)
        = (.8)(.7)(.7)(.5) = 0.196

  (c) P(passing all 4 subjects) = (.8)(.5)(.3)(.7) = 0.084

25.   (a) P(male|abstainer)

$$= \frac{P(male)\,P(abstain|male)}{P(male)\,P(abstain|male) + P(female)\,P(abstain|female)}$$

$$= \frac{(.45)(.20)}{(.45)(.20) + (.55)(.40)} = \frac{0.09}{0.31} = 0.29$$

  (b) P(female|heavy drinker)

$$= \frac{P(female)\,P(heavy\ drinker|female)}{P(female)\,P(heavy\ drink|female) + P(male)\,P(heavy\ drink|male)}$$

$$= \frac{(.55)(.05)}{(.55)(.05) + (.45)(.20)} = \frac{0.0275}{0.1175} = 0.23$$

27.   (a) 0   (b) 1/30   (c) P(64 or 46) = 2/30   (d) 15/30   (e) 7/30

29.   Let J, S, and G be the event of being a junior, senior, and graduate student, respectively.
  Let A be the event of receiving an A.

  P(J) = 10/50 = .2   P(A|J) = 2/10 = .2
  P(S) = 34/50 = .68   P(A|S) = 8/34 = .235
  P(G) = 6/50 = .12   P(A|G) = 3/6 = .5

$$P(J|A) = \frac{P(J)\,P(A|J)}{P(J)\,P(A|J) + P(S)\,P(A|S) + P(G)\,P(A|G)}$$

$$= \frac{(.2)(.2)}{(.2)(.2) + (.68)(.235) + (.12)(.5)} = 0.154$$

31.   This is a Bernoulli experiment with n = 8, p = 1/3

$$P(x = 6) = C(8, 6)(1/3)^6(2/3)^2 = (28)(.00137)(.444) = 0.017$$

33.   (a) 2 x 1 x 3 x 2 x 1 = 12
  (b) A semifinalist must be seated first, then a finalist, etc.
       3 x 2 x 2 x 1 x 1 = 12

35.   (a) P(First < 3 and second > 7) = $(\frac{2}{10})(\frac{3}{10})$ = .06

  (b) P(First < 4 and second < 4) = $(\frac{3}{10})(\frac{3}{10})$ = .09

37.   (a) P(C or above) = $\frac{225}{420}$ = .5357   (b) P(Low) = $\frac{68}{420}$ = .1619

  (c) P(Below C | Middle) = $\frac{118}{242}$ = .4876

  (d) P(High | C or above) = $\frac{98}{225}$ = .4356

39.   P(Seat belt not used) = $\frac{94}{192}$ P(Injuries) = $\frac{80}{192}$

  P(Seat belt not used and injuries) = $\frac{66}{192}$ = .344

  P(Seat belt not used)P(Injuries) = $(\frac{94}{192})(\frac{80}{192})$ = .204

  Since .344 $\neq$ .204 injuries and seat belt not used are dependent.

Chapter 7
Statistics

Section 7-1

1.
	Number	Frequency
(a)	-1	2
(b)	2	3
(c)	4	4
(d)	6	2
(e)	8	1

3.   Number of students who used swimming pool per day

Classes	Frequency
85-99	7
100-114	8
115-129	13
130-144	7
145-159	5

5.   (a)   67 students took the test.
      (b)   7 + 12 = 19 students scored below 70.
      (c)   14 + 8 = 22 students scored at least 80.
      (d)   Cannot be determined.
      (e)   26 + 14 = 40 students scored between 69 and 90.
      (f)   Cannot be determined.

7.

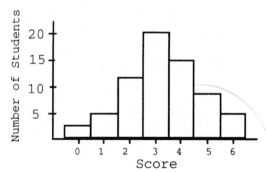

9.

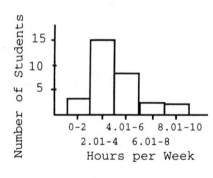

11.

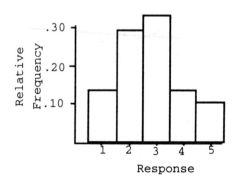

13.

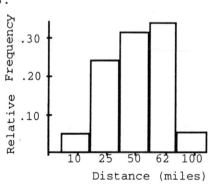

Section 7-2

15.

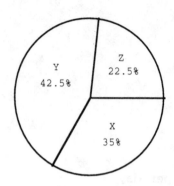

17.

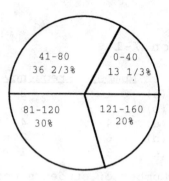

19.

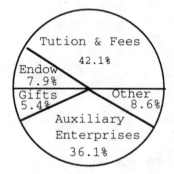

21.

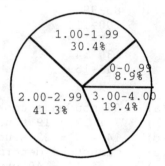

Section 7-2

1. $\mu = \dfrac{2 + 4 + 6 + 8 + 10}{5} = 6$ 3. $\mu = \dfrac{2.1 + 3.7 + 5.9}{3} = 3.9$

5. $\mu = \dfrac{6 - 4 + 3 + 5 - 8 + 2}{6} = 0.67$

7. $\mu = \dfrac{5.9 + 2.1 + 6.6 + 4.7}{4} = 4.825$

9. $\mu = \dfrac{80 + 76 + 92 + 64 + 93 + 81 + 57 + 77}{8} = 77.5$

11. $\mu = \dfrac{90.5 + 89.2 + 78.4 + 91.0 + 84.2 + 73.5 + 88.7}{7} = 85.07$ mi/hr

13. 9   15. $\dfrac{21 + 25}{2} = 23$ 17. $(9 + 14)/2 = 11.5$

19. 65, 68, 72, 72, 72, 81, 86, 90, 98   Median is 72

21. 5   23. 1 and 5   25. No mode

27. $\dfrac{2 \times 96 + 3 \times 91 + 7 \times 85 + 13 \times 80 + 12 \times 75 + 10 \times 70 + 8 \times 60 + 5 \times 50}{60} = 73.83$

29. $\dfrac{0 \times 430 + 1 \times 395 + 2 \times 145 + 3 \times 25 + 4 \times 5}{1000} = 0.78$

31. $\dfrac{2.5 \times 28 + 8.0 \times 47 + 15.5 \times 68 + 25.5 \times 7}{150} = 11.19$

33. $\dfrac{95 \times 8 + 84.5 \times 15 + 74.5 \times 22 + 64.5 \times 11 + 52 \times 5}{61} = 76$

35. $\dfrac{139.50 + 141.25 + 140.75 + 138.50 + 132.00}{5} = \$138.40$

37. $\dfrac{3.60 + 3.57 + 3.90 + 3.85 + 4.00 + 4.15 + 4.25 + 4.40}{8} = 3.965$

    Mean = $3.97
    For median, arrange in order:
          3.57, 3.60, 3.85, 3.90, 4.00, 4.15, 4.25, 4.40
    $\dfrac{3.90 + 4.00}{2} = 3.95$, median

39. (a)   5   (b)   2

    (c) $\dfrac{1 \times 5 + 2 \times 9 + 3 \times 3 + 4 \times 1}{18} = 2$ (d)   2

41. Let x = the unknown grade
    $78 = \dfrac{72 + 88 + 81 + 67 + x}{5}$
    $390 = 72 + 88 + 81 + 67 + x$
    $x = 82$

43. $\dfrac{21 \times 18000 + 9 \times 22000 + 14 \times 25000 + 26 \times 28000 + 13 \times 30000 + 8 \times 35000}{91}$

    $= \$25,538.46$

45. $\dfrac{8(27450) + 10(31400)}{18} = \dfrac{533600}{18} = \$29,644.44$

47. 65, 77, 82, 93
    Since there are an odd number of test scores, the median, 82, must be the third number in the ordered group of test scores. So the fifth test score must be 82 or larger.

49. $\dfrac{3(1.27) + 2(1.34)}{5} = \dfrac{6.49}{5} = \$1.30$

51. $\dfrac{1 \times 4 + 2 \times 28 + 3 \times 95 + 4 \times 24 + 5 \times 4}{155} = 2.97$

Section 7-3

1. $\mu = \dfrac{19 + 10 + 15 + 20}{4} = 16$
   $\text{var} = \dfrac{(19 - 16)^2 + (10 - 16)^2 + (15 - 16)^2 + (20 - 16)^2}{4} = 15.5,$
   $\sigma = \sqrt{15.5} = 3.94$

3. $\mu = \dfrac{4 + 8 + 9 + 10 + 14}{5} = 9$
   $\text{var} = \dfrac{(4 - 9)^2 + (8 - 9)^2 + (9 - 9)^2 + (10 - 9)^2 + (14 - 9)^2}{5} = 10.4$
   $\sigma = \sqrt{10.4} = 3.22$

Section 7-3

5. $\mu = \dfrac{17 + 39 + 54 + 22 + 16 + 46 + 25 + 19 + 62 + 50}{10} = 35$

$(17 - 35)^2 + (39 - 35)^2 + (54 - 35)^2 + (22 - 35)^2 + (16 - 35)^2$
$+ (46 - 35)^2 + (25 - 35)^2 + (19 - 35)^2 + (62 - 35)^2 + (50 - 35)^2$
$= 2662$

$\text{var} = \dfrac{2662}{10} = 266.2, \qquad \sigma = \sqrt{266.2} = 16.32$

7. $\mu = \dfrac{-8 - 4 - 3 + 0 + 1 + 2}{6} = -2$

variance =
$\dfrac{(-8 + 2)^2 + (-4 + 2)^2 + (-3 + 2)^2 + (0 + 2)^2 + (1 + 2)^2 + (2 + 2)^2}{6}$

$= 11.67, \qquad \sigma = \sqrt{11.67} = 3.42$

9. $\mu = \dfrac{-3 + 0 + 1 + 4 + 5 + 8 + 10 + 11}{8} = 36/8 = 4.5$

var =
$\dfrac{(-3-4.5)^2+(0-4.5)^2+(1-4.5)^2+(4-4.5)^2+(5-4.5)^2+(8-4.5)^2+(10-4.5)^2+(11-4.5)^2}{8}$

$= 174/8 = 21.75, \quad \sigma = 4.66$

11. $\mu = \dfrac{2 \times 1 + 5 \times 2 + 2 \times 3 + 3 \times 4 + 8 \times 5}{20} = 70/20 = 3.5$

variance $= \dfrac{2(1-3.5)^2 + 5(2-3.5)^2 + 2(3-3.5)^2 + 3(4-3.5)^2 + 8(5-3.5)^2}{20}$

$= 43/20 = 2.15, \qquad \sigma = 1.47$

13. $\mu = \dfrac{10(4.65) + 12(4.90) + 8(5.00) + 5(5.24)}{35} = 171.5/35 = 4.90$

$\text{var} = \dfrac{10(-.25)^2 + 12(0)^2 + 8(.10)^2 + 5(.34)^2}{35}$

$= 1.283/35 = 0.0367, \qquad \sigma = 0.191$

15. $\mu = \dfrac{5(5) + 12(15.5) + 8(25.5)}{25} = 415/25 = 16.6$

$\text{var} = \dfrac{5(-11.6)^2 + 12(-1.1)^2 + 8(8.9)^2}{25} = 1321/25 = 52.84 \qquad \sigma = 7.27$

17. $\mu = \dfrac{14(12.5) + 18(18) + 18(23)}{50} = 913/50 = 18.26$

$\sigma^2 = \dfrac{14(-5.76)^2 + 18(-.26)^2 + 18(4.74)^2}{50} = 17.4024$

$\sigma = \sqrt{17.4024} = 4.17$

19. $\mu = 217/7 = 31 \qquad \sigma = \sqrt{68/7} = \sqrt{9.714} = 3.12$

21.   (a) $Z = (180 - 160)/16 = 20/16 = 1.25$
       (b) $Z = -10/16 = -0.625$ (c) $Z = 0/16 = 0$
       (d) $1 = (x - 160)/16 \Rightarrow x = 16 + 160 = 176$
       (e) $-0.875 = (x - 160)/16 \Rightarrow x = 16(-0.875) + 160 = 146$

23.   (a)   <u>Lathe I</u>
    variance =
$$\frac{(.501-.5)^2+ (.503-.5)^2+ (.495-.5)^2+ (.504-.5)^2+ (.497-.5)^2}{5} = 0.000012$$

$\sigma = \sqrt{0.000012} = 0.00346$, for Lathe I.

<u>Lathe II</u>
variance =
$$\frac{(.502-.5)^2+ (.497-.5)^2+ (.498-.5)^2+ (.501-.5)^2+ (.502-.5)^2}{5} = 0.000044$$

$\sigma = \sqrt{0.000044} = 0.00210$, for Lathe II.

  (b)   Lathe II is more consistent because σ is smaller.

25.   Let x be the number of 2's in the set.
Let y be the number of 3's in the set.
Let 8 - x - y be the number of 4's in the set.

  (a) $\dfrac{2x + 3y + 4(8 - x - y)}{8} = 3$

$$.5 = \sqrt{\frac{x(2 - 3)^2 + y(3 - 3)^2 + (8 - x - y)(4 - 3)^2}{8}}$$

These can be rewritten as $2x + y = 8$

$.25 = \dfrac{x + (8 - x - y)}{8}$ or $2 = 8 - y$

so y = 6, the number of 3's
2x + y = 8
2x + 6 = 8
2x = 2
x = 1, the number of 2's
8 - x - y = 8 - 1 - 6 = 1, the number of 4's
The set of numbers is 2, 3, 3, 3, 3, 3, 3, 4

  (b)   The first equation is the same, $2x + y = 8$

$1 = \dfrac{x + (8 - x - y)}{8}$ or $8 = 8 - y$

so y = 0, the number of 3's
2x + 0 = 8
x = 4, the number of 2's
8 - x - y = 8 - 4 = 4, the number of 4's
The set of numbers is 2, 2, 2, 2, 4, 4, 4, 4

  (c)   No, because the largest possible value of the sum of the squared deviations is 8, for which $\sigma = 1$.

27.   30% scored above her so 110(.30) = 33 scored above.
She ranked 34th out of 110.

29.   2% scored higher so .02(1545) = 30.9 or 31 scored higher

31. $z_1 = (86 - 72)/8 = 14/8 = 1.75,$ $z_2 = (82 - 62)/12 = 20/12 = 1.67$
The 86 was the better score.

33. $z_R = (19 - 18)/1 = 1/1 = 1$
$z_C = (64 - 59)/3 = 5/3 = 1.7$
The runner's time was one z-score higher than the mean so the runner was slower than average. The cyclist's time was 1.67 z-scores above the mean so the cyclist was even slower than the average. The runner had the better performance.

Section 7-4

1.
HHH,	X = 3
HHT, HTH, THH,	X = 2
TTH, THT, HTT,	X = 1
TTT,	X = 0

3.
Ann, Betty	X = 2
Ann, Jason	X = 1
Ann, Tom	X = 1
Betty, Jason,	X = 1
Betty, Tom	X = 1
Jason, Tom	X = 0

5.   X = 0, 1, 2, or 3

7.   (a)   X = 0, 1, 2, 3, or 4   (b)   X = 0, 1, 2, or 3

9.   (a)   Discrete   (b)   Continuous
     (c)   Continuous   (d)   Discrete

11. (a)   Continuous   (b)   Discrete
     (c)   i) Discrete   ii) Continuous   iii) Discrete

13. Yes, since sum is 1.

15.
X	P(X)
0	1/8
1	3/8
2	3/8
3	1/8

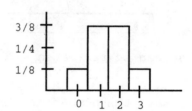

17.
X	P(X)
3	1/5
4	1/5
5	2/5
6	1/5

19.
X	P(X)
0	8/75
1	49/75
2	13/75
3	4/75
4	1/75

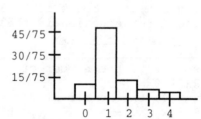

21.
	X	P(X)
(Red and black)	0	$\dfrac{4(6)}{C(10, 2)} = \dfrac{24}{45} = .533$
(2 black)	5	$\dfrac{C(6, 2)}{C(10, 2)} = \dfrac{15}{45} = .333$
(2 red)	10	$\dfrac{C(4, 2)}{C(10, 2)} = \dfrac{6}{45} = .133$

23. (a) X ∈ {1, 2, 3,...}
    (b) Discrete

25.   X = 0:   C(5, 0)·C(6, 2) = (1)(15) = 15
      X = 1:   C(5, 1)·C(6, 1) = (5)(6) = 30
      X = 2:   C(5, 2)·C(6, 0) = (10)(1) = 10

27.

X	P(X)	
0	$\dfrac{C(4,\ 0)\ C(4,\ 2)}{C(8,\ 2)} = \dfrac{6}{28} = \dfrac{3}{14}$	
1	$\dfrac{C(4,\ 1)\cdot C(4,\ 1)}{C(8,\ 2)} = \dfrac{4\cdot 4}{28} = \dfrac{4}{7}$	
2	$\dfrac{C(4,\ 2)\cdot C(4,\ 0)}{C(8,\ 2)} = \dfrac{6}{28} = \dfrac{3}{14}$	

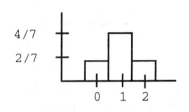

29.

X	P(X)	
0	$\dfrac{C(7,\ 2)}{C(10,\ 2)} = \dfrac{21}{45} = \dfrac{7}{15}$	
1	$\dfrac{C(7,\ 1)\ C(3,\ 1)}{C(10,\ 2)} = \dfrac{21}{45} = \dfrac{7}{15}$	
2	$\dfrac{C(3,\ 2)}{C(10,\ 2)} = \dfrac{3}{45} = \dfrac{1}{15}$	

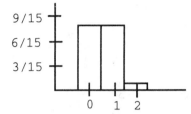

31. (a)

X	P(X)	
0	$\dfrac{C(4,\ 2)}{C(6,\ 2)} = \dfrac{2}{5}$	
1	$\dfrac{C(4,\ 1)C(2,\ 1)}{C(6,\ 2)} = \dfrac{8}{15}$	
2	$\dfrac{C(2,\ 2)}{C(6,\ 2)} = \dfrac{1}{15}$	

(b)

X	P(X)	
0	$\dfrac{C(5,\ 2)}{C(6,\ 2)} = \dfrac{2}{3}$	
1	$\dfrac{C(5,\ 1)\ C(1,\ 1)}{C(6,\ 2)} = \dfrac{1}{3}$	

33.

X	P(X)	
0	$C(4,\ 0)(1/5)^0(4/5)^4 = 0.4096$	
1	$C(4,\ 1)(1/5)^1(4/5)^3 = 0.4096$	
2	$C(4,\ 2)(1/5)^2(4/5)^2 = 0.1536$	
3	$C(4,\ 3)(1/5)^3(4/5)^1 = 0.0256$	
4	$C(4,\ 4)(1/5)^4(4/5)^0 = 0.0016$	

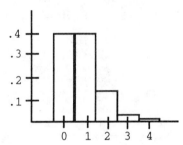

35.

X	P(X)	
0	$(7/12)^3 = 0.1985$	
1	$C(3,\ 1)(5/12)^1(7/12)^2 = 0.4253$	
2	$C(3,\ 2)(5/12)^2(7/12)^1 = 0.3038$	
3	$(5/12)^3 = 0.0723$	

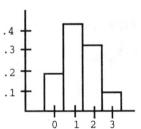

37. X = 0, 1 sequence (Gold, Gold);
X = 1, 2 sequences (Gold, Green, Gold or Green, Gold, Gold)
X = 2, 3 sequences (Green, Green or Green, Gold, Green or Gold, Green, Green)

39. (a) Weight   (b) Shirt size, suit size
(c) Shoe size   (d) Number of cavities

41. $X \in \{1,\ 2,\ 3,\ 4,...\}$

43.

X	P(X)
2	3/7
3	$(4/7)(3/6) = 2/7$
4	$(4/7)(3/6)(3/5) = 6/35$
5	$(4/7)(3/6)(2/5)(3/4) = 3/35$
6	$(4/7)(3/6)(2/5)(1/4)(3/3) = 1/35$

Section 7-5

45.
X	P(X)
1	1/2 (T)
2	(1/2)(1/2) = 1/4 (HT)
3	(1/2)(1/2)(1/2) + (1/2)(1/2)(1/2) = 1/4 (HHT or HHH)

47.
X	P(X)
0	$(.4)^2$ = 0.16
1	$2(.6)(.4)^2$ = 0.192 (BAB or ABB)
2	$(.6)^2 + 2(.6)^2(.4)$ = 0.648 (AA or ABA or BAA)

Section 7-5

1. $E(X) = .3(3) + .2(8) + .1(15) + .4(22) = 12.8$

3. $E(X) = .2(150) + .2(235) + .2(350) + .2(410) + .2(480) = 325$

5. $E(X) = (8)(1/2) + (2)(1/2) = \$5$

7. (a) $E(X) = (1)(1/2) + 0(1/2) = \$0.50$ so a charge of \$.50 will break
   even.
   (b) $\$1 + \$.50 = \$1.50$

9. (a) $(.15)(20) + (.65)(130) + (.20)(700) = \$227.50$
   (b) $(125)(\$227.50) = \$28,437.50$

11. $\mu = .4(100) + .5(140) + .1(210) = 131$
    $\sigma^2 = .4(-31)^2 + .5(9)^2 + .1(79)^2 = 1049 \qquad \sigma = 32.39$

13. $\mu = .4(10) + .2(30) + .3(50) + .1(90) = 34$
    $\sigma^2 = .4(-24)^2 + .2(-4)^2 + .3(16)^2 + .1(56)^2 = 624 \qquad \sigma = 24.98$

15. $E(X) = 0 + (1) \cdot \dfrac{4 \cdot 11}{C(15, 2)} + (2) \cdot \dfrac{C(4, 2)}{C(15, 2)} = \dfrac{44}{105} + \dfrac{12}{105} = \dfrac{56}{105} = .53$

17. $E(X_A) = (.60)(50,000) + (.30)(0) + (.10)(-70,000) = \$23,000$
    $E(X_B) = (.55)(100,000) + (.45)(-60,000) = \$28,000$
    B is the better risk

19. $E(X) = .75(0) + .10(1) + .06(2) + .04(3) + .04(4) + .01(5) = 0.55$

21. (a) $1(3/10) + 2(1/5) + 3(1/5) + 4(1/10) + 5(2/10) = 2.7$
    (b) $\mu = 2.7 \quad \sigma^2 = 2.21 \Rightarrow \sigma = 1.49$

23. (a) $E(X) = 0 + (2)C(3, 1)(.4)^1(.6)^2 + (4)C(3, 2)(.4)^2(.6)^1$
        $+ (6)C(3, 3)(.4)^3(.6)^0 = \$2.40$
    (b) $E(X) = 0 + (2)C(4, 1)(.4)^1(.6)^3 + (4)C(4, 2)(.4)^2(.6)^2$
        $+ (6)C(4, 3)(.4)^3(.6)^1 + (8)C(4, 4)(.4)^4(.6)^0 = \$3.20$

25. (a) $E(X) = .05(-23) + .95(18) = \$15.95$
    (b) $(150,000)(15.95) = \$2,392,500$

Section 7-6

1. $z = (3.1 - 4.0)/0.3 = -3$ 3. $z = (10.1 - 10.0)/2.0 = 0.05$

5. $z = (2.65 - 0)/1.0 = 2.65$ 7. $z = .50 \Rightarrow A = 0.1915$

9. $z = 0.25 \Rightarrow A = 0.0987$ 11. $z = 1.1 \Rightarrow A = 0.3643$

13. $z = -.75 \Rightarrow A = 0.2734$ 15. $z = 0.46 \Rightarrow A = 0.1772 = 17.72\%$

17. $z = 0.38 \Rightarrow A = 0.1480 = 14.8\%$

19. $z = -1.24 \Rightarrow A = 0.3925 = 39.25\%$

21. $z = -2.9 \Rightarrow A = 0.4981 = 49.81\%$ 23. $A = 2(0.3944) = 0.7888$

25. $A = 2(0.4861) = 0.9722$ 27. $A = 2(0.2422) = 0.4844 = 48.44\%$

29. $A = 2(0.1480) = 0.2960 = 29.6\%$

31. $A = A_1 + A_2 = 0.2258 + 0.3997 = 0.6255$

33. $A = A_1 + A_2 = 0.2881 + 0.4974 = 0.7855$

35. $A = 0.5 - 0.4032 = 0.0968$ 37. $A = 0.5 - 0.4918 = 0.0082$

39. $1 - 2(0.3051) = 0.3898 = 38.98\%$

41. $1 - 2(0.4332) = 0.1336 = 13.36\%$

43. $z = (98 - 85)/5 = 2.60 \Rightarrow 0.4953$

45. $z = (80 - 85)/5 = -1.00 \Rightarrow 0.3413$

47. $z_1 = (220 - 226)/12 = -0.5, z_2 = (235 - 226)/12 = 0.75$
$\Rightarrow A_1 + A_2 = 0.1915 + 0.2734 = 0.4649$

49. $z_1 = (211 - 226)/12 = -1.25, z_2 = (241 - 226)/12 = 1.25$
$\Rightarrow 2(A) = 2(0.3944) = 0.7888$

51. $z_1 = (144 - 140)/8 = 0.5, z_2 = (152 - 140)/8 = 1.5$
$\Rightarrow A_2 - A_1 = 0.4332 - 0.1915 = 0.2417$

53. $z_1 = (146 - 140)/8 = 0.75, z_2 = (156 - 140)/8 = 2$
$\Rightarrow A_2 - A_1 = 0.4773 - 0.2734 = 0.2039$

55. $z_1 = (80 - 75)/5 = 1, z_2 = (85 - 75)/5 = 2$
$\Rightarrow A_2 - A_1 = 0.4773 - 0.3413 = 0.1360$

57. $z = (76 - 75)/5 = 0.2 \Rightarrow 0.5 - 0.0793 = 0.4207$

59. $z_1 = (70 - 75)/5 = -1, z_2 = (80 - 75)/5 = 1$
$\Rightarrow 1 - 2(0.3413) = 0.3174$

61. $z_1 = (155 - 168)/10 = -1.3, z_2 = (169 - 168)/10 = 0.1$
$\Rightarrow A_1 + A_2 = 0.4032 + 0.0398 = 0.4430 = 44.3\%$

63. $z = (172 - 168)/10 = 0.4 \Rightarrow 0.5 + 0.1554 = 0.6554 = 65.54\%$

65. $z = (173 - 168)/10 = 0.5 \Rightarrow 0.5 - 0.1915 = 0.3085 = 30.85\%$

67. $z = (184 - 168)/10 = 1.6 \Rightarrow 0.5 + 0.4452 = 0.9452 = 94.52\%$

69. $.08 \Rightarrow A = .5 - .08 = .42 \Rightarrow z = 1.41$

71. $.86 \Rightarrow A = .86 - .5 = .36 \Rightarrow z = 1.08$

73. $.91 \Rightarrow A = (1/2)(.91) = .455 \Rightarrow z = 1.70$

Section 7-7

75.   (a) $z = (3.75 - 3.15)/.75 = 0.8$
              $\Rightarrow 0.5 - A = 0.5 - 0.2881 = 0.2119 = 21.19\%$
    (b) 0.2119

77.   (a) $z_1 = (120 - 110)/12 = 0.83,$
              $z_2 = (125 - 110)/12 = 1.25$
              $\Rightarrow A_2 - A_1 = 0.3944 - 0.2967 = 0.0977$
    (b) $z = (100 - 110)/12 = -0.83$
              $\Rightarrow 0.5 - A = 0.5 - 0.2967 = 0.2033$
    (c) $z_1 = (105 - 110)/12 = -0.42,$
              $z_2 = (115 - 110)/12 = 0.42 \Rightarrow 2(A) = 2(0.1628) = 0.3256$

79.   (a) $z_1 = (120 - 126)/6 = -1, \ z_2 = (132 - 126)/6 = 1$
              $\Rightarrow 2(0.3413)(700) = 477.82 \rightarrow 478$
    (b) $z = (114 - 126)/6 = -2$
              $\Rightarrow (.5 - 0.4773)(700) = 15.89 \rightarrow 16$
    (c) $z = (134 - 126)/6 = 1.33 \Rightarrow (.5 - 0.4082)(700) = 64.26$
         rounded to 64

81.   (a) $A = .5 - .12 = .38 \Rightarrow z \approx 1.175$
              $\Rightarrow X = 1.175 \dfrac{x - 66}{17} = 85.975 \rightarrow 86$
    (b) $A = .5 - .06 = .44 \Rightarrow z \approx 1.555$
              $\Rightarrow X = (1.555)(17) + 66 = 92.435 \rightarrow 92$

83.   (a) $z_1 = -0.75, \ z_2 = 0.75 \Rightarrow 2(0.2734) = 0.5468$
    (b) $z_1 = 12/40 = 0.3, \ z_2 = 30/40 = 0.75$
              $\Rightarrow 0.2734 - 0.1179 = 0.1555$
    (c) $.50$ score less than 300
          $z_1 = 26/40 = 0.65 \Rightarrow 0.5 + 0.2422 = 0.7422$ score less than 326
    (d) $A = .5 - .1 = 0.4 \Rightarrow z = 1.28 \Rightarrow x = 1.28 = \dfrac{x - 300}{40} = 351.2$
         $\rightarrow 352$ or higher.
    (e) $z_1 = 12/40 = 0.3, \ z_2 = 24/40 = 0.6 \Rightarrow 0.2258 - 0.1179 = 0.1079$

85. $z = 0.8 \Rightarrow (0.5 + 0.2881)^2 = (0.7881)^2 = 0.6211$

87. $z = (1140 - 1050)/50 = 1.8 \Rightarrow 0.5 - A = 0.5 - 0.4641 = 0.0359$

89.   (a) $.4332 - .1915 = .2417$ (b) $.4192 - .2258 = .1934$
    (c) $.4032 - .2580 = .1452$ (d) $.3849 - .2881 = .0968$
    (e) $.3643 - .3159 = .0484$ (f) $.3531 - .3289 = .0242$
    (g) $.3438 - .3389 = .0049$

Section 7-7

1.

X	P(X)	
0	$C(5,0)(.3)^0(.7)^5$	$= 0.16807$
1	$C(5,1)(.3)^1(.7)^4$	$= 0.36015$
2	$C(5,2)(.3)^2(.7)^3$	$= 0.3087$
3	$C(5,3)(.3)^3(.7)^2$	$= 0.1323$
4	$C(5,4)(.3)^4(.7)^1$	$= 0.02835$
5	$C(5,5)(.3)^5(.7)^0$	$= 0.00243$

3.

X	P(X)
0	$C(5,0)(.4)^0(.6)^5 = 0.07776$
1	$C(5,1)(.4)^1(.6)^4 = 0.2592$
2	$C(5,2)(.4)^2(.6)^3 = 0.3456$
3	$C(5,3)(.4)^3(.6)^2 = 0.2304$
4	$C(5,4)(.4)^4(.6)^1 = 0.0768$
5	$C(5,5)(.4)^5(.6)^0 = 0.01024$

5.

X	P(X)
0	$C(4,0)(1/6)^0(5/6)^4 = 0.4823$
1	$C(4,1)(1/6)^1(5/6)^3 = 0.3858$
2	$C(4,2)(1/6)^2(5/6)^2 = 0.1157$
3	$C(4,3)(1/6)^3(5/6)^1 = 0.0154$
4	$C(4,4)(1/6)^4(5/6)^0 = 0.0008$

7.

X	P(X)
0	$C(4,0)(1/2)^4 = 0.0625$
1	$C(4,1)(1/2)^4 = 0.2500$
2	$C(4,2)(1/2)^4 = 0.3750$
3	$C(4,3)(1/2)^4 = 0.2500$
4	$C(4,4)(1/2)^4 = 0.0625$

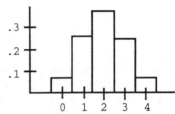

9.

X	P(X)
0	$C(4,0)(.6)^0(.4)^4 = 0.0256$
1	$C(4,1)(.6)^1(.4)^3 = 0.1536$
2	$C(4,2)(.6)^2(.4)^2 = 0.3456$
3	$C(4,3)(.6)^3(.4)^1 = 0.3456$
4	$C(4,4)(.6)^4(.4)^0 = 0.1296$

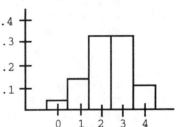

11. $P(40) = C(90, 40)(0.4)^{40}(0.6)^{50}$

13. $P(35) = C(75, 35)(0.25)^{35}(0.75)^{40}$

15. $n = 50, p = 0.4 \Rightarrow \mu = (50)(0.4) = 20,$
     $var = (50)(0.4)(0.6) = 12, \sigma = \sqrt{12} = 3.4641$

17. $n = 600, p = 0.52 \Rightarrow \mu = (600)(0.52) = 312,$
     $var = (600)(0.52)(0.48) = 149.76, \sigma = \sqrt{149.76} = 12.2376$

19. $n = 470, p = 0.08 \Rightarrow \mu = (470)(0.08) = 37.6,$
     $var = (37.6)(0.92) = 34.592, \sigma = \sqrt{34.592} = 5.8815$

21. $np = 50(.7) = 35 \geq 5, nq = (50)(.3) = 15 \geq 5 \Rightarrow$ yes

23. $np = (40)(.9) = 36, nq = (40)(.1) = 4 < 5 \Rightarrow$ no

25. $np = (25)(.5) = 12.5 \geq 5, nq = (25)(.5) = 12.5 \geq 5 \Rightarrow$ yes

27. $\mu = (50)(.7) = 35, \sigma = \sqrt{(35)(.3)} = \sqrt{10.5} = 3.24$
     (a) $x_1 = 39.5 \Rightarrow z_1 = (39.5 - 35)/3.24 = 1.39$
          $x_2 = 40.5 \Rightarrow z_2 = (40.5 - 35)/3.24 = 1.70$
          $P(x = 40) = A_2 - A_1 = 0.4554 - 0.4177 = 0.0377$

Section 7-7

(b) $\quad x_1 = 27.5 \Rightarrow z_1 = (27.5 - 35)/3.24 \ -2.31$

$\quad x_2 = 28.5 \Rightarrow z_2 = (28.5 - 35)/3.24 = -2.01$

$\quad P(X = 28) = A_2 - A_1 = 0.4896 - 0.4778 = .0118$

(c) $\quad x_1 = 31.5 \Rightarrow z_1 = (31.5 - 35)/3.24 = -1.08$

$\quad x_2 = 32.5 \Rightarrow z_2 = (32.5 - 35)/3.24 = -.77$

$\quad P(X = 32) = A_2 - A_1 = .3599 - .2794 = .0805$

29. $\quad \mu = 15(.4) = 6, \ \sigma = \sqrt{15(.4)(.6)} = \sqrt{3.6} = 1.90$

(a) $\quad x_1 = 4.5 \Rightarrow z_1 = (4.5 - 6)/1.90 = -.79$, so $A_1 = .2852$

$\quad x_2 = 7.5 \Rightarrow z_2 \Rightarrow (7.5 - 6)/1.90 = .79$, so $A_2 = .2852$

$\quad P(4 < x < 8) = .2852 + .2852 = .5704$

(b) $\quad x_1 = 3.5 \Rightarrow z_1 = (3.5 - 6)/1.90 = -1.32$, so $A = .4066$

$\quad x_2 = 8.5 \Rightarrow z_2 = (8.5 - 6)/1.90 = 1.32$, so $A = .4066$

$\quad P(4 \leq x \leq 8) = .4066 + .4066 = .8132$

(c) $\quad x_1 = 6.5 \Rightarrow z_1 = (6.5 - 6)/1.90 = .26$, so $A_1 = .1026$

$\quad x_2 = 8.5 \Rightarrow z_1 = 1.32$, so $A_2 = .4066$

$\quad P(7 \leq X \leq 8) = .4066 - .1026 = .3040$

31. $\quad \mu = 8, \ \sigma = 2$

(a) $\quad x = 5.5 \Rightarrow z = (5.5 - 8)/2 = -1.25$, so $A = .3944$

$\quad P(x > 5) = .5000 + .3944 = .8944$

(b) $\quad x = 4.5 \Rightarrow z = (4.5 - 8)/2 = -1.75$, so $A = .4599$

$\quad P(x \geq 5) = .5000 + .4599 = .9599$

(c) $\quad x = 9.5 \Rightarrow z = (9.5 - 8)/2 = .75$, so $A = .2734$

$\quad P(x > 9) = .5000 - .2734 = .2266$

33. $\quad \mu = 7.2, \ \sigma = 2.24$

(a) $\quad x = 9.5 \Rightarrow z = (9.5 - 7.2)/2.24 = 1.03$, so $A = .3485$

$\quad P(x < 10) = .5000 + .3485 = .8485$

(b) $\quad x = 10.5 \Rightarrow z = (10.5 - 7.2)/2.24 = 1.47$, so $A = .4292$

$\quad P(x \leq 10) = .5000 + .4292 = .9292$

(c) $\quad x = 5.5 \Rightarrow z = (5.5 - 7.2)/2.24 = -.76$, so $A = .2764$

$\quad P(x < 6) = .5000 - .2764 = .2236$

35. $\quad \mu = 60, \ \sigma = 4.90$

(a) $\quad x_1 = 49.5 \Rightarrow z_1 = (49.5 - 60)/4.90 = -2.14$, so $A_1 = .4838$

$\quad x_2 = 75.5 \Rightarrow z_2 = (75.5 - 60)/4.90 = 3.16$, so $A_2 = .4992$

$\quad P(50 \leq x \leq 75) = .4838 + .4992 = .9830$

(b) $\quad x = 75.5 \Rightarrow z = 3.16$, so $A = .4992$

$\quad P(x > 75) = .5000 - .4992 = .0008$

(c) $\quad x = 49.5 \Rightarrow z = -2.14$, so $A = .4838$

$\quad P(x \leq 50) = .5000 - .4838 = .0162$

37. $\quad \mu = (20)(1/3) = 6.67,$

$\quad \sigma = \sqrt{(20)(1/3)(2/3)} = \sqrt{4.44} = 2.11$

$\quad x_1 = 5.5 \Rightarrow z_1 = (5.5 - 6.67)/2.11 = -0.55$, so $A_1 = .2088$

$\quad x_2 = 8.5 \Rightarrow z_2 = (8.5 - 6.67)/2.11 = 0.87$, so $A_2 = .3079$

$\quad P(6 \leq x \leq 8) = 0.2088 + 0.3079 = 0.5167$

39. $\quad \mu = 50, \ \sigma = \sqrt{25} = 5$

$\quad x_1 = 49.5 \Rightarrow z_1 = (49.5 - 50)/5 = -0.1$, so $A_1 = .0398$

$\quad x_2 = 55.5 \Rightarrow z_2 = (55.5 - 50)/5 = 1.1$, so $A_2 = .3643$

$\quad P(50 \leq x \leq 55) = 0.0398 + 0.3643 = 0.4041$

41. $\mu = (64)(1/4) = 16$, $\sigma = \sqrt{(16)(3/4)} = \sqrt{12} = 3.46$
$x_1 = 19.5 \Rightarrow z_1 = (19.5 - 16)/3.46 = 1.01$, so A = .3438
$x_2 = 24.5 \Rightarrow z_2 = (24.5 - 16)/3.46 = 2.46$, so A = .4931
$P(20 \leq x \leq 24) = 0.4931 - 0.3438 = 0.1493$

43. $\mu = (270)(.9) = 243$, $\sigma = \sqrt{(243)(.1)} = \sqrt{24.3} = 4.93$
$x = 250.5 \Rightarrow z = (250.5 - 243)/4.93 = 1.52$
$P(x \leq 250) = 0.5 + 0.4357 = 0.9357$

45. $\mu = (250)(.3) = 75$, $\sigma = \sqrt{(75)(.7)} = \sqrt{52.5} = 7.25$
$x = 64.5 \Rightarrow z = (64.5 - 75)/7.25 = 1.45$, so A = .4265
$P(x \geq 65) = 0.5 + 0.4265 = 0.9265$

47. Let x = number correct
    (a) $3x - 1(90 - x) \geq 98 \Rightarrow 4x \geq 188 \Rightarrow x \geq 47$
    (b) $\mu = (90)(1/2) = 45$, $\sigma = \sqrt{(45)(1/2)} = \sqrt{22.5} = 4.74$
    $x = 46.5 \Rightarrow z = (46.5 - 45)/4.74 = 0.32$
    $P(x \geq 47) = 0.5 - 0.1255 = 0.3745$

Review Exercises, Chapter 7

1.

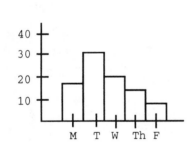
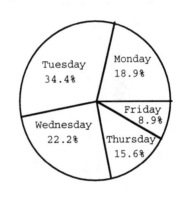

3. (a) 6   (b) $(9 + 12)/2 = 21/2 = 10.5$
   (c) $(1 + 3)/2 = 2$

5. $\mu = \dfrac{54(1.5) + 32(3.5) + 12(5.5)}{98} = 259/98 = 2.64$

7. $90.22/n = 3.47 \Rightarrow n = 90.22/3.47 = 26$ 9. $X \in \{0, 1, 2, 3\}$

11. $E(X) = .05(0) + .20(1) + .15(2) + .20(3) + .25(4) + .15(5) = 2.85$

13. $E(X) = .20(1) + .32(2) + .21(3) + .15(4) + .12(5) = 2.67$

15. $x = 400 \Rightarrow z = (400 - 350)/25 = 2 \Rightarrow .5 - A = .5 - 0.4773 = 0.0227$

17.

X	P(X)
0	$C(4, 0)(.25)^0(.75)^4 = 0.3164$
1	$C(4, 1)(.25)^1(.75)^3 = 0.4219$
2	$C(4, 2)(.25)^2(.75)^2 = 0.2109$
3	$C(4, 3)(.25)^3(.75)^1 = 0.0469$
4	$C(4, 4)(.25)^4(.75)^0 = 0.0039$

19. $\mu = (80)(.65) = 52$, $\sigma = \sqrt{(52)(.35)} = \sqrt{18.2} = 4.266$
   (a) $x = 50.5 \Rightarrow z = (50.5 - 52)/4.266 = -0.35$
         $\Rightarrow .P(X > 50) = .5 + 0.1368 = 0.6368$
   (b) $x_1 = 64.5 \Rightarrow z_1 = (64.5 - 52)/4.266 = 2.93$
         $x_2 = 65.5 \Rightarrow z_2 = (65.5 - 52)/4.266 = 3.16$
         $P(X = 65) = A_2 - A_1 = 0.4992 - 0.4983 = 0.0009$
   (c) $x_1 = 55.5 \Rightarrow z_1 = (55.5 - 52)/4.266 = 0.82$
         $x_2 = 59.5 \Rightarrow z_2 = (59.5 - 52)/4.266 = 1.76$
         $P(55 < X < 60) = A_2 - A_1 = 0.4608 - 0.2939 = 0.1669$

21. $(216 - 43 + 1)/216 = 174/216 = .805$, 81st percentile

23.

X	P(X)
1	20/800 = 0.025
2	160/800 = 0.200
3	370/800 = 0.4625
4	215/800 = 0.26875
5	35/800 = 0.04375

25.

X	Number of ways
0	10
1	30
2	15
3	1

27.

x	Number of ways
1	1
2	1
3	4

29. $\mu = \dfrac{8(3) + 13(8.5) + 6(12.5) + 15(17.5)}{42} = 11.24$

Chapter 8
Mathematics of Finance

Section 8-1

1. 7, 11, 15, 19   3.   5, 10, 20, 40   5.   -4, -3, -1, 3

7. 1, 2, 6, 22   9. $a = 2$, $b = 3$, $\frac{b}{a-1} = 3$

11. $a = 5$, $b = 0$, $\frac{b}{a-1} = 0$ 13. $a = .6$, $b = .5$, $\frac{b}{a-1} = -1.25$

15. $a = 1$, $b = 4$, $\frac{b}{a-1}$ is undefined   17. $x_n = x_{n-1} + 2$, $x_0 = 10$

19. $x_n = -x_{n-1}$, $x_0 = 5$ 21. $x_n = x_{n-1} - 5$, $x_0 = 1300$

23. $x_n = [1 + \frac{1}{3}]4^n - \frac{1}{3} = \frac{4}{3}(4^n) - \frac{1}{3}$

25. $x_n = [3 + \frac{7}{1}](2)^n - \frac{7}{1} = 10(2)^n - 7$

27. $x_n = [2 + \frac{1}{3}](-2)^n - \frac{1}{3} = \frac{1}{3}(-2)^n - \frac{1}{3}$

29. $x_n = 5 + 7n$ 31. Let x_n = population of year n.
$$x_n = x_{n-1} + 10$$

33. Let x_n = cost of living for year n.
$$x_n = x_{n-1} + .045x_{n-1} = 1.045x_{n-1}$$

35. Let x_n = amount in bank for week n.
$$x_n = x_{n-1} + .75, \quad x_0 = 5.35$$

37. x_n = amount in savings at the end of year n.
$$x_n = x_{n-1} + .08x_{n-1} - 6,000 = 1.08x_{n-1} - 6,000, \quad x_0 = 75,000$$

39. x_n = size of freshman class for year n.
$$x_n = x_{n-1} + 150$$

41. x_n = amount of material at the end of year n.
$$x_n = x_{n-1} - .0005x_{n-1} = .9995x_{n-1}$$

43. x_n = population for year n.
$$x_n = x_{n-1} - .005x_{n-1} = .995x_{n-1}$$

45. x_n = global temperature for year n
$$x_n = x_{n-1} + .2$$

47. x_n = amount in account at the end of month n, and M = amount withdrawn each month
$$x_n = x_{n-1} + .005x_{n-1} - M = 1.005x_{n-1} - M$$
$$x_0 = 25,000$$

$$x_n = [25,000 - \frac{M}{.005}](1.005)^n + \frac{M}{.005}$$
$$= [25,000 - 200M](1.005)^n + 200M.$$
Find M so that $x_{60} = 0$
$$25,000(1.005)^{60} - 200(1.005)^{60}M + 200M = 0$$
$$25,000(1.34885) - 269.77M + 200M = 0$$
$$69.77M = 33,721.25$$
$$M = 483.32 \text{ so} \qquad \$483.32 \text{ may be withdrawn each month}$$

Section 8-2

49. Let x_n = Tom's weight on day n.

    (a) $x_n = x_{n-1} + (3200 - 18x_{n-1})/3500$

    $\qquad = \dfrac{3482}{3500} x_{n-1} + \dfrac{3200}{3500} = .9949x_{n-1} + .9143$

    $x_0 = 240$

    We can also write x_n as

    $\qquad x_n = (240 + \dfrac{.9143}{-.0051})(.9949)^n - \dfrac{.9143}{-.0051}$

    $\qquad = 60.7255(.9949)^n + 179.2745$

    (b) $x_{30} = 60.7255(.9949)^{30} + 179.2745 = 231.36$

    so Tom weighed about 231 pounds after 30 days

    (c) $x_{n-1} = 179$ so the next month his weight is

    $\qquad x_n = .9949(179) + .9143 = 179.001$

    so the next month Tom's weight remains 179 pounds.

Section 8-2

1. $I = (1100)(.08)(9/12) = \$66$

3. $I = (600)(.10)(18/12) = \$90$

5. $I = (745)(.085)(6/12) = 31.6625 = \$31.66$

7. $I = (300)(.06)(1) = \$18 \quad A = P + I = 300 + 18 = \$318$

9. $I = (500)(.08)(3) = \$120$

11. $I = (700)(.015)(5) = \$52.50$

13. $I = (950)(.0175)(7) = 116.375 = \$116.38$

15. $P = I/rt = \dfrac{42.90}{(.13)(.5)} = \$660$

17. $P = I/rt = \dfrac{116.1}{(.09)(1.5)} = \$860$

19. $r = I/Pt = \dfrac{49.4}{(1140)(8/12)} = .065 = 6.5\%$

21. $r = I/Pt = \dfrac{616.25}{(5800)(1.25)} = .085 = 8.5\%$

23. $A = (2700)[1 + (.08)(1.5)] = \$3024$

25. $A = (6500)[1 + (0.086)(1.75)] = \$7478.25$

27. $P = \dfrac{1800}{1 + (.08)(1.5)} = 1607.142 = \$1607.14$

29. $D = (1850)(.075)(1) = \$138.75, \quad PR = M - D = \$1711.25$

31. $D = (485)(.13)(1.5) = \$94.58, \quad PR = \$390.42$

33. $I = (5000)(.07)(3) = \$1050$

35. For one year, $I = (50,000)(.075)(1) = \$3750$
    Total for 6 years = $22,500$

37. (a) $(100,000)(.09)(1/12) = \$750$ \quad (b) $250(12)(6) = \$54,000$

39. $I = Prt \Rightarrow t = I/Pr = 144/(800)(0.06) = 3$ years

41. $t = I/Pr = \dfrac{18}{(800)(.09)} = 0.25$ years $= 3$ months

43. $P = I/rt = \dfrac{48.75}{(0.075)(1)} = \$650$

45. $I = (20,000)(.09)(1/12) = \$150$ toward interest,
$179.95 - 150 = \$29.95$ toward principal

47. $A = P(1 + rt) \Rightarrow A = 900 = 860(1 + r(.5))$
$$40 = 430r$$
$$r = .0930 \quad = 9.3\%$$

49. $PR = M(1 - dt) \Rightarrow M = \dfrac{PR}{1 - dt} = \dfrac{6500}{1 - (.14)(1/12)} = 6576.728$
$$= \$6576.73$$

51. $M = \dfrac{PR}{1 - dt} = \dfrac{38000}{1 - (.12)(3/12)} = 39175.258 = \$39,175.26$

53. Simple interest: $I = (650)(.08)(2/12) = 8.6667 = \$8.67$
Simple discount: $M = \dfrac{PR}{1 - dt} = \dfrac{650}{1 - (.08)(2/12)} = 658.7838$
must be borrowed, so $D = 658.78 - 650.00 = \$8.78$

55. $50 = 950(r)(.5) \quad r = \dfrac{50}{475} = .10526 = 10.53\%$

57. Simple interest: $I = (3000)(.103)(4/12) = \$103$
Simple discount: $M = \dfrac{PR}{1 - dt} = \dfrac{3000}{1 - (.101)(4/12)} = 3104.5188$
$\Rightarrow D = \$104.52$. Simple interest at 10.3% results in the lower fee.

59. $I = (450)(.11)(1)$ billion $= \$49.5$ billion

61. $I = (500,000)(.09)(5) = \$225,000$

63. $I = (400,000)(.08)(.5) = \$16,000$ in interest payments semi-annually
$(10)(2)(16,000) = \$320,000$ in total interest

65. $PR = M(1 - dt) = (1 \text{ million})[1 - (.07)(90/360)] = \$982,500$

67. $982,000 = 1,000,000(1 - d(\dfrac{90}{360}))$
$-18000 = -250,000d$
$d = \dfrac{18,000}{250,000} = .072 = 7.2\%$

69. $PR = M(1 - dt) = (2 \text{ million})[1 - (.07125)(30/360)]$
$$= \$1,988,125$$

Section 8-3

1.   (a) $(1.07)^3 = 1.225043$ (b) $(1.02)^5 = 1.1040808$
      (c) $(1.015)^4 = 1.0613636$ (d) $(1.035)^2 = 1.071225$
      (e) $(1.045)^4 = 1.192519$ (f) $(1.025)^5 = 1.131408$

Section 8-3

3. (a) $i = .15/2 = .075 = 7.5\%$ (b) $i = .15/4 = .0375 = 3.75\%$
    (c) $i = .15/12 = .0125 = 1.25\%$

5. (a) $A = 4500(1.54330) = \$6,944.85$
    (b) $I = A - P = \$2,444.85$

7. (a) $A = 31,000(1.78348) = \$55,287.88$ (b) $I = \$24,287.88$

9. (a) $A = 5000(1.31080) = \$6,554.00$ (b) $I = \$1,554.00$

11. First quarter: $A = 800(1.03) = \$824$
     Second quarter: $A = 800(1.03)^2 = \$848.72$
     Third quarter: $A = 800(1.03)^3 = \$874.18$
     Fourth quarter: $A = 800(1.03)^4 = \$900.41$

13. $A = 1800(1.045)^2 = \$1,965.65$

15. (a) $A = (12,000)(1.10)^3 = \$15,972$
     (b) $A = (12,000)(1.05)^6 = \$16,081.20$
     (c) $A = (12,000)(1.025)^{12} = \$16,138.68$

17. $A = (10,000)(1.03)^{20} = \$18,061.10$

19. $A = (460)(1.008333)^6 = 460(1.051051) = \$483.48$

21. $A = (640)(1.02)^6 = \$720.74$ 23. $A = (32.75)(1.01)^4 = \$34.08$

25. $P = \dfrac{25000}{(1.03)^{30}} = \$10,299.68$

27. $P = \dfrac{A}{(1 + i)^n} = \dfrac{3000}{(1.025)^{16}} = \$2,020.87$

29. $x = (1.03)^2 - 1 = .0609 = 6.09\%$

31. $2 = (1.03)^n \Rightarrow n = 24$ semiannual periods $= 12$ years

33. $2 = (1.03)^n \Rightarrow n = 24$ quarters $= 6$ years

35. $2 = (1 + i)^{28}$ Look in the row for $n = 28$ to find 2. The nearest is
     in the $i = .025$ column so 2.5% quarterly rate gives 10% annual rate.

37. $3 = (1.05)^n \Rightarrow n = 23 \rightarrow 11.5$ years

39. $A = 260(1.016)^5 = \$281.48$

41. Ken had $1000(1.023)^{20} = 1000(1.575842) = \$1575.84$
     Barb had $1000(1.0076)^{60} = 1000(1.5750325) = \$1575.03$
     Ken had $.81 more.

43. The effective rate for 8.8% is $(1.044)^2 - 1 = .089936 = 8.9936\%$.
     The effective rate for 8.6% is $(1.0215)^4 - 1 = .088813 = 8.8813\%$,
     so 8.8% compounded semiannually is better.

45. The effective rate of 9.4% compounded annually is 9.4%.
     The effective rate of 9.2% compounded quarterly is
     $(1.023)^4 - 1 = .09522 = 9.522\%$, so 9.2% is better.

47. The effective rate of 10% compounded quarterly is
     $(1.025)^4 - 1 = .1038 = 10.38\%$, which is better than 10.2%
     compounded annually.

49. $A = (35,000)(1.02)^{10} = 35000(1.21899) = 42,665$

51. $A = (15,000)(1.02)^{28} = \$26,115.30$

53. $1485.95 = 1000(1 + r)^{20}$, so $(1 + r)^{20} = 1.48595$.   Look at the row for n = 20 for 1.48595.   It occurs under i = .02, so the annual rate is 8%.

55. $633.39 = 500(1 + i)^8$, so $1.26678 = (1 + i)^8$
       This occurs when i = .03 = 6% per year.

57.   For $6000 invested for 10 years, $A = (6,000)(1.05)^{20} = \$15,919.80$.
       Take the lump sum of $16,000

59. $18,000 = 8,000(1.03)^n$ $2.25 = (1.03)^n$ given n = 28 semiannual periods = 14 years.

61. $P = \dfrac{240,000}{(1.04)^{10}} = \$162,135.87$

Section 8-4

1.
Year Deposited	Value at End of 4 Years
1	$600(1.1)^3 = \$\ 798.60$
2	$600(1.1)^2 = \$\ 726.00$
3	$600(1.1)^1 = \$\ 660.00$
4	$600(1.1)^0 = \$\ \underline{600.00}$
	$2,784.60$ Final Value

3.   (a)   S = 18.59891   (b)   S = 29.77808
      (c)   n = 12, i = .12/4 = .03 $\Rightarrow$ S = 14.19203
      (d)   n = 14, i = .10/2 = .05 $\Rightarrow$ S = 19.59863
      (e)   n = 12, i = .12/12 = .01 $\Rightarrow$ S = 12.68250

5.   n = 15, i = .07 $\Rightarrow$ S = 25.12902
      A = 16,000(25.12902) = $402,064.32

7.   n = 20, i = .08/4 = .02 $\Rightarrow$ S = 24.29737
      A = 250(24.29737) = $6074.34

9.   n = 20, i = .01 $\Rightarrow$ S = 22.01900
      A = 200(22.01900) = $4403.80

11.   n = 20, i = .04 $\Rightarrow$ S = 29.77808
      A = 4000(29.77808) = $119,112.32

13.   n = 16, i = .12/4 = .03 $\Rightarrow$ S = 20.15688
      A = 750(20.15688) = $15,117.66

15.   2500 = R(4.57313)   R = $546.67

17.   14,500 = R(33.06595)   R = $438.52

19.   10,000 = R(13.79555)   R = $724.87

21.   75,000 = R(19.38022)   R = $3869.93

23.   15,000 = R(19.61475)   R = $764.73

Section 8-5

25. $n = 24$, $i = .01 \Rightarrow S = 26.97346$
    $A = 100(26.97346) = \$2697.35$

27. $n = 10$, $i = .04$ $S = 12.00611$
    $A = 400(12.00611) = \$4,802.44$

29. $n = 12$, $i = .015 \Rightarrow S = 13.04121$
    $4000 = R(13.04121)$ $R = \$306.72$

31. $n = 9$, $i = .07$, $S = 11.97799$
    $A = 5,000(11.97799) = \$59,889.95$

33. $n = 6$, $i = .07$, $S = 7.15329$ 35. $n = 16$, $i = .04$, $S = 21.82453$
    $150,000 = R(7.15329)$ $750,000 = R(21.82453)$
    $R = \$20,969.37$ $R = \$34,365.00$

37. $n = 5$, $A = 23,800$, $R = 4,000$,
    $23,800 = 4000S$
    $S = 5.95$. In the row for $n = 5$, the value nearest to $S = 5.95$
    is 5.98471 for $i = .09$. Thus, a 9% interest rate will yield at
    least $23,800.

39. (a) $R = 1000$, $n = 10$, $i = .08$, $S = 14.48656$
         $A = 1000(14.48656) = \$14,486.56$
    (b) $.08(14,486.56) = \$1158.92$

41. $A = 100 \left[\dfrac{(1.016)^{30} - 1}{.016} \right] = \$3812.16$

43. $15,000 = R \left[\dfrac{(1.0075)^{60} - 1}{.0075} \right] = R(75.424137)$
    $R = \$198.88$

45. $100,000 = R \left[\dfrac{(1.081)^{6} - 1}{.081} \right] = R(7.3544534)$
    $R = \$13,597.20$

Section 8-5

1. $K = 12.84926$

3. $n = 16$, $i = 5\% \Rightarrow K = 10.8377$

5. $n = 8$, $i = .07$, $P = 4000(5.97130) = \$23,885.20$

7. $n = 20$, $i = .02$, $P = 750(16.35143) = \$12,263.57$

9. $n = 20$, $i = .06$, $P = 500(11.46992) = \$5734.96$

11. $n = 22$, $i = .025$, $P = 300(16.76541) = \$5029.62$

13. $n = 12$, $i = .02 \Rightarrow K = 10.57534$
    $P = (226.94)(10.57534) = \$2,399.97$ rounded to $2,400

15. $n = 10$, $i = .07$, $K = 7.02358$
    $P = (2135.66)(7.02358) = \$14,999.98 \rightarrow$ rounded to $15,000

17. $n = 4$, $i = .07$, $K = 3.38721$,
    $5000 = R(3.38721)$ $R = \$1,476.14$

19. $n = 20$, $i = .025$, $K = 15.58916$, $50,000 = R(15.58916)$
    $R = \$3,207.36$

21. $n = 20$, $i = .06$, $K = 11.46992$
    $150,000 = R(11.46992)$ $R = \$13,077.68$

23. $n = 12$, $i = .025$, $K = 10.25773$,
    $2000 = R(10.25776)$ $R = \$194.97$

25. $n = 240$, $i = 2/3\%$, $K = 119.55429$
    $20,000 = R(119.55429)$ $R = \$167.29$

27. (a) $(360)(825.75) = \$297,270$ (b) $297,270 - 75,000 = \$222,270$

29. (a) $I = (68,000)(.15)(1/12) = \$850$ interest
        $870.96 - 850 = \$20.96$ to principal
    (b) Total paid $= (25)(12)(870.96) = \$261,288$

31. $n = 20$, $i = .025$, $S = 25.54466$
    Bal $= (75,000)(1.025)^{20} - (2987.72)(25.54466)$
        $= 122,896.50 - 76,320.29 = \$46,576.21$

33. $n = 18$, $i = 1.5\%$, $K = 15.67256$
    $P = (484.92)(15.67256) = 7599.94$ rounds to $\$7,600$

35. $n = 16$, $i = .025$, $K = 13.05500$,
    $7500 = R(13.05500)$
    $R = \$574.49$

37. $n = 20$, $i = .09$, $K = 9.12855$,
    $P = (10,000)(9.12855) = \$91,285.50$

39. $n = 24$, $i = .01$, $K = 21.24339$
    $12,000 = R(21.24339)$
    $R = \$564.88$

41. (i) Find amount needed at age 18 to pay $15,000 per year for 4 years.
        $n = 4$, $i = .08$, $K = 3.31213$
        $P = (15,000)(3.31213) = \$49,681.95$ needed at 18
    (ii) Find periodic payments of an annuity that will accumulate to
        $49,681.95 in 18 years.
        $n = 18$, $i = .08$, $S = 37.45024$
        $49,681.95 = R(37.45024)$
        $R = \$1,326.61$

43. $P = 200\left[\dfrac{(1.0075)^{60} - 1}{.0075(1.0075)^{60}}\right] = 200(48.173374) = \$9634.67$

45. $9700 = R\left[\dfrac{(1.0075)^{60} - 1}{.0075(1.0075)^{60}}\right] = R(48.173374)$
    $R = \$201.36$

47. $85,000 = R\left[\dfrac{(1.0075)^{120} - 1}{.0075(1.0075)^{120}}\right] = R(78.941693)$
    $R = \$1076.74$

Review Exercises, Chapter 8

1. $I = (500)(.09)(2) = \$90$

3. $P = \dfrac{A}{1 + rt} = \dfrac{1190.40}{1 + (.08)(3)} = \$960$

5. $I = (3000)(.09)(5) = \$1,350$

7. $D = (8500)(.09)(2) = \$1,530$, $PR = 8500 - 1530 = \$6970$

9. $A = (5000)(1.07)^3 = 6125.20$ so interest $= \$1,125.20$

11. $2 = (1.02)^n$, $n = 36$ quarters $= 9$ years

13. $x = (1.03)^2 - 1 = .0609 = 6.09\%$

15. $x = (1.02)^{12} - 1 = .26824 = 26.82\%$

17.   Effective rate of 18% $= (1.045)^4 - 1 = 0.1925 = 19.25\%$.
Effective rate of 19% $= (1.19)^1 - 1 = 0.19$, so 18% compounded quarterly is better.

19.   (a) $A = (8,000)(1.06)^4 = \$10,099.84$
(b) $I = 10099.84 - 8000 = \$2099.84$

21.   (a) $A = (5,000)(1.025)^{24} = \$9,043.65$
(b) $I = 9043.65 - 5000 = \$4,043.65$

23. $A = (15,000)(1.08)^2 = \$17,496$

25. $50,000 = P(1.02)^{20} = P(1.48595)$, $P = \$33,648.51$

27. $3500 = 2000(1.03)^n$, $1.75 = (1.03)^n$, $n = 19$ quarters $=$ 4 years, 9 months

29. $A = (200)(10.94972) = \$2,189.94$

31. $A = (1,000)(5.63709) = \$5,637.09$

33. $n = 10$, $i = .05$, $S = 12.57789$,
$A = (600)(12.57789) = \$7,546.73$

35. $n = 24$, $i = .02$, $S = 30.42186$,
$A = (250)(30.42186) = \$7,605.47$

37. $n = 10$, $i = .08$, $S = 14.48656$, $2,000,000 = R(14.48656)$
$R = \$138,059.00$

39. $P = 5000/(1.06)^5 = \$3,736.28$ 41. $P = 6000/(1.02)^{20} = \$4,037.82$

43. $P = 50,000/(1.02)^{20} = \$33,648.51$

45. $297,000 = 200,000(1.02)^n$,
$1.485 = (1.02)^n$, $n = 20$ quarters $= 5$ years

47. $n = 12$, $i = .03$, $K = 9.954$
$3000 = R(9.95400)$
$R = \$301.39$

49. $n = 5$, $i = .09$, $K = 3.88965$
$4800 = R(3.88965)$
$R = \$1234.04$

51.   n = 20, i = .07, K = 10.59401
       7.8 million = R(10.59401)
       R = \$736,265.12

53.   n = 8, i = .09, K = 5.53482
       98,000 = R(5.53482), R = \$17,706.09

55.   Amount at end of first five years
       $A = 1000(1.02)^{20} = \$1485.95$
       Amount at end of second five years
       $A = \$1485.95(1.025)^{20} = \$2434.91$

57. $A = 1700(1.0195)^{40} = \$3680.77$

59. $500,000 = R(1.025)^{160} = R(51.977868)$
       R = \$9619.48

61. $100,000 = R \left[\dfrac{(1.01)^{72} - 1}{.01} \right] = R(104.70993) \quad R = \$955.02$

Chapter 9

Game Theory

Section 9-2

1.

$$\begin{array}{cc} & C \\ & \begin{array}{cc} H & T \end{array} \\ R \begin{array}{c} H \\ T \end{array} & \begin{bmatrix} -1 & -.5 \\ -.5 & 2 \end{bmatrix} \end{array}$$

3.

$$\begin{array}{cc} & C \\ & \begin{array}{cc} 1 & 2 \end{array} \\ R \begin{array}{c} 1 \\ 2 \end{array} & \begin{bmatrix} 2 & -3 \\ -3 & 4 \end{bmatrix} \end{array}$$

5. (a) R receives 10 from C   (b) 10   (c) 10   (d) 8

7.

$$\begin{array}{ccc} & \begin{array}{cc} c_1 & c_2 \end{array} & \begin{array}{c} \text{row} \\ \text{min} \end{array} \\ \begin{array}{c} r_1 \\ r_2 \end{array} & \begin{bmatrix} 0 & 1 \\ -1 & 2 \end{bmatrix} & \begin{array}{c} 0 \\ -1 \end{array} \\ \text{col max} & \begin{array}{cc} 0 & 2 \end{array} \end{array}$$

The (1, 1) location is the saddle point. The value of the game is 0. The solution consists of the strategies r_1 and c_1. The game is strictly determined.

9.

$$\begin{array}{ccc} & \begin{array}{cc} c_1 & c_2 \end{array} & \begin{array}{c} \text{row} \\ \text{min} \end{array} \\ \begin{array}{c} r_1 \\ r_2 \end{array} & \begin{bmatrix} 3 & 1 \\ -1 & 2 \end{bmatrix} & \begin{array}{c} 1 \\ -1 \end{array} \\ \text{col max} & \begin{array}{cc} 3 & 2 \end{array} \end{array}$$

There is no saddle point, and the game is not strictly determined.

11.

$$\begin{array}{ccc} & \begin{array}{cc} c_1 & c_2 \end{array} & \begin{array}{c} \text{row} \\ \text{min} \end{array} \\ \begin{array}{c} r_1 \\ r_2 \end{array} & \begin{bmatrix} 0 & -3 \\ 3 & 0 \end{bmatrix} & \begin{array}{c} -3 \\ 0 \end{array} \\ \text{col max} & \begin{array}{cc} 3 & 0 \end{array} \end{array}$$

The (2, 2) location is the saddle point. The value of the game is 0. The solution consists of the strategies r_2 and c_2. The game is strictly determined.

13. (a)

$$\begin{array}{cc} & \begin{array}{c} \text{row} \\ \text{min} \end{array} \\ \begin{bmatrix} 2 & -1 & -2 \\ 1 & 0 & 1 \\ -2 & -1 & 2 \end{bmatrix} & \begin{array}{c} -2 \\ 0 \\ -2 \end{array} \\ \text{col max} \quad \begin{array}{ccc} 2 & 0 & 2 \end{array} \end{array}$$

The (2, 2) location is the saddle point. The value of the game is 0. The solution consists of the strategies r_2 and c_2.

(b)

$$\begin{bmatrix} 2 & 1 & -1 \\ 1 & 0 & -2 \\ 2 & 1 & -3 \end{bmatrix} \begin{matrix} \text{row} \\ \text{min} \\ -1 \\ -2 \\ -3 \end{matrix}$$

col max 2   1   -1

The (1, 3) location is the saddle point. The value of the game is -1. The solution consists of the strategies r_1 and c_3.

(c)

$$\begin{bmatrix} 1 & 3 & -1 \\ 4 & 2 & 0 \\ 1 & -3 & 2 \end{bmatrix} \begin{matrix} \text{row} \\ \text{min} \\ -1 \\ 0 \\ -3 \end{matrix}$$

col max 4   3   2

There is no saddle point.

(d)

$$\begin{bmatrix} 0 & -1 & 1 \\ 2 & 0 & 1 \\ 0 & -3 & 1 \end{bmatrix} \begin{matrix} \text{row} \\ \text{min} \\ -1 \\ 0 \\ -3 \end{matrix}$$

col max   2   0   1

The (2, 2) location is the saddle point. The value of the game is 0. The solution consists of the strategies r_2 and c_2.

15.

		C		row
		c_1	c_2	min
R	r_1	120	140	120
	r_2	80	60	60
col max		120	140	

Company R should adopt strategy r_1 and company C should adopt strategy c_1. R will gain 120 from C.

17.

			B		row
		b_1	b_2	b_3	min
A	a_1	30	-20	40	-20
	a_2	40	10	60	10
	col max	40	10	60	

A should adopt strategy a_2 and B should adopt strategy b_2.

Section 9-3

19.

$$
\begin{array}{c}
 & & \text{C} & & \text{row} \\
 & c_1 \quad c_2 \quad c_3 & & \text{min}
\end{array}
$$

$$
\text{R}
\begin{array}{c}
r_1 \\
r_2 \\
r_3
\end{array}
\left[
\begin{array}{ccc}
4 & -2 & 2 \\
-1 & 5 & 2 \\
5 & 4 & 3
\end{array}
\right]
\begin{array}{c}
-2 \\
-1 \\
3
\end{array}
$$

col max $\quad\; 5 \quad 5 \quad 3$

R should select strategy r_3 and C should select strategy c_3.

Section 9-3

1. $E = [1/2 \quad 1/2] \begin{bmatrix} 4 & 8 \\ 12 & 3 \end{bmatrix} \begin{bmatrix} 1/4 \\ 3/4 \end{bmatrix}$

$= [8 \quad 11/2] \begin{bmatrix} 1/4 \\ 3/4 \end{bmatrix} = 6.125$

3. $E = [2/5 \quad 3/5] \begin{bmatrix} 3 & -6 \\ -2 & 4 \end{bmatrix} \begin{bmatrix} 2/3 \\ 1/3 \end{bmatrix} = [0 \quad 0] \begin{bmatrix} 2/3 \\ 1/3 \end{bmatrix} = 0$

5. (a) $E = [1 \; 0 \; 0] \begin{bmatrix} 12 & 6 & -4 \\ 5 & 14 & 10 \\ 15 & 0 & -2 \end{bmatrix} \begin{bmatrix} 0 \\ 0 \\ 1 \end{bmatrix}$

$= [12 \; 6 \; -4] \begin{bmatrix} 0 \\ 0 \\ 1 \end{bmatrix} = -4$

(b) $E = [1/2 \; 1/2 \; 0] \begin{bmatrix} 12 & 6 & -4 \\ 5 & 14 & 10 \\ 15 & 0 & -2 \end{bmatrix} \begin{bmatrix} 0 \\ 1/2 \\ 1/2 \end{bmatrix}$

$= [17/2 \; 10 \; 3] \begin{bmatrix} 0 \\ 1/2 \\ 1/2 \end{bmatrix} = 6.5$

(c) $E = [0 \; 1/2 \; 1/2] \begin{bmatrix} 12 & 6 & -4 \\ 5 & 14 & 10 \\ 15 & 0 & -2 \end{bmatrix} \begin{bmatrix} 1/2 \\ 1/2 \\ 0 \end{bmatrix}$

$$= [10 \quad 7 \quad 4] \begin{bmatrix} 1/2 \\ 1/2 \\ 0 \end{bmatrix} = 8.5$$

(d) $\quad E = [0 \ 0 \ 1] \begin{bmatrix} 12 & 6 & -4 \\ 5 & 14 & 10 \\ 15 & 0 & -2 \end{bmatrix} \begin{bmatrix} 1 \\ 0 \\ 0 \end{bmatrix}$

$$= [15 \quad 0 \quad -2] \begin{bmatrix} 1 \\ 0 \\ 0 \end{bmatrix} = 15$$

(e) $\quad E = [.3 \ .5 \ .2] \begin{bmatrix} 12 & 6 & -4 \\ 5 & 14 & 10 \\ 15 & 0 & -2 \end{bmatrix} \begin{bmatrix} .2 \\ .2 \\ .6 \end{bmatrix}$

$$= [9.1 \ 8.8 \ 3.4] \begin{bmatrix} .2 \\ .2 \\ .6 \end{bmatrix} = 5.62$$

(f) $\quad E = [.1 \ .7 \ .2] \begin{bmatrix} 12 & 6 & -4 \\ 5 & 14 & 10 \\ 15 & 0 & -2 \end{bmatrix} \begin{bmatrix} .3 \\ .2 \\ .5 \end{bmatrix}$

$$= [7.7 \ 10.4 \ 6.2] \begin{bmatrix} .3 \\ .2 \\ .5 \end{bmatrix} = 7.49$$

7. $\quad p_1 = \dfrac{8 + 3}{6 + 8 - 4 + 3} = \dfrac{11}{13}, \qquad p_2 = \dfrac{2}{13}$

$\quad q_1 = \dfrac{8 - 4}{13} = \dfrac{4}{13}, \qquad q_2 = \dfrac{9}{13}$

The optimal strategies for R and C are [11/13   2/13] and [4/13   9/13], respectively. The value of the game is

$E = \dfrac{6(8) - 4(-3)}{13} = \dfrac{60}{13} = 4.62$

9. Row 1 dominates row 2, and column 1 dominates column 2, so row 2 and column 2 can be deleted, giving

$\begin{bmatrix} 6 & 3 \\ 5 & 8 \end{bmatrix}$ $\qquad p_1 = \dfrac{8 - 5}{8 + 6 - 3 - 5} = \dfrac{3}{6} = \dfrac{1}{2} \quad p_2 = \dfrac{1}{2}$

$\qquad\qquad\qquad q_1 = \dfrac{8 - 3}{6} = \dfrac{5}{6} \qquad\qquad\qquad q_2 = \dfrac{1}{6}$

The optimal strategies for R and C are [1/2   0   1/2] and [5/6   0   1/6], respectively. The value of the game is

$$E = \frac{6(8) - 3(5)}{6} = \frac{33}{6} = \frac{11}{2}$$

11. Row 2 dominates row 1 and column 1 dominates column 2.
So row 1 and column 2 can be deleted, giving

Defense

$$\begin{array}{cc} & c_1 \quad c_2 \\ \begin{array}{c} r_2 \\ \\ r_3 \end{array} & \begin{bmatrix} 6 & 3 \\ -4 & 10 \end{bmatrix} \end{array}$$

The strategy of the offense should be $P = [0 \quad p_2 \quad p_3]$, where

$$p_2 = \frac{10 + 4}{6 + 10 - 3 + 4} = \frac{14}{17} \quad \text{and} \quad p_3 = \frac{3}{17}$$

The strategy of the defense should be $Q = [q_1 \quad 0 \quad q_3]$, where

$$q_1 = \frac{10 - 3}{17} = \frac{7}{17}, \qquad q_3 = \frac{10}{17}$$

The value of the game is

$$E = \frac{6(10) - (3)(-4)}{17} = \frac{72}{17} = 4.24$$

13. (a) Row 1 dominates row 4 and column 2 dominates column 1.

So row 4 and column 1 can be deleted to give $\begin{bmatrix} 2 & 3 \\ 0 & 4 \\ 2 & 1 \end{bmatrix}$

(b) Row 3 dominates row 4, so deleting row 4 gives

$$\begin{bmatrix} 6 & 2 & -2 & 1 \\ 4 & 1 & 9 & 2 \\ 2 & 4 & 6 & 8 \end{bmatrix}$$

15. (a) $E = \frac{3(5) - (2)(-1)}{3 + 5 - 2 + 1} = \frac{17}{7}$ This is not a fair game.

(b) $E = \frac{5(4) - (-10)(-2)}{5 + 4 + 10 + 2} = \frac{0}{21} = 0$

This is a fair game.

(c) This game is strictly determined. Its value is 7.
This is not a fair game.

17. $p_1 = \frac{100 - 150}{50 + 100 - 200 - 150} = \frac{-50}{-200} = 0.25 \qquad p_2 = 0.75$

The restaurateur should plan for 25% tourists and 75% locals.

19. $p_1 = \frac{150 - 60}{100 + 150 - 90 - 60} = \frac{90}{100} = 0.90 \qquad p_2 = 0.10$

They should devote 90% of the relative emphasis to industry
and 10% to tourism.

21. $p_1 = \frac{2000 - 3000}{2700 + 2000 - 2900 - 3000} = \frac{-1000}{-1200} = 0.83 \qquad p_2 = 0.17$

The company should plan on manufacturing 83% standard cars and 17%
economy cars.

Review Exercises, Chapter 9

1. (a) $\begin{bmatrix} 5 & -1 \\ 2 & 4 \end{bmatrix} \begin{matrix} -1 \\ 2 \end{matrix}$ This game is not strictly determined.

     5   4

    (b) $\begin{bmatrix} 1 & 3 & 9 \\ 7 & 4 & 8 \\ -5 & 3 & 4 \end{bmatrix} \begin{matrix} 1 \\ 4 \\ -5 \end{matrix}$ This game is strictly determined. The (2, 2) location is the saddle point. The value of the game is 4.

     7   4   9

    (c) $\begin{bmatrix} 140 & 210 \\ 300 & 275 \end{bmatrix} \begin{matrix} 140 \\ 275 \end{matrix}$ This game is strictly determined. The (2, 2) location is the saddle point. The value of the game is 275.

     300   275

    (d) $\begin{bmatrix} -6 & 2 & 9 & 1 \\ 5 & -4 & 0 & 2 \\ 4 & 2 & 8 & 3 \end{bmatrix} \begin{matrix} -6 \\ -4 \\ 2 \end{matrix}$ This game is strictly determined. The (3, 2) location is the saddle point. The value of the game is 2.

     5   2   9   3

3. (a) This game is not strictly determined, so there is no solution.
   (b) This game is strictly determined with value 4. The saddle point is at location (2,1). So the solution consists of the offense adopting strategy 2 and the defense adopting strategy 1.

5. (a) $E = [.3 \quad .7] \begin{bmatrix} 5 & 9 \\ 11 & 2 \end{bmatrix} \begin{bmatrix} .6 \\ .4 \end{bmatrix} = [9.2 \quad 4.1] \begin{bmatrix} .6 \\ .4 \end{bmatrix} = 7.16$

   (b) $E = [.5 \quad .5] \begin{bmatrix} -2 & 6 \\ 3 & 9 \end{bmatrix} \begin{bmatrix} .1 \\ .9 \end{bmatrix} = [.5 \quad 7.5] \begin{bmatrix} .1 \\ .9 \end{bmatrix} = 6.8$

   (c) $E = [.1 \quad .4 \quad .5] \begin{bmatrix} -3 & 2 & 1 \\ 4 & -2 & 5 \\ 3 & 1 & 2 \end{bmatrix} \begin{bmatrix} .2 \\ .2 \\ .6 \end{bmatrix} = [2.8 \quad -0.1 \quad 3.1] \begin{bmatrix} .2 \\ .2 \\ .6 \end{bmatrix} = 2.4$

7. $p_1 = \dfrac{210 - 175}{250 + 210 - 140 - 175} = \dfrac{35}{145} = 0.24 \qquad p_2 = 0.76$

   The farmer should plant 24% of the crop in the field and 76% in the greenhouse.

Appendix A
Algebra Review

Section A-1

1. $(-1)13 = -13$ 3. $-(-23) = 23$ 5. $(-5)(6) = -30$ 7. $5(-7) = -35$

9. $-(7 - 2) = -5$ 11. $21/(-3) = -7$ 13. $(-4) + (-6) = -10$

15. $(-4)(2) = -8$ 17. $5/3 + 4/3 = 9/3 = 3$

19. $12/5 - 3/5 = 9/5$ 21. $2/3 + 3/4 = 8/12 + 9/12 = 17/12$

23. $5/6 - 7/4 = 10/12 - 21/12 = -11/12$

25. $2/5 + 1/4 = 8/20 + 5/20 = 13/20$

27. $4/7 - 3/5 = 20/35 - 21/35 = -1/35$

29. $(3/4)/(9/8) = (3/4) \times (8/9) = 2/3$

31. $(2/7)/(4/5) = (2/7) \times (5/4) = 5/14$

33. $(1/3)(1/5) = 1/15$ 35. $2/5 \times 4/3 = 8/15$

37. $(-3/5)(-4/7) = 12/35$ 39. $3/11 + 1/3 = 9/33 + 11/33 = 20/33$

41. $5/7 \div 15/28 = (5/7) \times (28/15) = 4/3$

43. $(5/8) \div (1/3) = (5/8)(3) = 15/8$

45. $(3/4 + 1/5) \div (2/9) = (15/20 + 4/20)(9/2) = (19/20)(9/2) = 171/40$

47. $-2(3a + 11b) = -6a - 22b$ 49. $-5(2a + 10b) = -10a - 50b$

Section A-2

1. $2x - 4 = -10$
   $x = -3$ is a solution, since $2(-3) - 4 = -6 - 4 = -10$

3. $2x - 3 = 5$
   $2x = 8$
   $x = 4$

5. $4x - 3 = 5$
   $4x = 8$
   $x = 2$

7. $7x + 2 = 3x + 4$
   $4x = 2$
   $x = 1/2$

9. $12x + 21 = 0$
   $12x = -21$
   $x = -21/12 = -7/4$

11. $3(x - 5) + 4(2x + 1) = 9$
    $3x - 15 + 8x + 4 = 9$
    $11x = 20$
    $x = 20/11$

13. $\dfrac{2x + 3}{3} + \dfrac{5x - 1}{4} = 2$
    $8x + 12 + 15x - 3 = 24$
    $23x = 15$
    $x = \dfrac{15}{23}$

15. $\dfrac{12x + 4}{2x + 7} = 4$

    $12x + 4 = 8x + 28$

    $4x = 24$

    $x = 6$

17. (a) $y = 0.20(650) + 112 = \$242$
    (b) $y = 0.20(1500) + 112 = \$412$
    (c) Solve $0.20x + 112 = 302$
         $0.20x = 190$
         $x = 950$ miles

19. (a) $y = 0.42(42 - 8) = 0.42(34) = \$14.28$
    (b) $y = 0.42(113 - 8) = 0.42(105) = \$44.10$
    (c) Solve $0.42(x - 8) = 22.26$
         $x - 8 = 53$
         $x = 61$ pounds

Section A-3

1.

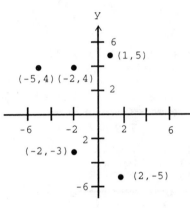

3.

5. (a) Second quadrant: negative x-coordinates,
                          positive y-coordinates
   (b) Third quadrant: negative x-coordinates,
                          negative y-coordinates
   (c) Fourth quadrant: positive x-coordinates,
                          negative y-coordinates

7.

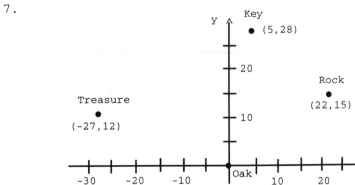

Section A-4

1. (a) 9 > 3 is True, since 9 - 3 = 6.
    (b) 4 > 0 is True, since 4 - 0 = 4.
    (c) -5 > 0 is False, since -5 - 0 = -5.
    (d) -3 > -15 is True, since -3 - (-15) = 12.
    (e) 5/6 > 2/3 is True, since 5/6 - 2/3 = 5/6 - 4/6 = 1/6.

3. 3x - 5 < x + 4
    2x < 9
    x < 9/2

5. 5x - 22 ≤ 7x + 10
    -2x ≤ 32
    x ≥ -16

7. 3(2x + 1) < 9x + 12
    6x + 3 < 9x + 12
    -3x < 9
    x > -3

9. 3x + 2 ≤ 4x - 3
    -x ≤ -5
    x ≥ 5

      5

11. 6x + 5 < 5x - 4
    x < -9

      -9

13. 3(x + 4) < 2(x - 3) + 14
    3x + 12 < 2x - 6 + 14
    x < -4

      -4

15. 3(2x + 1) < -1(3x - 10)
    6x + 3 < -3x + 10
    9x < 7
    x < 7/9

      7/9

17. -16 < 3x + 5 < 22
    -21 < 3x < 17
    -7 < x < 17/3

      -7   17/3

19. 14 < 3x + 8 < 32
    6 < 3x < 24
    2 < x < 8

      2   8

21. 3x + 4 ≤ 1
    3x ≤ -3
    x ≤ -1

    (-∞, -1]

23. -7x + 4 ≥ 2x + 3
    -9x ≥ -1
    x ≤ 1/9

    (-∞, 1/9]

25. -45 < 4x + 7 ≤ -10
    -52 < 4x ≤ -17
    -13 < x ≤ -17/4
    (-13, -17/4]

27. $\frac{6x + 5}{-2} \geq \frac{4x - 3}{5}$
    30x + 25 ≤ -8x + 6
    38x ≤ -19
    x ≤ -1/2

29. $\frac{2}{3} < \frac{x + 5}{-4} \leq \frac{3}{2}$
    -8 > 3x + 15 ≥ -18
    -23 > 3x ≥ -33
    -23/3 > x ≥ -11

31. 75 ≤ 35 + 5x < 90
    40 ≤ 5x < 55
    8 ≤ x < 11
    8, 9, or 10 correct answers

33. 85 ≤ 3x + 25 ≤ 100
    60 ≤ 3x ≤ 75
    20 ≤ x ≤ 25
    20, 21, 22, 23, 24, or 25

Appendix B
Logic

Section B-1

1. (a) Statement. It is a true declarative sentence.
    (b) Statement. It is a false declarative sentence.
    (c) Not a statement. It is a question.
    (d) Not a statement. It is an opinion.

3. (a) Statement. It is a true declarative sentence.
    (b) Statement. It is a false declarative sentence.
    (c) Statement. It is a true declarative sentence.
    (d) Not a statement. It is a command.
    (e) Not a statement. It is an opinion.

5. (a) Neither   (b) Disjunction
    (c) Conjunction   (d) Disjunction

7. (a) Betty has blonde hair or Angela has dark hair.
    (b) Angela does not have dark hair.
    (c) Betty has blonde hair and Angela has dark hair.
    (d) Betty does not have blonde hair and Angela does not
         have dark hair.

9. (a) $p \wedge q$ (b) $p \vee q$ (c) $(\sim p) \wedge q$

11. (a) False because $4^2 = 15$ is false.
    (b) False because the first part is false.
    (c) True because both statements in the conjunction are true.

13. (a) False because both parts are false.
    (b) True because both parts are true.
    (c) True because the first part is true.

15. (a) I do not have six one-dollar bills in my wallet.
    (b) Roy cannot name all 50 states.
    (c) A quorum was present for the meeting.

17. (a) I drink coffee at breakfast and I eat salad for lunch and I
         like a dessert after dinner.
    (b) I drink coffee at breakfast, or I eat salad for lunch and I
         like a dessert after dinner.
    (c) I drink coffee at breakfast and I eat salad for lunch, and I
         do not like a dessert after dinner.
    (d) I drink coffee at breakfast and I eat salad for lunch, or I
         drink coffee at breakfast and I like dessert after dinner.

19. (a) T because all parts are T   (b) F because $\sim p$ is F
    (c) F because $\sim p$ is F   (d) F because $\sim r$ is F
    (e) T because $p \vee q$ is T

Section B-2

1.   (a)   If I have $5.00, then I can rent a video.
      (b)   If I can rent a video, then I have $5.00.

3.   (a)   True because the hypothesis and the conclusion are both true.
      (b)   True because the hypothesis is false.
      (c)   False because the hypothesis is true and the conclusion is false.

5.   Converse: If I live in Colorado, then I live in Denver.
      Inverse: If I do not live in Denver, then I do not live in Colorado.
      Contrapositive: If I do not live in Colorado, then I do not live in Denver.

7.   (a)   False because the components have different truth values, true and false, respectively.
      (b)   True because both components are true.
      (c)   True because both components are true.

9.

p	q	$p \wedge q$	$\sim(p \wedge q)$
T	T	T	F
T	F	F	T
F	T	F	T
F	F	F	T

11.

p	q	$\sim q$	$p \wedge \sim q$
T	T	F	F
T	F	T	T
F	T	F	F
F	F	T	F

13.

p	q	$\sim p$	$\sim q$	$\sim p \vee \sim q$
T	T	F	F	F
T	F	F	T	T
F	T	T	F	T
F	F	T	T	T

15.

p	q	$q \vee p$	$\sim p \rightarrow (q \vee p)$
T	T	T	T
T	F	T	T
F	T	T	T
F	F	F	F

17.

p	q	r	$p \vee q$	$(p \vee q) \wedge r$
T	T	T	T	T
T	F	T	T	T
F	T	T	T	T
F	F	T	F	F
T	T	F	T	F
T	F	F	T	F
F	T	F	T	F
F	F	F	F	F

19.

p	q	r	$p \rightarrow q$	$q \rightarrow r$	$(p \rightarrow q) \wedge (q \rightarrow r)$
T	T	T	T	T	T
T	F	T	F	T	F
F	T	T	T	T	T
F	F	T	T	T	T
T	T	F	T	F	F
T	F	F	F	T	F
F	T	F	T	F	F
F	F	F	T	T	T

21.

p	q	r	p ∨ q	(p ∨ q) ↔ r
T	T	T	T	T
T	F	T	T	T
F	T	T	T	T
F	F	T	F	F
T	T	F	T	F
T	F	F	T	F
F	T	F	T	F
F	F	F	F	T

23.

p	~p	~(~p)	~(~p) ↔ p
T	F	T	T
F	T	F	T

Section B-3

1.

p	q	p → q	~q → ~p
T	T	T	T
T	F	F	F
F	T	T	T
F	F	T	T

Equivalent

3.

p	q	~p	p ∧ q	~p ∨ (p ∧ q)	~p ∨ q
T	T	F	T	T	T
T	F	F	F	F	F
F	T	T	F	T	T
F	F	T	F	T	T

Equivalent

5.

p	q	r	~p	q ∧ r	~p ∨ (q ∧ r)	p → (q ∧ r)
T	T	T	F	T	T	T
T	F	T	F	F	F	F
F	T	T	T	T	T	T
F	F	T	T	F	T	T
T	T	F	F	F	F	F
T	F	F	F	F	F	F
F	T	F	T	F	T	T
F	F	F	T	F	T	T

Equivalent

7.

p	q	p → q	~(p → q)	p
T	T	T	F	T
T	F	F	T	T
F	T	T	F	F
F	F	T	F	F

Not equivalent

9.

p	q	r	q ∨ r	p ∧ q	p ∧ (q ∨ r)	(p ∧ q) ∨ r
T	T	T	T	T	T	T
T	F	T	T	F	T	T
F	T	T	T	F	F	T
F	F	T	T	F	F	T
T	T	F	T	T	T	T
T	F	F	F	F	F	F
F	T	F	F	F	F	F
F	F	F	F	F	F	F

Not equivalent

Section B-4

1.   p: Eat your beans.
        q: You may have dessert.

$$p \rightarrow q$$
$$\underline{p}$$
$$q$$ Valid, Law of Detachment

3.   p: You do not study.
        q: You cannot do the homework.
        r: You cannot pass the course.

$$p \rightarrow q$$
$$\underline{q \rightarrow r}$$
$$p \rightarrow r$$ Valid, syllogism

5.   p: You eat your beans.
        q: You may have dessert.

$$p \rightarrow q$$
$$\underline{\sim p}$$
$$\sim q$$ Not valid. See Example 5.

7.   p: The ice is six inches thick.
        q: Shelley will go skating.

$$p \rightarrow q$$
$$\underline{\sim q}$$
$$\sim p$$

p	q	$p \rightarrow q$	$(p \rightarrow q) \wedge \sim q$	$(p \rightarrow q) \wedge \sim q \rightarrow \sim p$
T	T	T	F	T
T	F	F	F	T
F	T	T	F	T
F	F	T	T	T

Valid

9.   p: Inflation increases.
        q: The price of new cars will increase.
        r: More people will buy used cars.

$$p \rightarrow q$$
$$\underline{q \rightarrow r}$$
$$p \rightarrow r$$ Valid, Syllogism

11.   Check $[(p \rightarrow q) \wedge (q \wedge r)] \rightarrow (p \vee r)$

p	q	r	$p \rightarrow q$	$q \wedge r$	$p \vee r$	$[(p \rightarrow q) \wedge (q \wedge r)] \rightarrow (p \vee r)$
T	T	T	T	T	T	T
T	F	T	F	F	T	T
F	T	T	T	T	T	T
F	F	T	T	F	T	T
T	T	F	T	F	T	T
T	F	F	F	F	T	T
F	T	F	T	F	F	T
F	F	F	T	F	F	T

Valid

13. Check [(p ∧ q) ∧ (p → ~q)] → (p ∧ ~q)

p	q	p ∧ q	p → ~q	p ∧ ~q	[(p ∧ q) ∧ (p → ~q)] → (p ∧ ~q)
T	T	T	F	F	T
T	F	F	T	T	T
F	T	F	T	F	T
F	F	F	T	F	T

Valid

15. Check [(q → r) ∧ (~p ∨ q) ∧ p] → r

p	q	r	q→r	~p∨q	[(q→r) ∧ (~p∨q) ∧p] →r
T	T	T	T	T	T
T	F	T	T	F	T
F	T	T	T	T	T
F	F	T	T	T	T
T	T	F	F	T	T
T	F	F	T	F	T
F	T	F	F	T	T
F	F	F	T	T	T

Valid

17. Check [(p → q) ∧ (p → r)] → (q ∧ r)

p	q	r	p→q	p→r	q∧r	[(p → q) ∧ (q→r)] → (q∧r)
T	T	T	T	T	T	T
T	F	T	F	T	F	T
F	T	T	T	T	T	T
F	F	T	T	T	F	F
T	T	F	T	F	F	T
T	F	F	F	F	F	T
F	T	F	T	T	F	F
F	F	F	T	T	F	F

Not valid

19. Check [(p → q) ∧ (q → r) ∧ ~q] → ~r

p	q	r	p→q	q→r	~q	~r	[(p→q) ∧ (q→r) ∧~q] →~r
T	T	T	T	T	F	F	T
T	F	T	F	T	T	F	T
F	T	T	T	T	F	F	T
F	F	T	T	T	T	F	F
T	T	F	T	F	F	T	T
T	F	F	F	T	T	T	T
F	T	F	T	F	F	T	T
F	F	F	T	T	T	T	T

Not valid

21. Check [(p ∧ q → r) ∧ q] → (p → r)

p	q	r	p∧q	p∧q→r	p→r	[(p∧q →r) ∧q] → (p→r)
T	T	T	T	T	T	T
T	F	T	F	T	T	T
F	T	T	F	T	T	T
F	F	T	F	T	T	T
T	T	F	T	F	F	T
T	F	F	F	T	F	T
F	T	F	F	T	T	T
F	F	F	F	T	T	T

Valid